A
SENTIMENTAL JOURNEY,
&c. &c.

LAURENCE STERNE

Professing themselves to be wise, they became fools.

> Romans 1:22—the text of Yorick's sermon
> on "Advantages of Christianity to the world"
> (*Sermons*, II, 53–64 [IV.xi])

This fellow is wise enough to play the fool,
And to do that well craves a kind of wit.

Twelfth Night, III.i.67–68

LAURENCE STERNE

A

SENTIMENTAL JOURNEY

THROUGH

FRANCE AND ITALY

BY

MR. YORICK

Edited by Gardner D. Stout, Jr.

UNIVERSITY OF CALIFORNIA PRESS

BERKELEY AND LOS ANGELES

1967

University of California Press
Berkeley and Los Angeles, California

Cambridge University Press
London, England

PREFACE

Laurence Sterne "lusted earnestly, and endeavoured carefully . . . that [his] little books . . . might stand instead of many bigger books." The big book I have made of his little one would surely have amused him; but I hope he would have appreciated my admiration for his wit and wisdom. I hope too that his readers will find this edition helpful in "sailing and posting" with Yorick "through the politer kingdoms of the globe in pursuit of knowledge and improvements."

It is a pleasure to express my gratitude to a few of the many persons who have helped me in various ways: to Professor John Loftis, for his unfailing assistance and kindness; to Professor Ralph Rader, for his generous advice and aid; to Professor Robert Bloom, for his encouragement and friendship; to Professors Sheldon Sacks, Bertrand Bronson, John Traugott, Ernest Tuveson, Arthur Cash, and Louis Milic, for their help; to James Benson, William Chace, and Peter Howard; to the staff of the University of California Press, for their patient and painstaking care with a very difficult work; to Professor Samuel Monk, for the privilege of his counsel and the joy of his friendship; to Mr. and Mrs. Charlton M. Lewis, Jr., for their devotion to the cause; and to my mother and father, for their sustaining confidence.

Finally, I wish to acknowledge, though I shall not try to express, my debt to my beloved wife. This edition is dedicated to her.

G. D. S., Jr.

Berkeley, California

ACKNOWLEDGMENTS

I am indebted to the following institutions for their courteous permission to use unpublished material and to reproduce illustrations: the Trustees of the British Museum, for permission to quote from and reproduce folios of Sterne's holograph MS. of Vol. I of *A Sentimental Journey* (Egerton MS. 1610), and for plate 7; the Pierpont Morgan Library, for permission to quote from and reproduce folios of their MS. of *A Sentimental Journey* (MA 1046–1047); the New York Public Library, for the frontispiece; P. & D. Colnaghi & Co., Ltd., London, and the Yale University Press, for plate 3; the National Portrait Gallery, London, and the Yale University Press, for plate 4; the Curator of the Harry Elkins Widener Collection in the Harvard College Library, for plates 8 and 9; the Harvard College Library, for plate 12. I am also indebted to the Odyssey Press for permission to quote from James A. Work's edition of *Tristram Shandy*, and to Professor Lewis P. Curtis and the Clarendon Press for permission to quote from *Letters of Laurence Sterne*.

An earlier version of section iv of the Introduction appeared in *ELH*, XXX (1963), 395–412, under the title "Yorick's *Sentimental Journey*: A Comic 'Pilgrim's Progress' for the Man of Feeling." An earlier version of the note to pp. 83.100–85.126 (App. E, pp. 332–336) appeared in *English Language Notes*, II (1965), 196–200, under the title "Sterne's Borrowings from Bishop Joseph Hall's *Quo Vadis?*"

Professor Louis Milic generously allowed me to use his master's thesis, "An Annotated Critical Edition of Sterne's *Sentimental Journey*" (Columbia University, 1950).

Finally, I wish to acknowledge my general indebtedness to Alan H. Vrooman's Ph.D. dissertation, "The Origin and Development of the *Sentimental Journey* as a Work of Travel Literature and of Sensibility" (Princeton University, 1940), which points out many of the verbal parallels between *A Sentimental Journey* and Sterne's other writings that are noted in the present edition.

CONTENTS

Index to the Chapters of *A Sentimental Journey*

NOTE ON THE ILLUSTRATIONS

FRONTISPIECE. Laurence Sterne. In the Ford Collection of the New York Public Library. This drawing closely resembles the first portrait of Sterne by Sir Joshua Reynolds, in the Lansdowne Collection (see the frontispiece to *Letters*), but it has never been definitely attributed to Reynolds.

PLATE 1 (p. 4). Title page to Vol. I of the first edition of *The Sermons of Mr. Yorick.*

PLATE 2 (p. 14). Title page to Vol. I of the first edition of Smollett's *Travels through France and Italy.*

MAP (facing p. 162). *Paris au XVIIIe siècle: Plan de Paris . . . dessiné et gravé sous les ordres de Michel-Étienne Turgot . . . levé et dessiné par Louis Bretez,* Paris, 1734–1739. (The plate in the present edition is reproduced from a facsimile publ. Paris, 1851.) Yorick's journey to Paris is set in 1762, the same year as Sterne's first trip there (see p. 192.7–8*n*, below), and this map agrees in all details relevant to the present edition with Deharme's flat map of Paris, publ. Paris, 1762–1763.

Plates 3–12 follow p. 292.

PLATE 3. Laurence Sterne. Engraving from the watercolor sketch by Louis Carogis, *dit* Carmontelle, in the Musée Condé at Chantilly. (The plate in the present edition is taken from the reproduction of the engraving facing p. 308 in *Life.*) On 19 March 1762 Sterne wrote Garrick from Paris: "The Duke of Orleans has suffered my portrait to be added to the number of some odd men in his collection; and a gentleman [Carmontelle] who lives with him has taken it most expressively, at full length" (*Letters,* No. 85, pp. 157–158; for Carmontelle, see *Letters,* p. 159, n. 9).

PLATE 4. Laurence Sterne. Marble replica in the National Portrait Gallery, London, of the bust executed by Joseph Nollekens when Sterne was in Rome in 1766 (see *Life,* pp. xix, 404). The plate in the present edition is taken from the plate facing p. 404 in *Life.*

xi

PLATE 5. A *désobligeante*, as pictured in the edition of *A Sentimental Journey* published by J. E. Nicholls, London [1840?] (see App. A, p. 296, n. 8).

PLATE 6. Untitled engraving by Thomas Stothard of the old man lamenting the death of his ass, facing p. 56 in the edition of *A Sentimental Journey* published by J. Good and E. and S. Harding, London, 1792. Stothard's illustrations for this edition typify the emphasis placed on the sentimental and "pathetic" aspects of the book by illustrators during the period 1770–1800; see T. C. Duncan Eaves, "Graphic Illustration of the Principal English Novels of the Eighteenth Century" (unpubl. dissertation, Harvard, 1944), I, 241–243, 248–249; II, 632–634.

PLATE 7. William Bunbury, "A Tour to Foreign Parts" (publ. 1778). From a copy in the British Museum. The young English gentleman (center) is holding a volume entitled "Chesterfield Letters"—presumably Lord Chesterfield's letters to his son, publ. 1774 (see *Catalogue of Prints and Drawings in the British Museum*, IV, 798–799, No. 4732). (This print is used as frontispiece in Maxwell.)

PLATE 8. "The Dance at Amiens," etched by Thomas Rowlandson, facing p. 99 in *The Beauties of Sterne: Comprising his Humorous and Descriptive Tales, Letters, &c. &c. Embellished by Caricatures, by Rowlandson, from Original Drawings by Newton*, published by Thomas Tegg, London, 1809 (from a copy in the Harvard Library). Rowlandson's etchings in this volume are described in Eaves, "Graphic Illustration," I, 257–258; II, 643–644. On Newton's illustrations of *A Sentimental Journey*, see the note on plate 12, below.

PLATE 9. "Yorick Feeling the Grisset's Pulse," etched by Thomas Rowlandson. Frontispiece to *The Beauties of Sterne* (see the note on plate 8, above).

PLATE 10. Untitled engraving by Thomas Stothard of Yorick and Maria, facing p. 162 in the edition of *A Sentimental Journey* described in the note on plate 6, above.

PLATE 11. Untitled engraving by Thomas Stothard of "The Grace," facing p. 175 in the edition of *A Sentimental Journey* described in the note on plate 6, above.

PLATE 12. "The Grace," etched by Richard Newton, facing p. 174 in *Sterne's Sentimental Journey through France and Italy, with Twelve Illustrative Prints, Designed and Etched by Richard Newton,* published by William Holland, London, 1795 [error for 1797] (from a copy in the Harvard College Library). Newton's illustrations for this edition are described by Eaves in "Graphic Illustration," I, 254–256, II, 635–640. Eaves points out (I, 254–256) that Newton's designs, from which Rowlandson's etchings were executed (see the note on plate 8, above), were almost the only ones during the period 1770–1800 that emphasized the humor of *A Sentimental Journey.*

SHORT TITLES AND ABBREVIATIONS

n explanatory note; p. 65.7–8*n* = explanatory note to p. 65, ll. 7–8, of the text.

tn textual note; p. 65.5–6*tn* = textual note to p. 65, ll. 5–6, of the text.

A Sentimental Journey Laurence Sterne, *A Sentimental Journey through France and Italy By Mr. Yorick.* All references are to the present edition, unless otherwise specified.

CASH, "Sterne Letters" Arthur H. Cash, "Some New Sterne Letters," *London Times Literary Supplement,* 8 April 1965, p. 284.

COLE, *Journey to Paris* Rev. William Cole, *A Journal of my Journey to Paris in the Year 1765,* ed. Francis G. Stokes, London, 1931.

CRANE Ronald S. Crane, "Suggestions Toward a Genealogy of the 'Man of Feeling,' " *ELH,* I (1934), 205–230.

Don Quixote Miguel de Cervantes, *Don Quixote,* Motteux–Ozell translation, Modern Library edition, New York, 1930. References are given to part, book, chapter, and page.

FERRIAR John Ferriar, *Illustrations of Sterne,* 2d ed., 2 vols., London, 1812.

HAMMOND Lansing V. Hammond, *Laurence Sterne's "Sermons of Mr. Yorick,"* New Haven, 1948.

HOOKER Edward N. Hooker, "Humour in the Age of Pope," *Huntington Library Quarterly,* XI (1948), 361–385.

HOWES Alan B. Howes, *Yorick and the Critics: Sterne's Reputation in England, 1760–1868,* New Haven, 1958.

Journal *Journal to Eliza,* in *Letters.*

Letters *Letters of Laurence Sterne,* ed. Lewis P. Curtis, Oxford, 1935.

Life Wilbur L. Cross, *The Life and Times of Laurence Sterne,* 3d ed., New Haven, 1929.

McKillop   Alan D. McKillop, *The Early Masters of English Fiction*, Lawrence, Kansas, 1956.

Maxwell   Constantia Maxwell, *The English Traveller in France 1698–1815*, London, 1932.

Mead   William E. Mead, *The Grand Tour in the Eighteenth Century*, Boston and New York, 1914.

Milic   Louis T. Milic, "An Annotated Critical Edition of Sterne's *Sentimental Journey*," unpubl. master's thesis, Columbia University, 1950.

Milic, "Sterne and Smollett's 'Travels' "   Louis T. Milic, "Sterne and Smollett's 'Travels,' " *Notes & Queries*, CCI (1956), 80–81.

Millard   [John Millard], *The Gentleman's Guide in his Tour through France. Wrote by an Officer*, 4th ed., London, 1770.

Putney   Rufus Putney, "The Evolution of *A Sentimental Journey*," *Philological Quarterly*, XIX (1940), 349–369.

Rabelais, *Gargantua and Pantagruel*   François Rabelais, *Gargantua and Pantagruel*, Everyman's Library, 2 vols., London and New York, 1954.

Sermons   *The Sermons of Mr. Yorick*, 2 vols., in *The Writings of Laurence Sterne*, Shakespeare Head Press, Oxford, 1927. References to this edition (by volume and page) are followed (in parentheses) by the volume and number of the sermon in the first editions of *The Sermons of Mr. Yorick*, Vols. I–II (London, 1760), Vols. III–IV (London, 1766), and of *Sermons by The late Rev. Mr. Sterne*, Vols. V–VII (London, 1769); see *Life*, pp. 600–604. All quotations are from the first editions.

Sharp, *Letters from Italy*   Samuel Sharp, *Letters from Italy, Describing the Customs and Manners of that Country, In the Years 1765, and 1766. To which is Annexed, An Admonition to Gentlemen who pass the Alps, in their Tour through Italy*, London, 1766.

Smollett, *Travels*   Tobias Smollett, M.D., *Travels through France and Italy*, 2 vols., London, 1766 (see facsimile title page, p. 14, below). All quotations are from this (the first) edition; for convenience, page references are given to the World's Classics edition, ed. Thomas Seccombe, Oxford, 1935.

Spectator *The Spectator*, ed. Donald F. Bond, 5 vols., Oxford, 1965.

TAVE   Stuart M. Tave, *The Amiable Humorist: A Study in the Comic Theory and Criticism of the Eighteenth and Early Nineteenth Centuries*, Chicago, 1960.

THICKNESSE, *Observations*   Philip Thicknesse, *Observations on the Customs and Manners of the French Nation, in a Series of Letters, in which That Nation is vindicated from the Misrepresentations of some Late Writers*, London, 1766.

THICKNESSE, *Useful Hints*   Philip Thicknesse, *Useful Hints to Those Who Make the Tour of France, in a Series of Letters, Written from that Kingdom*, London, 1768.

TRAUGOTT   John Traugott, *Tristram Shandy's World: Sterne's Philosophical Rhetoric*, Berkeley and Los Angeles, 1954.

Tristram Shandy   Laurence Sterne, *The Life and Opinions of Tristram Shandy, Gentleman*, ed. James A. Work, New York, 1940. References are given to volume, chapter, and page. All quotations are from this edition; however, the length of the long dash has been changed to accord with the first edition.

TS   *Tristram Shandy*, ed. Work (see above).

VROOMAN   Alan H. Vrooman, "The Origin and Development of the *Sentimental Journey* as a Work of Travel Literature and of Sensibility," unpubl. dissertation, Princeton University, 1940.

WATKINS   Walter B. C. Watkins, *Perilous Balance: The Tragic Genius of Swift, Johnson, and Sterne*, Princeton, 1939.

INTRODUCTION

I

In December 1767, when he had almost completed *A Sentimental Journey*, Sterne informed a friend: "I am going to ly-in; being at Christmas at my full reckoning . . . [and] shall have the honour of presenting to you a *couple of as clean brats* as ever chaste brain conceiv'd—they are frolicksome too, *mais cela n'empeche pas*—"[1]

The origins of Sterne's last literary offspring can be traced back to his initial plans for *Tristram Shandy*, and their conception was influenced by the contemporary reception of his writings.[2]

Sterne's "first Plan" for *Tristram Shandy* was, according to John Croft, "to travell his Hero . . . all over Europe and after making his remarks on the different Courts, proceed with making strictures and reflections on the different Governments of Europe and finish the work with an eulogium on the superior constitution of England and at length to return Tristram well informed and a compleat English Gentleman."[3] Although he did not execute this plan, Sterne clearly intended from the outset of Tristram's *Life and Opinions* to incorporate in them a Shandean burlesque of the Grand Tour, for in Vol. I Tristram promised that a "delectable narrative" of his tour through Europe as governor to "Mr. *Noddy*'s eldest son . . . will be given in the progress of this work."[4]

During the first week of January 1762, a fortnight after Vols. V and VI of *Tristram Shandy* were published (on 21 December 1761),

---

[1] *Letters*, No. 223, Coxwold, to Sir George Macartney, p. 405. Sterne's ref. to a "*couple*" of brats is to the two vols. of *A Sentimental Journey*.

[2] In this section of the Introduction, I am extensively indebted to Vrooman, pp. 14–142; Putney, pp. 358–366; Howes, pp. 1–39; and McKillop, pp. 213–217.

[3] *The Whitefoord Papers*, ed. W. A. S. Hewins (Oxford, 1898), p. 228. The reliability of Croft's anecdotes of Sterne is questionable (see Howes, p. 7, n. 4; and James M. Kuist, "New Light on Sterne: An Old Man's Recollections of the Young Vicar," *PMLA*, LXXX [1965], 549–553). However, Croft's report of Sterne's description of his initial plan for *Tristram Shandy* tallies quite closely with Tristram's description, in Vol. VII, of the Shandy family's grand tour; see App. E, pp. 345–347, note to p. 176.27–37.

[4] *TS*, 1.11.24–25.

1

Sterne left England on his first trip to the Continent.[5] He traveled
with Death at his heels, having gone abroad in hope of recovering
from a severe attack of his chronic consumption; and shortly after
his departure for France the London papers were reporting that he
had died in Paris.[6] However, he mended, and after two weeks'
triumphant progress through the salons of Paris in the role of
"Chevalier Shandy," he informed David Garrick: "I could write
six volumes of what has passed comically in this great scene, . . .
but more of this hereafter."[7] After spending about six months in
Paris, Sterne set out for southern France, staying in Toulouse and
Montpellier during most of August 1762–February 1764, with his
wife and daughter.[8] In October 1762 he informed John Hall-
Stevenson: "I . . . am busy playing the fool with my uncle Toby,
who I have got soused over head and ears in love.—I have many hints
and projects for other works."[9]

It is clear that Sterne had commenced Vol. VIII of *Tristram
Shandy*, and, as Vrooman points out,[10] his reference to "hints and
projects for other works" suggests that he was considering writing

---

[5] Cross's conjecture (*Life*, pp. 56–57) that Sterne may have made the
Grand Tour in 1741 is incorrect; see Lewis P. Curtis, *The Politicks of Laurence
Sterne* (Oxford, 1929), p. 119.

[6] The papers soon denied the rumor; see *Life*, pp. 289–290; *Letters*, p. 148,
n.1; Howes, pp. 15–16. In a letter from Paris dtd. 8 March 1762, Sterne remarked, in apologizing for not having written sooner: "If I chose it I could
tell You I was above all Epistolary Correspondence, after my death—but that's
a Lye—for I have wrote three Letters since that period to Hall & Garrick—I
find by the last english papers here, I am once more alive, & now tis high
time to write to You or never—Strange! that a man should be so inconsistent!—" (Cash, "Sterne Letters"). See also *Letters*, No. 88, Paris, 10 May
1762, p. 164: "When I arrived here, the Faculty thought I could not live a
month—I have lived however, . . . 5 Months, & in a gradual restoration of
my health . . ."

[7] *Letters*, No. 83, Paris, 31 Jan. 1762, p. 152. For the duc de Choiseul's
reference to Sterne as "Chevalier Shandy," see *Letters*, No. 85, p. 157, quoted
p. 226.33–35*n*, below.

[8] His sojourn in southern France did not, as he had hoped, restore his
health: see *Letters*, No. 107, Toulouse, 29 April 1763, p. 194; No. 113, Montpellier, 30 Sept. 1763, p. 200; No. 118, Montpellier, 5 Jan. 1764, pp. 207–208.

[9] *Letters*, No. 100, Toulouse, 19 Oct. 1762, p. 186.

[10] P. 15.

something independent of Tristram's *Life and Opinions*, possibly
an account of his travels. For the first time, Sterne was able to view
with a Shandean eye his fellow-Englishmen "sailing and posting
through the politer kingdoms of the globe in pursuit of knowledge
and improvements" (p. 83).[11] The spectacle afforded him fresh
literary inspiration, and in June 1763 he wrote Robert Foley: "I
shall cross the Pyreneans, and spend a week in . . . [Spain],
which is enough for a fertile brain to write a volume upon.—When
I write the history of my travels—Memorandum! I am not to forget
how honest a man I have for a banker at Paris."[12]

Sterne returned to England in early June 1764. Just before he
retired to Coxwold, he informed Elizabeth Montagu that he intended to "write a world of Nonsense . . . [with which] I am
pretty well provided . . . both by nature & Travel."[13] After six
months' labor on the fourth installment of *Tristram Shandy,* he
wrote Foley: "You will read a comic account of my journey from
Calais thro' Paris to the Garonne, in these volumes."[14] Vol. VII, "a
laughing good temperd Satyr against Traveling (as puppies
travel)," and Vol. VIII, an account of Uncle Toby's amours "for
the laughing part of the world," were published on 22 January
1765.[15]

Sterne's decision to insert a Shandean burlesque of the Grand
Tour at this point in Tristram's *Life and Opinions* was partly determined by their declining popularity. The first two volumes had
been a brilliant success. One critic had rhapsodized: "Oh rare
Tristram Shandy!—Thou very sensible—humourous—pathetick
—humane—unaccountable!—what shall we call thee?—Rabelais,

---

[11] *A Sentimental Journey,* p. 83, below. All page refs. are to the present
text.
[12] *Letters,* No. 111, Toulouse, 12 June 1763, p. 198; he never went to Spain.
Sterne also considered traveling to Italy on his first trip abroad; see *Letters,*
p. 193.
[13] *Letters,* No. 124, [? June 1764], p. 216.
[14] *Letters,* No. 136, York, 16 Nov. 1764, p. 234.
[15] See *Letters,* No. 134, York, 11 Nov. 1764, p. 231; No. 101, Toulouse,
9 Nov. 1762, p. 189. For an excellent study of Vol. VII of *Tristram Shandy* as
a satire on the Grand Tour, see Vrooman, ch. ii, pp. 14–99, "The Seventh
Book of *Tristram Shandy* and the Background of Travel and Travel Literature."

THE
SERMONS

O F

Mr. YORICK.

VOL. I.

LONDON:

Printed for R. and J. DODSLEY in
Pall-Mall.

Cervantes, What?" Declining to conjecture "who thou art," he
assured Tristram he would be "read and admir'd" if he published
fifty volumes.[16] However, Sterne had Shandyed his way through
London society after the first installment of *Tristram* made him
famous, and he had identified himself with his hero in the eyes of a
public eager for new humorists and humorous characters.[17] Many
were offended to find that the indecent and indecorous Tristram
was a clergyman. And when this ribald buffoon hawked the first two
volumes of *The Sermons of Mr. Yorick* under his pseudonym as the
heteroclite parson in *Tristram Shandy*,[18] a storm of protest arose.
The sermons themselves were generally praised,[19] but for "Mr.
Yorick" to offer them to the public was, according to Owen Ruffhead, Sterne's severest critic (writing in the *Monthly Review*), "the
greatest outrage against Sense and Decency" since the establishment of Christianity.[20]

---

[16] *London Magazine*, XXIX (Feb. 1760), 111. On the critical reception of
Vols. I and II of *Tristram Shandy*, see Howes, pp. 2–5; *TS*, ix–xiv; *Life*, pp.
205–217. Vols. I and II went through four editions during 1760 (*Life*, p. 600).

[17] See Hooker, pp. 376 ff.

[18] See esp. *TS*, 1.10–12.17–32. Sterne's use of the pseudonym Yorick on
the title pages of the *Sermons* (Vols. I–IV) and of *A Sentimental Journey* recalls Burton's use of the pseudonym "Democritus Junior" in *The Anatomy of
Melancholy* and his defense of his title page ("Democritus Junior to the
Reader," 6th ed. [London, 1651], p. 5): "If the title and inscription [Democ-
ritus Junior] offend your gravity, were it a sufficient justification to accuse
others, I could produce many sober treatises, even sermons themselves,
which in their fronts carry more phantastical names." On Democritus and
on Sterne's indebtedness to Burton in *Tristram Shandy* and *A Sentimental
Journey*, see the notes to pp. 130–131, below.

[19] They were popular and financially successful, and went through four
editions within a year and through five more by 1768; see Howes, pp. 10–12.

[20] *Monthly Review*, XXII (May 1760), 422–431. Ruffhead observed that a
"Fool's cap does but ill become a Reverend head," and asked: "Would any
man believe that a Preacher was in earnest, who should mount the pulpit in
a *Harlequin's coat?*" On the other hand, though he found the *"manner"* of
their publication outrageous, Ruffhead recommended the *"matter"* of *The
Sermons of Mr. Yorick* as a model for his clerical brethren. The concluding
portion of the review (written by William Rose) praised the "many fine and
delicate touches of the human heart and passions, which . . . shew marks
of great benevolence and sensibility of mind." The sermon on Philanthropy
(*Sermons*, I, 25–36 [I.iii]) was particularly commended as certain to strength-

When Vols. III and IV of *Tristram Shandy* appeared in January 1761, Ruffhead renewed his attack. Noting that the *Monthly Review* had not criticized the "indelicacies" of the first two volumes because the identity of their author was unknown, he declared that the *Monthly* could never have supposed they were "the production of a Dignitary of the Church of England, had not the wanton brat been publicly owned by its reverend Parent." Ruffhead quoted Tristram's reply to his attack on Vols. I and II of *The Sermons of Mr. Yorick*—in which Tristram declares that, in spite of the cuts and slashes Ruffhead had given his jerkin, "the lining to it . . . is not a three-penny piece the worse"[21]—and invited him to "imagine . . . what an antic figure" his jerkin "must cut upon a prunella gown and cassock! As well might . . . a right Reverend Bishop clap a grenadier's cap over his mitre. Do, for shame, Mr. Shandy, hide your jerkin, or, at least, send the lining to the Scowerer's." Remarking that "there is a certain faculty called *Discretion,* which, reasonable men will ever esteem," Ruffhead observed: "you, the arch *Prebend* Mr. *Yorick,* alias *Tristram Shandy,* have done all in your power to laugh it out of fashion." He declared that the "whimsical notions" of Tristram's father were "worn threadbare" and that the "novelty and extravagance" of Tristram's manner had become "insipid," and charged: "your Indiscretion, good Mr. Tristram, is not all we complain of in the volumes now before us. We must tax you with what you will dread above the most terrible of all imputations—nothing less than DULLNESS."[22]

en "the dispositions of tenderness and compassion in the breast of every humane Reader."

As Howes points out (p. 10), the other periodicals reviewed the *Sermons* more favorably: the *Critical Review* (IX [May 1760], 405), for example, was not "offended at Yorick's name prefixed" and declared: "we will ever esteem religion when smoothed with good humour, and believe that piety alone to be genuine, which flows from a heart, warm, gay, and social."

[21] *TS,* 3.4.161–162.

[22] *Monthly Review,* XXVI (Jan. 1761), 101–106. The *Critical Review* (XI [April 1761], 314–317) asserted that, although Tristram claims Cervantes is dearer to him than Rabelais (*TS,* 3.19.191), Rabelais is "the pattern and prototype" of *Tristram Shandy.* Declaring that the book is written "merely *pour la refection corporelle,*" the reviewer deplored its "gross expressions, impure ideas, and . . . general want of decorum." Howe notes (p. 13) that the critical reaction to Vols. III and IV in the other periodicals was divided.

Although Sterne may have lost some readers because of the impropriety of his authorship of *Tristram Shandy* and the indecencies of the book, Ruffhead was surely correct in predicting that he would consider the charge of indiscretion much less serious than that of dullness. Writing for a heterogeneous and generally imperceptive public, he recognized that the originality of the first two volumes had been primarily responsible for their success at a time when readers were eager for something new.[23] The third and fourth volumes sold fairly well, but for many readers the diverting oddities of the first installment had become the tedious "nonsense" of the second, and Sterne later admitted to David Hume that his "vogue had lasted only one winter."[24]

Vols. V and VI, published just before Sterne's departure for France, were more favorably reviewed. The charges of obscenity were less severe, and the story of Le Fever's death was warmly praised and widely reprinted. The *Monthly Review* declared that it "does greater honour to the abilities and disposition of the Author, than any other part of his work." The reviewer quoted the entire episode and observed:

Since Mr. Sterne published his Sermons, we have been of opinion, that his excellence lay not so much in the humourous as in the pathetic; and in this opinion we have been confirmed by the . . . story of Le Fever. We appeal to the Heart of every reader whether our judgment is not right?[25]

Uncle Toby's whimsical benevolence in the first two installments had won him universal esteem, and the story of Le Fever raised his

---

[23] As Howes points out (p. 1), no major novel had been published since *Sir Charles Grandison,* in 1754; and between 1754 and 1760 the periodicals had been "deploring the low level of the usual contemporary novel and its fall from past greatness."

[24] J. Y. T. Greig, *David Hume* (New York, [1931]), p. 304. Sir Horace Mann was "diverted . . . extremely" by the first two volumes of *Tristram Shandy,* although he admitted he didn't understand them; but after seeing Vols. III and IV, he declared that "Nonsense pushed too far becomes insupportable" (*Horace Walpole's Correspondence with Sir Horace Mann,* ed. W. S. Lewis, Warren Hunting Smith, and George L. Lam, V [New Haven, 1960], 446, 521).

[25] *Monthly Review,* XXVI (Jan. 1762), 31–41. The reviewer, John Langhorne, found Vols. V and VI "not so much interlarded with obscenity as the former."

8   Introduction

reputation to new heights. The *Critical Review* declared that
the episode "is beautifully pathetic, and exhibits the character of
Toby and his corporal in such a point of view, as must endear them
to every reader of sensibility. The author has contrived to make us
laugh at the ludicrous peculiarity of Toby, even while we are weep-
ing with tender approbation at his goodness of heart."[26]

Vols. V and VI of *Tristram Shandy* did not, however, sell nearly
so well as the earlier ones, and in March 1763 Becket (the publisher) still had one-quarter of the original edition on hand.[27] At
this point Sterne's boast at the outset of his literary career that he
wrote "not [to] be *fed* but to be *famous*"[28] must have echoed hol-
lowly in his ears, for the expense of maintaining himself and his
wife and daughter in France had strained his finances. Dr. Johnson's later pronouncement—"Nothing odd will do long. 'Tristram
Shandy' did not last"[29]—seemed likely to be fulfilled, and Sterne
found himself casting about for ways of regaining the interest of the
public.

Vols. VII and VIII of *Tristram Shandy* were published in January 1765.[30] As we have seen, Sterne's journey to France in 1762–
1764 provided the basic inspiration for the experiment of Vol. VII;
and he expressed his determination to offer the public something
novel, in his assurance to Foley that he would find Tristram's
Shandean journey "as odd a Tour thro' france, as ever was pro-

---

[26] *Critical Review*, XIII (Jan. 1762), 66–69. The reviewer observed that
there were "some pathetic touches of nature" which compelled him "to wish
the author had never stooped to . . . buffoonery." But he acknowledged
there were some fine "strokes of humour," especially the blank page which
Tristram declares will escape being blackened by malice and misrepresented
by ignorance, because he has invited the reader to picture the Widow Wadman on it according to his own fancy (*TS*, 6.37–38.472; see p. 170.2–9*n*,
below).

[27] See *Letters*, No. 104, to Thomas Becket, Toulouse, 12 March 1763, pp.
191–192; and *TS*, 8.6.545.

[28] *Letters*, No. 47, [? York], 30 Jan. 1760, p. 90.

[29] Boswell, *Life of Johnson*, ed. G. B. Hill and L. F. Powell (Oxford, 1934),
II, 449; Wed., 20 March 1776.

[30] According to Sterne, they sold "well" (*Letters*, No. 137, London, 16
March 1765, p. 235), but Howes points out (p. 18) that "the general tone of
criticism was not favorable."

jected or executed by traveller or travell Writer, since the world began—"[31]

Sterne must have found the critical reception of Vol. VII both disappointing and instructive. The reviewers, as usual, charged it with indecency, and several professed to be baffled by what one described as "an unconnected, unmeaning, account of our author's journey to France."[32] Ralph Griffiths, the editor of the *Monthly Review,* was generally pleased with Tristram's journey, though he found parts dull and obscene, particularly the misadventure of the Abbess of Andoüillets. On the other hand, he praised the good-humored gaiety of Tristram's dance with the peasants in the Languedoc vineyard (bating the slit in Nannette's petticoat) as "Admirable!—Mr. Shandy, you understand the art, the true art of travelling, better than any other mortal I ever knew or heard of!"[33]

Griffiths was even more delighted with Uncle Toby's courtship of the Widow Wadman in Vol. VIII. He praised Sterne's mastery of "the science of *human feelings,* and the art of describing them" and asserted that "*Richardson*—the delicate, the circumstantial RICHARDSON himself, never produced any thing equal to the amours of Uncle Toby and the Widow Wadman!" Regretting that "ever any grosser colours should daub and defile that pencil of thine," Griffiths observed:

> Ah, Mr. Shandy, your *ninth* and *tenth!* that's talking of things at a great distance! Better take a friend's advice. Stop where you are. The Public, if I guess right, will have *had enough,* by the time they get to the end of your eighth volume.——Your health, Mr. Shandy, and hearty thanks for the entertainment you have given me—but,—excuse me if I hazard a bold conjecture,—I am inclined to think that, all this while, you have not sufficiently cultivated your best talents. Give up your Long Noses . . . your Andoüillets. . . . try your strength another way. One of our gentlemen once remarked, in *print* Mr. Shandy——that he thought your excellence lay in the PATHETIC. I think so too. In my opinion, the little story of Le Fevre has done you more honour than every thing else you have wrote, except your Sermons. Suppose you were to strike out a new plan? Give us none but amiable or worthy, or exemplary characters; or, if you will, to enliven the drama, throw in the *innocently humorous.* . . . Paint Nature in her loveliest dress—her

[31] *Letters,* No. 134, York, 11 Nov. 1764, p. 231.
[32] *Critical Review,* XIX (Jan. 1765), 65.
[33] *Monthly Review,* XXXII (Feb. 1765), 128.

native simplicity. Draw natural scenes, and interesting situations——In fine, Mr. Shandy, do, for surely you can, excite our passions to *laudable* purposes—awake our affections, engage our hearts—arouze, transport, refine, improve us. Let morality, let the cultivation of virtue be your aim —let wit, humour, elegance and pathos be the means; and the grateful applause of mankind will be your reward.[34]

Although the influence of Griffiths' advice should not be exaggerated, it is difficult to believe that it was lost on a shrewd opportunist like Sterne, particularly when he needed funds. As the novelty of the first two volumes of *Tristram Shandy* wore off, many readers became indifferent to the oddities and hostile to the indecencies of Vols. III–VIII. On the other hand, they were consistently charmed by the humorous benevolence of the Shandy household and with the comic treatment of their foibles, provided it was chaste. Almost certainly, the shift from Tristram's "laughing good temperd Satyr" on the Grand Tour to Yorick's *Sentimental Journey* was made at least partly in response to the admonitions of the reviewers, and in recognition that Griffiths was correct in maintaining that a public whose tastes were largely dominated by the standards of the "man of feeling" wanted (and would pay for) pathos, refined sentiments, and chaste humor.[35]

---

[34] *Monthly Review*, XXXII (Feb. 1765), 132–139.

[35] Putney (p. 363), Vrooman (p. 128), and Curtis (*Letters*, p. 285, n. 3) quote Griffiths' advice to Tristram and suggest that it may have influenced Sterne's decision to interpolate Yorick's *Sentimental Journey* between installments of *Tristram Shandy* (see *Letters*, No. 169, quoted p. 12, below) Putney notes (p. 363) that the *Critical Review* (XIX [Jan. 1765], 66) gave Tristram much the same advice as the *Monthly*: reminding him that Uncle Toby's breeches had become so thin as to be unserviceable, they remarked: "Indeed, Tristram, your wit and humour, we are afraid, will very soon be in the same predicament." As Howes points out (p. 24), in Vols. V, VI, VIII, and IX of *Tristram Shandy* Sterne "focuses the spotlight on Uncle Toby, Trim, and the Widow Wadman and develops the . . . sentimental vein which critics referred to as 'the pathetic.' . . . The tremendous popularity of the episode of Le Fever [in Vol. VI] must have led Sterne to cater to the public taste in working this sentimental vein, and the critics obliged with the highest praise for it wherever it occurred. As the character of *Tristram Shandy* changed in this way with the later installments, the earlier praise for Sterne as a satirist tended to be replaced by praise for Sterne as a master of the pathetic."

By sending Tristram on a Shandean variation of the Grand Tour governed by the principles of laughter and good humor, rather than by the spleen, Sterne took an important step toward Yorick's *Journey*. And by diverting Tristram from the beaten track of his forerunners in order to demonstrate that such digressions can lead to delightful experiences for the man of good humor and sensibility who is willing to seize "every handle" which chance holds out to him in his journey, he indicated the route which Yorick, the Sentimental Traveller, was to take.[36]

Shortly after Vols. VII and VIII of *Tristram Shandy* were published, Sterne wrote Garrick:

I am taxing the publick with two more volumes of sermons, which will more than double the gains of Shandy—It goes into the world with a prancing list of *de toute la noblesse* . . . I shall be rich . . . but I scorn . . . to pocket all this trash—I set out to lay a portion of it in the service of the world, in a tour round Italy, where I shall spring game, or the duce is in the dice.—In the beginning of September I quit England, that I may avail myself of the time of the vintage, when all nature is joyous, and so saunter philosophically for a year or so, on the other side the Alps.[37]

As he remarked to another correspondent, he was "doing penance" for "my 7 & 8 graceless Children . . . in begetting a couple of more ecclesiastick ones— . . . they will appear in the Shape of the 3ᵈ & 4 Volˢ of Yorick. These you must know are to keep up a kind of balance, in my shandaic character."[38] Vols. III and IV of *The Sermons of Mr. Yorick* appeared in January 1766, and this time Yorick's name on the title page caused no furor. The reviewers were generally favorable and reprinted extensive extracts. The *Critical Review* observed that, although "the author sometimes forgets the dignity of his character . . . and condescends . . . to excite a jocular idea, or display a frivolous turn of wit," the sermons exhibit "the same acute remarks on the manners of mankind, the same striking characters, the same accurate investigation of the

---

[36] See p. 114.10–12n, below.
[37] *Letters*, No. 137, London, 16 March 1765, p. 235.
[38] *Letters*, No. 145, York, 5 July 1765, p. 252.

passions, the same delicate strokes of satire, and the same art in moving the tender affections of nature" as *Tristram Shandy*.[39]

In October 1765, before his third and fourth ecclesiastical children appeared, Sterne set out for Italy, on his second (and last) trip abroad. He was again fleeing Death[40] and (as his remark to Garrick that he hoped to "spring game" in Italy suggests) pursuing fresh literary inspiration. After a few days in Paris, he set out for Italy, traveling through the Bourbonnais and the mountains of Savoy, and reached Turin in mid-November. From Turin he proceeded to Florence, stopping in Milan, and then went on to Rome and Naples, where he found himself "infinitely better than I was— and hope to have added at least ten years to my life by this journey to Italy." By the end of March he was back in Rome; and having "pass'd a jolly laughing winter of it,"[41] he returned to England early in June 1766. In late July he told a friend:

Never man, my dear Sir, has had a more agreeable tour than your Yorick —and at present I am in my peaceful retreat, writing the ninth volume of Tristram—I shall publish but one this year, and the next I shall begin a new work of four volumes, which when finish'd, I shall continue Tristram with fresh spirit.[42]

---

[39] *Critical Review*, XXI (Jan. and Feb. 1766), 49. Howes notes (p. 20) that the *Monthly Review* (XXXIV [March 1766], 207–215) "as usual commended the 'pathetic touches.' " The reviewer declared that, though "there is an air of levity" in some of the sermons "altogether unbecoming the dignity and seriousness of pulpit-discourses," Sterne "is possessed . . . of such a fund of good humour, . . . native pleasantry, . . . [and] philanthropy, that it is impossible, for us at least, to be long displeased with him. . . . every subject, indeed, is treated in such a manner as shews the originality of his genius, and as will, in some measure, soften the severity of censure, in regard to his ill-timed pleasantry and want of discretion."

[40] See *Letters*, No. 149, Coxwold, 20 [? Sept.] 1765, p. 257: "I find I must once more fly from death whilst I have strength—I shall go to Naples and see whether the air of that place will not set this poor frame to rights—"

[41] See *Letters*, No. 157, to Lydia Sterne, Naples, 3 Feb. 1766, p. 267; No. 162, Rome, 30 March 1766, p. 275.

[42] *Letters*, No. 169, Coxwold, 23 July 1766, p. 284. See also No. 171, to Becket, Coxwold, 30 Aug. 1766, p. 288: "I shall publish the 9th and 10 of Shandy the next winter"; No. 175, Coxwold, 17 Dec. 1766, p. 290: "Tristram goes on busily—what I can find appetite to write, is so so"; No. 177, London, [? 7-9 Jan. 1767], p. 294: "I miscarried of my tenth Volume by the Violence

The "new work" is certainly *A Sentimental Journey*, and Sterne's reference to four volumes suggests that he may have already decided to write two volumes of travels in France and two of travels in Italy.

In Vol. IX of *Tristram Shandy* (publ. 30 January 1767), Sterne digressed from Uncle Toby's amours with the Widow Wadman to Tristram's encounter with Maria of Moulines, in order to give his readers a foretaste of his projected work and to state its principles, already suggested in Vol. VII—both in Tristram's renunciation of traveling on the spleen and in his journey through the plains of Languedoc.[43] After invoking the "Gentle Spirit of sweetest humour, who erst didst sit upon the easy pen of my beloved CERVANTES," Tristram beseeches it to

——Turn in hither, . . . behold these breeches!——they are all I have in the world——that piteous rent was given them at *Lyons*——[44]

My shirts! see what a deadly schism has happen'd amongst 'em—for the laps are in *Lombardy,* and the rest of 'em here—I never had but six, and a cunning gypsey of a laundress at *Milan* cut me off the *fore*-laps of five—To do her justice, she did it with some consideration—for I was returning *out* of *Italy.*[45]

And yet, notwithstanding all this, and a pistol tinder-box which was moreover filch'd from me at *Sienna,* and twice that I pay'd five Pauls for two hard eggs, once at *Raddicoffini,* and a second time at *Capua*—I do

---

of a fever, I have just got thro'—I have however gone on to my reckoning with the ninth, ⟨in⟩ of wch I am all this week in Labour pains; & if to Day's Advertiser is to be depended upon shall be safely deliver'd by tuesday."

[43] Tristram declares that the "SPLEEN" is "the best principle in the world to travel speedily upon; for, as few objects look very inviting in that mood—you have little or nothing to stop you"; however, "though you do get on at a tearing rate, yet you get on but uneasily to yourself at the same time; for which reason I here quit it entirely, and for ever, and 'tis heartily at any one's service—it has spoiled me the digestion of a good supper, and brought on a bilious diarrhæa" (*TS,* 7.16.497, 7.19.502). On his journey through Languedoc, see p. 268.1–10*n,* below.

[44] In his encounter with the ass (*TS,* 7.32.522–524).

[45] Curtis notes that this anecdote in *Tristram Shandy* had previously been reported, in the *St. James's Chronicle,* 14–17 June 1766 (*Letters,* p. 278, n. 3). For a similar instance in which Sterne used in *A Sentimental Journey* an anecdote about his travels that had previously been reported in the papers, see p. 232.34–42*n,* below.

T R A V E L S

T H R O U G H

FRANCE AND ITALY.

CONTAINING OBSERVATIONS ON

CHARACTER,	POLICE,
CUSTOMS,	COMMERCE,
RELIGION,	ARTS, AND
GOVERNMENT,	ANTIQUITIES.

With a particular DESCRIPTION of the

TOWN, TERRITORY, and CLIMATE of NICE:

To which is added,

A Regifter of the Weather, kept during a Refidence of Eighteen Months in that City.

BY T. SMOLLETT, M.D.

Ut Homo qui erranti comiter monftrat viam,
Quafi lumen de fuo lumine accendat, facit :
Nihilominus ipfi luceat, cum illi accenderit.   ENNIUS,

IN TWO VOLUMES.

V O L. I.

L O N D O N,

Printed for R. BALDWIN, in Pater-nofter-Row.

MDCCLXVI,

PLATE 2.

Title page to Vol. I of the first edition of Smollett's *Travels through France and Italy*.

not think a journey through *France* and *Italy,* provided a man keeps his temper all the way, so bad a thing as some people would make you believe: there must be *ups* and *downs,* or how the duce should we get into vallies where Nature spreads so many tables of entertainment.— 'Tis nonsense to imagine they will lend you their voitures to be shaken to pieces for nothing; and unless you pay twelve sous for greasing your wheels, how should the poor peasant get butter to his bread?—We really expect too much—and for the livre or two above par for your suppers and bed . . . who would embroil their philosophy for it? for heaven's and for your own sake, pay it———[46]

Sterne certainly expected many readers to recognize that Tristram was alluding to Tobias Smollett's *Travels through France and Italy,* published in May 1766.[47] Smollett's account of his travels had been well received and extensively quoted by the reviewers.[48] And it conveniently epitomized, for Sterne's purposes, the dullness and spleen which he thought typical of the "travels and observations" (p. 82) of the average Englishman on the Grand Tour and had ridiculed, in the "laughing good temperd Satyr" of Vol. VII of *Tristram Shandy,* the year before Smollett's book appeared.

To demonstrate that "a journey through *France* and *Italy*" need not be "so bad a thing" as people like Smollett "would make you believe," Tristram recounts his meeting with Maria of Moulines, as an example of the entertainment Nature affords the good-humored traveler of benevolent sensibility. He observes that he encountered Maria while Uncle Toby's amours were running through his head and that he was, therefore, "in the most perfect state of bounty and good will; and felt the kindliest harmony vibrating within me, with every oscillation of the chaise alike; so that whether the roads were rough or smooth, it made no difference; every thing I saw, or had to do with, touch'd upon some secret spring either of sentiment or

---

[46] *TS,* 9.24.628–629. On Smollett's exasperation at the (to him) exorbitant prices he was charged on his travels, see p. 80.43–53*n,* below.

[47] Smollett spent June 1763–July 1765 on the Continent. He and Sterne may have met in Montpellier in Nov. 1763 (see p. 117.33*n,* below).

[48] See Lewis M. Knapp, *Tobias Smollett, Doctor of Men and Manners* (Princeton, 1949), pp. 262–263. As Vrooman points out (p. 27), Smollett's *Travels* was the most distinguished book of travels through Europe which had been published by an Englishman since 1705, when Addison's *Remarks on Several Parts of Italy* appeared.

rapture."[49] In describing his meeting with Maria, he strikes almost
as delicate a balance between humor and pathos as Yorick does in
his "sentimental commerce" with her (pp. 268–276).

Sterne almost certainly intended this incident as a kind of "advertisement" for *A Sentimental Journey*,[50] which, as we have seen,
he had projected as early as July 1766. Ralph Griffiths, who had
urged him to strike out on a new plan and to cultivate his talent for
pathos, was delighted with this episode. He found his sensibility
vibrating in sympathetic harmony with the motions of Tristram's
literary vehicle and reprinted the entire incident, except for his
praise of the inn at Moulines:

> What a pretty, whimsical, affecting kind of episode has he introduced,
> in his chapter entitled INVOCATION! . . . our Readers shall have the
> chapter entire, except the abrupt transition [to the inn] in the last two
> lines, which, in our opinion, serve but to *spoil all*, by an ill-tim'd stroke
> of levity; like a ludicrous epilogue, or ridiculous farce, unnaturally
> tagged to the end of a deep tragedy, only as it were, to efface every
> elevated, generous, or tender sentiment that might before have been
> excited by the nobler part of the evening's entertainment.[51]

---

[49] *TS,* 9.24.629.

[50] See *Life,* p. 425. Possibly in anticipation of Yorick's encounter with
Maria, Tristram remarks, as he is bidding farewell to her: "some time, but not
now, I may hear thy sorrows from thy own lips——but I was deceived; for
that moment she took her pipe and told me such a tale of woe with it, that I
rose up, and with broken and irregular steps walk'd softly to my chaise"
(*TS,* 9.24.631).

[51] *Monthly Review,* XXXVI (Feb. 1767), 93–102. Commenting on the two
blank chapters (see *TS,* 9.18–19.621–622, 9.25.632–633), Griffiths remarked:
"well would it have been for thy reputation S——! had some scores of *thine*
[pages] . . . been left in the like state of primæval innocence!" (see Tristram's remark on the blank page in *TS,* 6.38.470–471, quoted p. 170.2–9*n,*
below). Griffiths praised Mrs. Wadman's "*kind* solicitude about the cure of
the wound in [Toby's] groin" as "an amiable picture of SENSIBILITY," and
exclaimed: "O what pity that Nature should . . . capriciously have embroidered the choicest flowers of genius, on a paultry groundwork of buffoonery!" In a similar vein, he asserted that, although Sterne had been compared
to Cervantes and (more justly) to Rabelais, his "*real* prototype" is "HARLE-
QUIN": "To *us* . . . it is a clear case, that the *Reverend Tristram,* does not
sound half so well as *Harlequin-Shandy;* and that, after all the scholia, com-
mentaries and glossaries that have appeared, in order to explain the nature
and design of these whimsical volumes, and to ascertain the class and order of

Griffiths characteristically chose to ignore the fact that Tristram's "INVOCATION" was to the Cervantic "Spirit of sweetest humour," the same spirit which guides Yorick's pen in *A Sentimental Journey*. In finding the motions of Tristram's "vehicle" disobligingly irregular, and in wanting to eliminate its humorous oscillations, Griffiths typifies the reactions of many of Sterne's contemporaries to their literary journey with Tristram. And, as we shall see, he also typifies their failure to understand the motions of Yorick's *"Vehicle."*[52]

By inserting Tristram's encounter with Maria near the conclusion of his *Life and Opinions,* Sterne suggested the sort of entertainment a journey through France and Italy could afford; and, by alluding to Smollett, he hinted that he had such a book in mind. The fashionable world of London knew that "the celebrated Tristram Shandy" had just been abroad again,[53] and the publication of Smollett's splenetic *Travels* enabled Sterne to excite his readers' curiosity by giving them a preview of a new work quite different both from the tedious and ill-humored accounts of many of his forerunners and from Tristam's "Satyr" on them in Vol. VII.

II

During the winter and spring of 1767, following the appearance of Vol. IX of *Tristram Shandy,* Sterne was busy in London publicizing his intention to write a travel book and collecting subscriptions for it.[1] Toward the end of January he wrote a friend: "Im going to publish a *Sentimental Journey* through *France & Italy*— the undertaking is protected & highly encouraged by all our

---

literary composition to which they belong, we scruple not to affirm, that so motley a performance, taking the whole together, . . . can only be denominated the PANTOMIME OF LITERATURE."

Howes notes (pp. 20–21) that the other reviews of Vol. IX were perfunctory and that the book apparently could no longer cause the furor it had once aroused. However, some readers were sufficiently outraged by the indecencies of Vol. IX to request that the Archbishop of York censure Sterne: see *Life,* pp. 423–424; *Letters,* p. 300, n. 2.

[52] See pp. 82.77, 85.127–133, below.

[53] See *Letters,* p. 278, n. 3.

[1] In January 1767 Sterne met Elizabeth Draper, whom he immortalized as "Eliza" in *A Sentimental Journey*. His relationship with her and its influence on *A Sentimental Journey* are discussed in App. E, pp. 322–326, note to p. 67.21.

Noblesse—& at the rate tis subscribed—for, will bring me a thousand guineas (au moins)—twil be an Original—" And he told Lydia, "'I shall not begin my Sentimental Journey till I get to Coxwould—I have laid a plan for something new, quite out of the beaten track."²

Sterne arrived in Coxwold at the beginning of June, and spent most of June through December there, writing *A Sentimental Journey*. On June 9 he informed a friend,

I am now seriously set down to it—that is, I began this morning; a five weeks illness, which by the by, *ought* to have killed me—but that I made a point of it, not to break faith with the world, and in short *would* not die, (for in some cases, I hold this affair to be an act of the will) . . . reduced me and my imagination with me, to such mere shadows, that it was not till last night that I felt the least powers or temptations . . . within me for what I had undertaken. I have now set to, and shall not take my pen from my paper till I have finished.³

On June 13 he told Eliza he had "immortalized" her picture in *A Sentimental Journey*.⁴ In early July he was "beginning to be truly busy at my Sentimental Journey—the pains and sorrows of this life having retarded its progress—but I shall make up my lee-way, and overtake every body in a very short time.—"⁵ However, the work progressed more slowly than he anticipated. According to Richard Griffith, who saw him in Scarborough early in September, he had by then completed only half the first volume. Recounting his conversations with "the modern Democritus, Tristram Shandy," Griffith wrote: "He has communicated a Manuscript to us, that he means soon to publish. It is stiled a Sentimental Journey through Europe, by Yoric. It has all the Humour and Address of the best Parts of Tristram, and is quite free from the Grossness of the worst. There is but about Half a Volume wrote of it yet. He promises to spin the Idea through several Volumes, in the same chaste Way, and calls it his *Work of Redemption* . . ."⁶

---

² *Letters*, No. 182, London, 20 Feb. 1767, p. 300; No. 183, London, 23 Feb. 1767, p. 301.

³ Earl R. Wasserman, "Unedited Letters by Sterne, Hume, and Rousseau," *Modern Language Notes*, XLVI (1951), 74–75.

⁴ See p. 67.20–21*n*, below.

⁵ *Letters*, No. 204, Coxwold, 6 July 1767, p. 375.

⁶ *A Series of Genuine Letters, between Henry and Frances* (London, 1786), V, 66, 83; quoted from *Letters*, p. 398, n. 3.

On the third of October Sterne assured the Jameses that he was spurring on his "Pegasus . . . violently" and was "determined not to draw bit, till I have finish'd"—by Christmas, if possible.[7] However, Mrs. Sterne and Lydia had just arrived from France to spend October in Coxwold, and their visit "robb'd [him] of a month's writing."[8] Sterne probably hoped to have Yorick enter the London literary scene in January (1768), the month Tristram had usually made his appearance, and it is hardly surprising that he found this interruption galling.

In mid-November he wrote Mrs. William James (whose "sentimental turn of mind" he had praised to Lydia)[9] that *A Sentimental Journey* would please her, in a letter he paraphrased in the book:

It is a subject which works well, and suits the frame of mind I have been in for some time past—I told you my design in it was to teach us to love the world and our fellow creatures better than we do—so it runs most upon those gentler passions and affections, which aid so much to it.[10]

In a somewhat different vein, he wrote to "Hannah":

I have something . . . for you, which I am fabricating at a great rate, & that is my Journey, which shall make you cry as much as ever it made

[7] *Letters*, No. 217, Coxwold, 3 Oct. 1767, p. 398.

[8] *Letters*, No. 223, to Sir George Macartney, Coxwold, 3 Dec. 1767, p. 405.

[9] In *Letters*, No. 183, London, 23 Feb. 1767, p. 302.

[10] *Letters*, No. 218, Coxwold, 12 Nov. 1767, pp. 400–401. It should be noted that in paraphrasing this passage in *A Sentimental Journey* (p. 219.75–78, below), Sterne omitted "gentler." Cf. his statement to Mrs. James with *Letters*, No. 214, quoted p. 277.8–9n, below, and with Sterne's prediction that Yorick's *Journey* "will take with the generality—the women will read this book in the parlour, and Tristram in the bed-chamber" (*Letters*, No. 230, London, [? 17 Feb. 1768], p. 412). In a similar vein, Tristram had predicted that his "life and opinions . . . [would] take in all ranks, professions, and denominations of men whatever,—be no less read than the *Pilgrim's Progress* itself—and, in the end, prove the very thing which *Montaigne* dreaded his essays should turn out, that is, a book for a parlour-window" (*TS*, 1.4.7). Tristram is referring to Montaigne's vexation "that my *Essays* only serve the *Ladies* for a common moveable, a Book to lye in the Parlour Window; this Chapter shall prefer me to the Closet" ("Upon Some Verses of Virgil," Cotton's trans., quoted from *TS*, p. 7, n. 1). In considering whether to tell the reader the two words which will make a French post-horse go forward (see p. 137.42–50n, below), Tristram remarks that if he does so, "though their reverences may laugh at it in the bed-chamber—full well I wot, they will abuse it in the parlour" (*TS*, 7.20.503).

me laugh—or I'll give up the Business of sentimental writing—& write to the Body . . .[11]

At the beginning of December, Sterne anticipated being in London at Christmas.[12] On December 28 he wrote the Jameses from York, on his way from Coxwold to London, that he had been confined to his room three weeks "with a fever, & bleeding at my lungs . . . Youl see Me enter like a Ghost."[13] By January 3 Sterne was in London, and was soon "tyed down neck and heels (twice over) by engagements."[14] He predicted on February 9 that he would in "a week's time . . . be deliver'd of two volumes of the sentimental travels of *Mr. Yorick* through France and Italy," but the book was not published until February 27.[15]

Yorick's *Sentimental Journey* was accompanied by an advertisement acknowledging the subscribers' claim on Sterne for two more volumes, which ill health had prevented him from completing, and promising their delivery "early the next Winter."[16] Shortly after the book appeared, however, Sterne contracted a "vile influenza."[17] At first he thought that he could get the better of it, and wrote Elizabeth Montagu:

I brave evils.—et quand Je serai mort, on mettra mon nom dans le liste de ces Heros, qui sont Morts en plaisantant. . . . when y[r] kind Billet came in—I was writing a Romance, in truth, & which, as it is most comic—if my Sickness continues but 7 days—I shall finish—[18]

---

[11] *Letters*, No. 219, Coxwold, 15 Nov. 1767, p. 401 (cf. "I laugh . . . laugh," in *Letters*, No. 87, p. 163, quoted p. 226.33–35*n*, below). Cf. his description of the book to Sir George Macartney as "*clean*" and "frolicksome too," in *Letters*, No. 223, quoted p. 1, above.

[12] See *Letters*, No. 223, 3 Dec. 1767, quoted p. 1, above. On 19 Nov. he wrote: "I am in earnest at my sentimental work—and intend being in town soon after Christmas" (*Letters*, No. 220, p. 402).

[13] *Letters*, No. 226, York, 28 Dec. 1767, pp. 408–409.

[14] *Letters*, No. 231, to the William Jameses, London, [? 18 Feb. 1768], p. 414.

[15] *Letters*, No. 229, to Dr. John Eustace, London, 9 Feb. 1768, p. 411. See App. D, p. 316, n. 1.

[16] See App. D, §3.

[17] *Letters*, No. 235, to Lydia, London, March 1768, p. 417.

[18] *Letters*, No. 234, London, [? March 1768], p. 416. Sterne refers admiringly in this letter to Cervantes' ability to write *Don Quixote* in prison (see pp. 201.10–202.17*n*, below) and to Scarron's ability to write his *Roman comique*

But this time he was not to escape his "vile cough," and less than three weeks after Yorick's uncompleted *Journey* was published, Sterne died of a pleurisy.[19] That "*son of a whore*" Death, the "long-striding scoundrel of a scare-sinner" whom he had led such a merry chase, had overtaken him and found out his lodgings.[20]

III

While he was writing *A Sentimental Journey*, Sterne told Becket (his publisher): "some Genius[e]s in the North declare it an Original work, and likely to take in all Kinds of Readers—the proof of the pudding is in the eating."[1]

The soundness of their judgment, and of Sterne's prediction that though his "*clean brats*" were "frolicksome . . . *cela n'empeche pas*,"[2] was fully proven by the favorable reception of the book. In general, readers found Yorick's *Journey* exactly suited to their taste, and his "travels and observations" were as popular as the first installment of Tristam's "life and opinions." Soon after the book was published, Sterne wrote Lydia from London: "My Sentimental Journey, you say, is admired in York by every one—and 'tis not vanity in me to tell you that it is no less admired here."[3]

In fashionable circles Yorick's *Journey* was generally praised, even by some who had consistently disparaged *Tristram Shandy*.

(from which Sterne had borrowed in Yorick's *Journey:* see p. 178.57–73*n*, below) while in "bodily pain." As Curtis notes (*Letters*, p. 416, n. 1), in Walter's oration upon Bobby's death (which is announced while he is planning Bobby's Grand Tour), he refers to Vespasian's dying "in a jest upon his close stool" (*TS*, 5.3.356).

[19] On 18 March 1768; for the circumstances of his death and an eye-witness account of his last moments by John Macdonald (for whom see App. E, p. 355, note to p. 286.28–34), see *Letters*, p. 419, n. 3; *Life*, pp. 486 ff.

[20] See *TS*, 7.1.479–480, 7.7.487 (when Death comes for Tristram, forcing him to flee abroad, he is telling Eugenius a "tawdry" story of a nun).

[1] *Letters*, No. 211, Coxwold, 3 Sept. 1767, p. 393. Cf. his prediction that the book would "take with the generality," in *Letters*, No. 230, quoted p. 19, n. 10, above.

[2] *Letters*, No. 223, quoted p. 1, above.

[3] *Letters*, No. 235, London, March 1768, p. 417. On the popularity of *A Sentimental Journey* and the innumerable "sentimental" imitations and fads it engendered, see Howes' discussion (pp. 40–44) of the reception of the book, to which I am indebted throughout this section of the introduction.

Horace Walpole, who had pronounced the earlier book an "insipid and tedious performance," grudgingly conceded that Sterne
had partly redeemed himself with the "great good nature and
strokes of delicacy" in his sentimental travels.[4] Elizabeth Montagu,
who had been distressed by the indecency of *Tristram Shandy,* declared: "Poor Tristrams last performance was the best."[5] There
were, to be sure, some hostile reactions. One reader observed: "I
have seen the reverend Prebendary's new publication; in his former
writings I saw evident marks of his genius and benevolence, but
who that indulges serious reflection can read his obscenity and ill-
applied passages of Holy Scripture without horror!"[6] Others ob-
jected to the book on the grounds that the sentiments of "Yorick"
Sterne were exaggerated, insincere, even depraved. One female
reader asserted that a "feeling heart is certainly a right heart; no-
body will contest that: but when a man chooses to walk about the
world with a cambrick handkerchief always in his hand, that he
may always be ready to weep, either with man or beast,—he only
turns me sick."[7] Such dissenting voices were, however, a small
minority.

The periodicals were almost unanimous in their praise, and
only the *Critical Review* attacked a book which one reviewer said
"cannot fail to please every one who is not a stranger to social feelings."[8] The *Critical* charged that Sterne had "set out in a delerium,
. . . a fatal symptom of his approaching dissolution," which had
"the happy temporary effect of making the sufferings of others the
objects of his mirth, and not only rendering him insensible to the
feelings of humanity, but superior to every regard for taste, truth,
observation, or reflection." The reviewer accused Sterne of "sub-
stituting immorality, impudence, and dullness, in the room of

---

[4] *Correspondence with Sir David Dalrymple,* ed. W. S. Lewis (New Haven,
1951), p. 66; *Correspondence with George Montagu,* ed. W. S. Lewis and
Ralph S. Brown, Jr. (New Haven and London, 1941), II, 255.

[5] *Letters,* p. 441.

[6] Joseph Cockfield, as cited in John Nichols, *Illustrations of the Literary
History of the Eighteenth Century* [London, 1817–1858], V, 580; quoted from
Howes, p. 44.

[7] Fanny Greville, as cited in Frances Burney D'Arblay, *Memoirs of Doctor
Burney* [London, 1832], I, 201; quoted from Howes, p. 42.

[8] *Court Miscellany,* IV (Feb. 1768), 87; quoted from Howes, p. 43.

virtue, decency, and wit," and of instructing "young travellers in what the author meant for the *bon ton* of pleasure and licentiousness"; and declared that he had imposed upon his countrymen "*whim* for *sentiment*, and *caprice* for *humour!*"[9] However, the *Critical*'s attack was the only dissenting voice in a general chorus of admiration. The reviewer in the *Political Register* was gratified to find that, to the "original vein of humour which was so natural to him, and which constitutes the chief merit of his works, [Sterne] has here added the moral and the pathetic; so that even while he is entertaining (as he always is) we are agreeably instructed, and our passions are sometimes touched with the strongest sensations of pity and tenderness."[10]

Ralph Griffiths, editor of the *Monthly Review,* who had repeatedly urged Sterne to cultivate his talent for pathos, was delighted, and reprinted generous extracts from the book.[11] He found Yorick's catalogue of travelers (pp. 79–82) "diverting, edifying, and satirical," and declared that in the description of Parisian society (pp. 261–266) "the agreeable though unsubstantial characteristics of the French, may be seen in a truer light, than in the laboured drawings of more serious travellers." In the chapter in which Yorick dispenses alms to the beggars (pp. 132–134), "the heart of the humane reader will," he predicted, "revel in all the luxury of benevolence." Praising the "delicacy of feeling, . . . tender-

---

[9] *Critical Review,* XXV (March 1768), 181–185. Smollett had formerly been the editor of the *Critical,* and Sterne's castigation of him in *A Sentimental Journey* as the splenetic Smelfungus may well have been the main motive for the attack, even though Smollett's connection with the *Critical* had ended before he went abroad in 1763 (see Howes, p. 44). (Tristram alludes sarcastically to Smollett as editor of the *Critical* in *TS,* 6.11.428–429).

[10] *Political Register,* II (May 1768), 383. The *London Magazine,* XXXVII (March 1768), 163, described *A Sentimental Journey* as "the beginning of a work which death has commanded never to be finished—The author's great talents notwithstanding his disregard of order, are universally known, and though some illiberal pen has meanly endeavoured to injure his reputation, by hinting at his want of wisdom, still we may say in his own words at the conclusion of Lefevre's story, that if the accusing spirit flies up to heaven's chancery with his indiscretions, it will blush to give them in, and we doubt not, but the recording angel in writing them down will drop a tear upon each, and wash it away for ever."

[11] *Monthly Review,* XXXVIII (March, April 1768), 174–185, 309–319.

ness of sentiment," and "simplicity of expression" in Yorick's sentimental commerce with Madame R****'s fille de chambre (pp. 187–191), Griffiths exclaimed: "Is it *possible* that a man of *gross ideas* could ever *write* in a strain so pure, so refined from the dross of sensuality!" In the "effusions of this extraordinary pen" he found "reprehensible" only the final chapter, with its "ludicrous *hiatus*" at the end.[12] On the whole, Griffiths declared, the book is Sterne's best production and vindicates the *Monthly*'s judgment that "the highest excellence of this genuine, this legitimate son of humour, lies not in his humorous, but in his pathetic vein."

<h1 style="text-align:center">IV</h1>

Shortly before *A Sentimental Journey* was published, Sterne received a double-handled walking stick from Dr. John Eustace, an admirer of *Tristram Shandy*, who believed this piece of "shandean statuary" would afford him an "ample . . . field for meditation."[1] In acknowledging the gift, Sterne recorded the thoughts it had occasioned:

Your walking stick is in no sense more *shandaic* than in that of its having *more handles than one*—The parallel breaks only in this, that in using the stick, every one will take the handle which suits his convenience. In *Tristram Shandy*, the handle is taken which suits their passions, their ignorance or sensibility. There is so little true feeling in the *herd* of the *world*, that I wish I could have got an act of parliament, when the books first appear'd, "that none but wise men should look into them." It is too much to write books and find heads to understand them. . . . it is not in the power of any one to taste humor, however he may wish it—'tis the gift of God—and besides, a true feeler always brings half the entertainment along with him. His own ideas are only call'd forth by what he

---

[12] See p. 291.152–154*n*, below. Observing that Sterne "had scarce closed" the final hiatus in *A Sentimental Journey* "before the fatal *hiatus* of DEATH put at once a final period to [his] ramblings and writings," Griffiths bade him "eternal adieu": "Farewell, then, admirable Yorick! Be thy wit, thy benevolence, and every blameless part of thy *life* and thy *works*, remembered:—but, on the imperfections of *both*, 'MAY THE RECORDING ANGEL DROP A TEAR, AND BLOT THEM OUT FOR EVER!' "

[1] *Letters*, No. 222, p. 404.

reads, and the vibrations within, so entirely correspond with those excited, 'tis like reading *himself* and not the *book*.[2]

Like Dr. Eustace's walking stick and *Tristram Shandy*, *A Sentimental Journey* has more than one handle. The title page epitomizes the resemblance: *A Sentimental Journey through France and Italy By Mr. Yorick*. Two handles are presented and seem to be paradoxically juxtaposed: the travels are "sentimental"—the traveler is a fellow of infinite jest.[3]

In the course of his journey, Yorick becomes involved by accident and design in situations enabling him to display, with manifest self-approval, all the benevolent sentiments widely regarded during the eighteenth century as the essence of virtue, particularly by those who shared the credo of the "man of feeling."[4] On the other hand, his account of his travels consistently exhibits the comic incongruities between his exalted impulses and the situations which occasion them, exposes their instability and radical impurity, and reveals his susceptibility to all the venial imperfec-

---

[2] *Letters*, No. 229, London, 9 Feb. 1768, p. 411. Cf. *Letters*, No. 136, "we must . . . with us," quoted p. 224.10–13n, below; No. 66, Coxwold, 3 Aug. 1760, p. 120: "I have just finished one volume of Shandy [prob. Vol. III], and I want to read it to someone who I know can taste and rellish humour—"; *TS*, 8.19.559: in listening to a merry story, "a man should ever bring one half of the entertainment along with him"; *Sermons*, II, 25 (IV.viii): "a man's mind must be like your proposition before it can be relished; and 'tis the resemblance between them, which brings over his judgment, and makes him an evidence on your side."

[3] See facsimiles of the title pages of Vols. I and II of the first edition, pp. 63 and 185, below. Sterne certainly intended the book to be ambivalent; see pp. 19–20, above.

According to Lady Bradshaigh, writing to Richardson in 1749 to ask him what "sentimental" meant, the word was then "much in vogue among the polite" (*Correspondence of Samuel Richardson*, ed. Anna L. Barbauld [London, 1804], IV, 282–283). Her use of the word is the first recorded in the *OED;* Curtis argues convincingly (*Letters*, pp. 14–15) that Sterne did not use it in a letter in 1739/40. The word was first given general (especially literary) currency by *A Sentimental Journey:* see Howes, pp. 42–43; Erik Erämetsä, *A Study of the Word "Sentimental" and of Other Linguistic Characteristics of Eighteenth Century Sentimentalism in England* (Helsinki, 1951), esp. pp. 19–21, 46–54.

On Yorick as a fellow of infinite jest, see p. 223.20–23n, below.

[4] See Crane.

tions of human nature, including pruriency, concupiscence, selfishness, and vanity.

Confronted with this equivocal spectacle, many readers have shown the tendency Sterne noted in meditating upon Dr. Eustace's walking stick: to take the handle of the book which accords with their sensibility. As we have seen, Yorick's *Journey* was valued by Sterne's contemporaries mainly for its "tenderness of sentiment" and "delicacy of feeling." During the later eighteenth and early nineteenth centuries, it was admired principally for its sentimental and pathetic aspects.[5] More recently, it has been described as "a text-book on feeling, an exposition of how, in any given set of circumstances, to behave in a sentimental and civilised mode."[6] On the other hand, Yorick has been accused of being a knave who exhibits virtues he knows to be sham. During much of the nineteenth century, though Sterne's humorous characters, particularly Toby, were universally praised, for many readers "Yorick" was synonymous with "pharisee."[7] Even Coleridge, one of Sterne's most admiring and perceptive critics, considered *A Sentimental Journey* "poor sickly stuff" and found "little beyond a clever affectation" in it.[8] Although Thackeray's virulent attack on Sterne is not typical of his age as a whole, his aggressive question about Sterne's general sincerity expressed the uneasy feelings the book aroused in many of his contemporaries: "How much was deliberate calculation and imposture—how much was false sensibility—and how much true feeling? Where did the lie begin, and did he know where? and where did the truth end in the art and scheme of this man of genius, this actor, this quack?"[9]

Several recent critics of Yorick's *Journey* have attempted to resolve its paradoxes by arguing that the "sentimental" aspects of the book are essentially insincere—a pose Sterne adopted to

[5] See Howes, p. 141.

[6] Peter Quennell, *Four Portraits; Studies of the Eighteenth Century* (London, 1945), p. 183.

[7] See Howes, esp. pp. 89–93, 110, 174–175.

[8] See Howes, pp. 118–119.

[9] *The English Humourists of the Eighteenth Century* (New York, 1853), Lecture VI, "Sterne and Goldsmith," p. 240 (first delivered in London, 1851). For an excellent summary and analysis of Thackeray's criticism of Sterne, and of contemporary reactions to it, see Howes, pp. 144–150.

regain the favor of the public, which had been pleased with the
benevolent and "pathetic" aspects of Tristram's "life and opinions" and offended by their wit. According to this view, Sterne's
real feelings are expressed in the comic aspects of the book, and
the Sentimental Traveller is a self-deluded fool who is unwittingly
exposed and ironically mocked, by Sterne, for his naïve faith in
his benevolent sentiments.[10]

Such an interpretation of Yorick's travels cannot, I believe,
account adequately for the evidence that he observes *himself* with
comic detachment. The "*knowingness*"[11] with which he describes
the equivocal motions of his sensibility and seeks to communicate them to the reader's sensibility constantly makes us feel the
presence of a lucid, objective, and witty intelligence. Furthermore,
his analysis, in the Preface to his *Journey,* of what he terms "the
efficient as well as the final causes of travelling" (p. 79), his
frequent asides to the reader, his statement to the Count de B****
that he has "come laughing all the way from London to Paris"
(p. 216), and, above all, his name, are explicit warnings against
regarding Yorick as an *ingénu*-gull whose faith in his own virtue
is a largely unconscious form of self-deception.

Professor Alan McKillop has recently described Yorick as "a
comic figure representing at the same time sentimentalism and the

---

[10] See esp. Rufus Putney's description of *A Sentimental Journey* as "a hoax
by which [Sterne] persuaded his contemporaries that the comedy he must
write was the pathos they wished to read. He accomplished this by making
Yorick weep in order that 'in the same tender moment' he himself might
laugh. . . . Yorick is a dramatically presented comic hero . . . Occasionally Sterne's identification of himself with Yorick becomes almost complete.
But for the most part the writer records with amused irony the false, ludicrous,
or humiliating postures into which Yorick is thrust by his intrepid sensi-
bility" ("Laurence Sterne, Apostle of Laughter," in *The Age of Johnson:
Essays Presented to Chauncey Brewster Tinker* [New Haven, 1949], p. 168).
Putney expresses the same view in "The Evolution of *A Sentimental Journey,*"
(*Philological Quarterly,* XIX [1940], pp. 368–369), where he characterizes
Yorick as "a Cervantic hero" mocked by Sterne for being "led into ludicrous
extravagances by the hyper-sensibility of his heart." See also Ernest N.
Dilworth, *The Unsentimental Journey of Laurence Sterne* (New York, 1948),
esp. ch. v; Lawrance Thompson, *A Comic Principle in Sterne—Meredith—
Joyce* (British Institute, Univ. of Oslo, 1954), pp. 3–11.

[11] Coleridge's term; see p. 40, n. 44, below.

ultimate refinement or attenuation of the comedy of humors. This is not to say that the portrayal of such a character intends a mere burlesque of sentiment; the comedy of humors had long been moving toward sympathetic presentation, and Sterne caps the climax by sympathizing with the humorous aspects of his own personality."[12] Professor McKillop's remarks indicate, I think, a way of grasping both the "sentimental" and the comic handles of Yorick's *Journey* as complementary aspects of a unified, comic vision of life.[13]

Let us consider first the "sentimental" aspects of Yorick's *Journey*. Sterne intended, I believe, that by traveling with Yorick—by attuning his sensibility to Yorick's—a "man of feeling" should strengthen the benevolent virtues he *and Yorick* tended to regard as a sign of goodness and a means of redemption in this world, and even as a partial condition of salvation in the next. These virtues include a capacity for philanthropic benevolence, an ability to share sympathetically the joys and sorrows of our fellow-creatures, and a faculty for good-humored cheerfulness enabling man to participate in all the God-given pleasures and joys of a benign universe.

This aspect of *A Sentimental Journey . . . By Mr. Yorick* corresponds with the faith Sterne preached in *The Sermons of Mr. Yorick*. As a successor of the "anti-Puritan, anti-Stoic, and anti-Hobbesian divines of the Latitudinarian school," Yorick views man as a creature made in the image of "a Being infinitely kind" and bearing

---

[12] McKillop, p. 216. Observing that "sentimentalism involves a highly self-conscious and even self-critical attitude toward feeling, [and] . . . can never be called 'sincere' if by that word we mean 'simple' or 'direct'," he maintains, correctly, I think, that the paradoxes of the book cannot be resolved "simply by setting laughter over against tears, or sincerity over against insincerity" (pp. 215–216).

[13] Although I disagree with Putney's description of *A Sentimental Journey* as a "hoax," my interpretation of the book is indebted to his articles (see p. 27, n. 10, above) and to Traugott; Watkins; Herbert Read, "Sterne," *Collected Essays in Literary Criticism* (London, 1951); and Lawrance Thompson, *op. cit.*, p. 27, n. 10, above.

For an important interpretation of *A Sentimental Journey,* and of the relationship between it and Sterne's *Sermons,* which differs in various respects from mine, see Arthur H. Cash, *Sterne's Comedy of Moral Sentiments: The Ethical Dimensions of the Journey* (Pittsburgh, 1966).

the "natural impressions of benevolence" graven upon his heart by his Creator.[14] He consistently maintains that we can strengthen our natural goodness most effectively through benevolent intercourse with our fellow-men, and through enjoyment of all the pleasurable sensations which emanate from the benign Being whom Yorick, the Sentimental Traveller, apostrophizes as the "great— great SENSORIUM of the world!" (p. 278). True religion enjoins us to participate in "social intercourse" and "peaceable commerce with each other," and in all the "fugacious and innocent pleasures" and joys of the world, by which "the Author of nature intended to sweeten this journey of life,—and bear us up under the many shocks and hard jostlings, which we are sure to meet with" in our "weary pilgrimage."[15] We should also share compassionately the sufferings of others, for if "even the most insensible man" will "comfort the captive, or cover the naked with a garment, . . . he will feel what is meant by that moral delight arising in the mind from the conscience of a humane action."[16] Indeed, can the fact that God, "who is infinitely happy," has

made such provision for our happiness . . . given us so many powers and faculties for enjoyment, and adapted so many objects to gratify and entertain them . . . be reconciled to [His] wisdom, . . . or can it be accounted for on any other supposition, but that the author of our Being, who has given us all things richly to enjoy, wills us a comfortable existence even *here,* and seems moreover . . . to have ordered things . . . [so] that the ways which lead to our future happiness, when rightly understood, he has made to be ways of pleasantness, and all her paths peace[?][17]

---

[14] Crane, p. 230. *Sermons,* II, 177 (VI.x); I, 64 (I.v), 82–83 (II.vii).

[15] *Sermons,* II, 224 (VII.xiv); II, 177–179 (VI.x).

[16] See *Sermons,* II, 24–25, quoted in App. E, p. 339, n. 6. This and many similar passages in the *Sermons* exhibit what Crane has described (pp. 229– 230) as "that curious type of hedonism—the often frankly avowed pursuit of altruistic emotions for egoistic ends"—foreshadowed in the preaching of many Anglican divines of Latitudinarian persuasion from the Restoration onward, and characteristic of "most of the representative 'men of feeling' of the next two generations. Sir Charles Grandison might have been a parishioner of Parker or Brent, and Parson Yorick their successor."

[17] *Sermons,* "Penances," II, 177–178 (VI.x). Cf. Proverbs 3:17: the ways of wisdom "are ways of pleasantness, and all her paths are peace." Sterne's text in this sermon is I John 5:3: "For this is the love of God, that we keep

Underlying this and other passages in the *Sermons*[18] is an assumption which may be briefly stated as follows: that the joys afforded us by the goods of *this* world are essentially akin to the perfect joy which will be afforded us by God, the supreme Good, in the *next* world, and therefore require the same faculties for their enjoyment.[19] Parson Yorick consistently affirms his belief that participation in the God-given joys and pleasures of our present state is a redemptive process,[20] in two principal senses: first, it

---

his commandments: and his commandments are not grievous." He argues (II, 175–176): that "amongst the many prejudices which at one time or other have been conceived against our holy religion, there is scarce any one which has done more dishonour to christianity, or which has been more opposite to the spirit of the gospel, than this, in express contradiction to the words of the text, 'That the commandments of God *are* grievous.'—That the way which leads to life is not only strait, for that our Saviour tells us, and that with much tribulation we shall seek it;—but that christians are bound to make the worst of it, and tread it barefoot upon thorns and briers,—if ever they expect to arrive happily at their journey's end.—And in course,—during this disastrous pilgrimage, it is our duty so to renounce the world, and abstract ourselves from it, as neither to interfere with its interests, or taste any of the pleasures, or any of the enjoyments of this life." The Methodists "discant upon the necessity of alienating themselves from the world" on this "same mistaken enthusiastic principle, which would cast so black a shade upon religion, as if the kind Author of it had created us on purpose to go mourning, all our lives long, in sack-cloth and ashes,—and sent us into the world, as so many saint-errants, in quest of adventures full of sorrow and affliction."

[18] See esp. the passages quoted from the *Sermons*, p. 39 and pp. 283.15–284.27n, below, and in App. E, pp. 338–342, note to pp. 120.54–64. These passages are consistently qualified by Sterne's awareness that, because man's "affections" are radically imperfect, his participation in the virtuous pleasures and joys of the world often becomes excessive and licentious; see esp. *Sermons,* I, 16–20 (I.ii), II, 182–184 (VI.x), and p. 45, n. 54, below.

[19] The foundations and rationale of this assumption are to be found partly in the writings of the Cambridge Platonists and their Latitudinarian successors, particularly in their reformulation of the Platonic doctrine of Eros; see Ernst Cassirer, *The Platonic Renaissance in England* (Austin, Texas, 1953); Ralph W. Rader, "Idea and Structure in Fielding's Novels" (unpubl. diss., Indiana Univ., 1957), pp. 1–82.

[20] Ernest Tuveson has traced the "steps whereby nature became a source of redemption and the imagination a means of grace" during the eighteenth century, and has described the resulting tendency to regard the "pleasures" of this world as essentially similar to the "true and eternal 'joy' " of the next

enables us to achieve a measure of temporal blessedness and, thereby, to strengthen the virtues which will enable us to participate in the joyful beatitude of eternal blessedness. And second, it saves us from the vices which can deprive us of the joys of this world and even, perhaps, of the next.

As Yorick points out in *A Sentimental Journey,* chief among these vices is the spleen:

> The learned SMELFUNGUS travelled from Boulogne to Paris—from Paris to Rome—and so on—but he set out with the spleen and jaundice, and every object he pass'd by was discoloured or distorted—He wrote an account of them, but 'twas nothing but the account of his miserable feelings. . . .
>
> Mundungus . . . made the whole tour . . . without one generous connection or pleasurable anecdote to tell of; but he had travell'd straight on looking neither to his right hand or his left, lest Love or Pity should seduce him out of his road.
>
> Peace be to them! if it is to be found; but heaven itself, was it possible to get there with such tempers, would want objects to give it—every gentle spirit would come flying upon the wings of Love to hail their arrival—Nothing would the souls of Smelfungus and Mundungus hear of, but fresh anthems of joy, fresh raptures of love, and fresh congratulations of their common felicity—I heartily pity them: they have brought up no faculties for this work; and was the happiest mansion in heaven to be allotted to Smelfungus and Mundungus, they would be so far from being happy, that the souls of Smelfungus and Mundungus would do penance there to all eternity. [pp. 116–120]

Yorick's ironic benediction upon Smelfungus and Mundungus as Splenetic Travellers is paraphrased from one of Sterne's sermons.[21] It clearly implies that the spleen is a vice which, by tingeing everything in the traveler's way "with sable, or with a sickly green,"[22] deprives its victims of the redeeming joys and pleasures emanating from the great SENSORIUM of the world. Like Tristram's

---

(*The Imagination as a Means of Grace* [Berkeley and Los Angeles, 1960], pp. 55, 108). Sterne's *Sermons* and *A Sentimental Journey,* show, I think, the influence of this revolution, with the qualification that Sterne emphasizes the redeeming pleasures afforded by benevolent intercourse with our fellowman, rather than those afforded by contemplating the sublimities of physical nature.

[21] See App. E, pp. 338–342, note to pp. 120.54–64.

[22] See *TS,* 7.1.479, quoted p. 224.10–13*n,* below.

Life and Opinions, Yorick's *Journey* is written "against the spleen,"[23] and in this as in other respects, his "travels and observations" are, as he points out, "altogether of a different cast" from those of many of his English "fore-runners" on the Grand Tour (p. 82).

Smelfungus is, of course, Tobias Smollett, whose *Travels through France and Italy* Tristram had attacked as typifying the morose and splenetic observations of many of his fellow-Englishmen on their travels abroad. By Tristram's and Yorick's standards, Smollett's *Travels* simply prove that in general "a man would act as wisely, if he could prevail upon himself, to live contented without foreign knowledge or foreign improvements" (p. 84). For, like many British travellers during the eighteenth century, Smollett suffered from the prejudices and afflictions Yorick specifies in the Preface to his *Journey* as the "efficient as well as the final causes of travelling" which prevented many of his countrymen from gaining "useful knowledge and real improvements" abroad (pp. 79, 83).

As a Proud Traveller, Smollett found almost everything worse ordered in France than in England, and praised his native country as "the land of liberty, cleanliness, and convenience."[24] As a Vain and Inquisitive Traveller, he proclaimed the *"Novelty of [his] Vehicle"* (p. 82, below) and promised he would not repeat the empty generalizations about foreign customs, culture, and institutions or the trite catalogues of *videnda* furnished by his predecessors on the beaten track of the Grand Tour.[25] However, like many of his forerunners, Smollett was frequently betrayed into dullness and absurdity by his uninspired efforts to be original. He compiled statistics on the weather at Nice, remeasured Roman ruins with a

---

[23] *TS,* 4.22.301.

[24] *Travels,* Letter No. 41, p. 339.

[25] See p. 218.66–69*n,* below. Smollett assures his readers that his remarks on Rome "are all my own" and that, "upon my word and honour, I have described nothing but what actually fell under my own observation" (*Travels,* Letter No. 31, p. 264; No. 33, p. 290). However, in this respect Smollett was, like many of his predecessors, a Lying Traveller (p. 81, below) who cribbed from other travelers; see Louis L. Martz, *The Later Career of Tobias Smollett* (New Haven, 1942), pp. 73–89. Tristram makes fun of the way travelers steal each other's "remarks," in *TS,* 7.36.528–529.

packthread,[26] and catalogued the horrors of European closestools. His original judgment on the Pantheon and his novel perspective on the Venus de Medici—"there is no beauty in the features of Venus . . . [but] the back parts . . . are executed so happily, as to excite the admiration of the most indifferent spectator"— were given an unenviable immortality by Yorick.[27] Above all, as a Splenetic Traveller driven abroad by "infirmity of body," Smollett complained incessantly about the discomforts, inconveniences, and expenses of traveling abroad.[28] In his endless campaign against ill health, filthy inns, and rapacious innkeepers, he encountered nothing but "VEXATION upon VEXATION,"[29] and in a moment of splenetic exasperation he declared that his experiences on the road would "not bear a recital."[30]

Yorick's conduct as the Sentimental Traveller shows how to gain "useful knowledge and real improvements" in "sailing and posting through the politer kingdoms of the globe" (pp. 83–84). His travels are partly intended to teach his contemporaries the value of behaving in a civilized manner. As V. S. Pritchett has observed, Smollett's writings, like Rowlandson's and Hogarth's pictures, delineate "the nightmare lying behind the Augustan manner." Peopled by genteel Yahoos "done up in ribbons or breeches," this nightmare luridly illustrates the urgent necessity for the reform of manners undertaken by English writers during the eighteenth century, particularly in the *Tatler* and the *Specta-*

---

[26] *Travels,* Letter No. 16, p. 144.

[27] See p. 117.33–35*n*, p. 117.35–39*n*, below.

[28] Smollett left England to travel in France and Italy partly in hope of improving his health, which had been broken by his prolonged literary labors; see Lewis M. Knapp, *Tobias Smollett, Doctor of Men and Manners* (Princeton, 1949), pp. 243–247. Knapp points out (p. 265) that "it is reasonably certain that Smollett . . . did not have to worry too much about travelling expenses after 1763," the year he went abroad; and Smollett probably exaggerates his financial vexations in his *Travels.* On the other hand, he had to be careful to stay within his means. George M. Kahrl observes that Smollett "went abroad, depending on his limited resources but undoubtedly intending to pay part of his expenses by writing a book of travels" (*Tobias Smollett, Traveller-Novelist* [Chicago, 1945], p. 95).

[29] *TS,* 7.30.518.

[30] See *Travels,* Letter No. 8, quoted p. 268.1–10*n*, below.

tor.[31] *A Sentimental Journey* is part of this program of reform and
is intended to demonstrate that delicacy and decorum, good manners and cosmopolitan tolerance are civilizing and humanizing
virtues conducive to a benevolent disposition toward our fellowmen. This aspect of Yorick's travels is comically exemplified by
his service at Madame de Rambouliet's fountain (pp. 181–183).
It is also expressed in his conversation with the old French officer
at the opera, who comments that "the advantage of travel, as it
regarded the *sçavoir vivre*, was by seeing a great deal both of men
and manners; it taught us mutual toleration; and mutual toleration, concluded he, making me a bow, taught us mutual love. . . .
'twas my own way of thinking—the difference was, I could not
have expressed it half so well" (p. 181).

Yorick's conversation with the officer also exemplifies the importance of mastering the *"short hand"* of translating "the several
turns of looks and limbs, with all their inflections and delineations,
into plain words." For the Sentimental Traveller, "There is not
a secret so aiding to the progress of sociality" (p. 171), because,
as Yorick observes to the Count de B***, he wishes

to spy the *nakedness* of . . . hearts, and through the different disguises
of customs, climates, and religion, find out what is good in them, to
fashion my own by—and therefore am I come.

It is for this reason . . . that I have not seen the Palais royal . . .
nor the Façade of the Louvre—nor have attempted to swell the catalogues we have of pictures, statues, and churches . . . —'tis a quiet
journey of the heart in pursuit of NATURE, and those affections which
rise out of her, which make us love each other—and the world, better
than we do. [pp. 217–219]

Cosmopolitan benevolence for our fellowmen and mastery of
the *"short hand"* which enables us to share their feelings are in-
dispensable aids in overcoming the difficulty which

must have been observed by many a peripatetic philosopher, That nature
has . . . [laid man] under almost insuperable obligations to work out
his ease, and to sustain his sufferings at home. . . . 'Tis true we are endued with an imperfect power of spreading our happiness sometimes
beyond *her* limits, but 'tis so ordered, that from the want of languages,
connections, and dependencies, and from the difference in education,

---

[31] *The Living Novel* (New York, 1947), p. 33.

customs and habits, we lie under so many impediments in communicating our sensations out of our own sphere, as often amount to a total impossibility.

It will always follow from hence, that the balance of sentimental commerce is always against the expatriated adventurer. [p. 78]

Read with Locke and with Tristram's *Life and Opinions* in mind, the Sentimental Traveller's observations describe, in terms of the frustrations of traveling "abroad," a dilemma fundamental to our shandean existence—"the great game of cross-purposes called communication."[32] The comic perplexities, and the possibilities, of playing this game successfully are central to the drama of Tristram's world, and to the "rhetoric" of attitude, look, and gesture, as well as of words, which informs that world and makes it accessible to the reader. Walter, Toby, and the reader speak languages which are largely foreign to one another, but they do succeed in communicating their sensations out of their own spheres, largely through the mysterious operation of intuition and sympathy, aided by look and gesture.

Yorick's *Sentimental Journey* is a triumph of communication between his own and foreign sensibilities, in traveling through France and Italy, and in traveling with the reader. It is intended to persuade us that the real profits of "sailing and posting through the politer kingdoms of the globe in pursuit of knowledge and improvements" (p. 83) derive from carrying on a sentimental commerce in the benevolent affections with our fellowmen and from participating in all the joys of a beneficent universe. As Yorick asks rhetorically in one of his sermons: "For what purpose do you imagine, has GOD made us? for the social sweets of the well watered vallies where he has planted us, or for the dry and dismal deserts of a *Sierra Morena?*"[33] Indeed, the Sentimental Traveller—"who interests his heart in every thing, and who . . . [has] eyes to see, what time and chance are perpetually holding out to him as he journeyeth on his way"—can carry on a benevolent commerce with a beneficent world even in a *Sierra Morena:* "I pity the man who can travel from *Dan* to *Beersheba,* and cry, 'Tis all barren—

[32] See McKillop, pp. 195, 206–207; and Traugott, pp. 6–14.
[33] *Sermons,* I, 14 (I.ii); for the "*Sierra Morena,*" see *Don Quixote,* 1.3.9.161 ff.

and so it is; and so is all the world to him who will not cultivate the
fruits it offers. I declare, said I, clapping my hands chearily together, that was I in a desart, I would find out wherewith in it to
call forth my affections—" (pp. 114–115).

Yorick's "travels and observations" illustrate the importance
of digressing from the beaten track of the Grand Tour and of interesting one's heart in everything. The traveler who has eyes to
see more than the standard *videnda* can grasp the significance of
apparently trivial experiences and objects. An exchange of snuff-
boxes, the hiring of a valet, a caged starling, the throbs of a grisette's pulse, the dance of a peasant family are, rightly understood,
more important than the Palais Royal and the façade of the Louvre.
As Yorick remarks, "Nature is shy," and the "precise and distinguishing marks of national characters" can be seen better in
"nonsensical *minutiae*" like a Parisian barber's encomium on a
wig "than in the most important matters of state" (pp. 257, 160).
The episodes of Yorick's *Journey* are rendered with a minute fidelity to details of posture, gesture, and feeling which illustrates
the importance of grasping such experiences "within this little
span of life" (p. 114)—in which one travels with Death close behind. This fidelity to detail makes us feel, as in *Tristram Shandy*,
the way the present moment epitomizes reality, and individual
experience "images in little and simultaneously a moral order and
a cosmic order."[34] The underlying principle is expressed in a fragment attributed to Sterne:

It's hard to say whether [*sic*] side of yᵉ prospects strikes yᵉ imagination most; whether yᵉ solar system or a drop of pepper water afford a
nobler subject of contemplation; in short whether we owe more to yᵉ
Telescope or microscope. On one side infinite Power and wisdom appear
drawn at *full extent;* on yᵉ other, in *miniature.* The infinitely *strong and
bold Strokes there,* yᵉ infinitely *nice and delicate Touches here,* shew equally
in both yᵉ divine hand.[35]

For the traveler with eyes to see, the small things of the world
correspond with the great and are equally significant; and they
have the added advantage of being everywhere close at hand and

---

[34] McKillop, p. 196.

[35] "*Fragment Inédit,*" in Paul Stapfer, *Laurence Sterne* (Paris, 1870), p.
xxii, misnumbered xii.

easily accessible. The correspondence and interaction of small and great, of microcosm and macrocosm, is expressed by Yorick in his apostrophe to his sensibility and to the "great—great Sensorium of the world! which vibrates, if a hair of our heads but falls upon the ground, in the remotest desert of thy creation" (p. 278).

Like many of Yorick's forerunners on the Grand Tour, Smollett failed to gain "useful knowledge and real improvements" abroad partly because he spent much of his time cataloguing pictures, statues, churches, and closestools, rather than spying the nakedness of hearts and pursuing Nature and the benevolent affections which rise out of her. However, as Yorick's ironic benediction upon Smelfungus suggests, Smollett failed, in Yorick's opinion, to profit from his Grand Tour primarily because he suffered from that peculiarly English malady—the spleen. Thus afflicted, he could not engage in sentimental commerce with his fellowmen; and, thus rendered incapable of seeing any beauty in the features of Venus, he could admire only her backsides.

In his *Travels*, Smollett casts himself partly in the role of the "splenetic humourist, the man of fierce independence and of a difficult temper"—a prickly and angular individualist admired by Englishmen during the eighteenth century as a bulwark of English liberty and a singular instance of "that agreeable Variety of original Characters" produced by the English climate.[36] Smollett also plays the part of Matthew Bramble, "an odd kind of humourist" who is "always on the fret," but who "affects misanthropy, in order to conceal the sensibility of a heart, which is tender, even to a degree of weakness."[37] However, as Smelfungus, Smollett becomes a

---

[36] See Hooker, pp. 379–381, and p. 231.27–33*n*, below.

[37] *Humphrey Clinker*, Modern Library ed. (New York, 1929), pp. 5, 29. See Lewis M. Knapp, "Smollett's Self-Portrait in *The Expedition of Humphrey Clinker*," in *The Age of Johnson: Essays Presented to Chauncey Brewster Tinker* (New Haven, 1949), pp. 153–154. As V. S. Pritchett has acutely remarked, "Smollett may have enjoyed the brutality he described, but his protests and his hypochondria suggest that he felt the pleasure and the agony of the man who has a skin too few. His coarseness, like that of Joyce, is the coarseness of one whose senses were unprotected and whose nerves were exposed" (*The Living Novel*, p. 34). Tave notes (pp. 146–147) that Goldsmith's man in black is a humorist of the same kind as Bramble and conceals a benevolent heart beneath a misanthropic manner.

partially allegorical figure epitomizing all those "splenetick and
morose souls"—particularly those of puritanical and stoic persua-
sions—"whose natural pleasures are burthens" and who fly "from
joy . . . as if it was really an evil in itself."[38] For the Splenetic
Travellers of this world, life is merely a "disastrous pilgrimage"
through "the dry and dismal deserts of a *Sierra Morena.*"

Yorick's *Sentimental Journey* may be said to culminate the program initiated by the Latitudinarian divines and carried forward
in Shaftesbury's *Characteristics* and in the *Tatler* and *Spectator*—
to raise to the status of a spiritual virtue "cheerfulness, the good
humor of the man who recognizes that the true spirit of religion is
amiable and sociable," and to play it off "against the spleen and
melancholy of the puritanical saint of a sorrowful countenance."[39]
This aspect of his *Journey* is illustrated by the supper he shares
with the peasant family in the Bourbonnais and by the grace which
follows it. After partaking of bread and wine with them, he observes:

> If the supper was to my taste—the grace which follow'd it was much
> more so. . . . [In] the middle of the second dance, . . . from some
> pauses in the movement wherein they all seemed to look up, I fancied
> I could distinguish an elevation of spirit different from that which is the
> cause or the effect of simple jollity.—In a word, I thought I beheld *Re-
> ligion* mixing in the dance—but as I had never seen her so engaged, I
> should have look'd upon it now, as one of the illusions of an imagination
> which is eternally misleading me, had not the old man, as soon as the
> dance ended, said, that this was their constant way; and that all his life
> long he had made it a rule, after supper was over, to call out his family
> to dance and rejoice; believing, he said, that a chearful and contented
> mind was the best sort of thanks to heaven that an illiterate peasant
> could pay—
> ——Or a learned prelate either, said I. [pp. 282–284]

---

[38] *Sermons,* II, 13 (IV.vii). In ridiculing the "pious fooleries of penances and
sufferings" practiced by the Methodists and Papists, Yorick observes that
"such mockery became a part of religion . . . [and] were imagined to
be services acceptable to God," because "men of melancholy and morose
tempers, conceiving the Deity to be like themselves, a gloomy, discontented
and sorrowful being,—believed he delighted, as they did, in splenetic and
mortifying actions . . ." (*Sermons,* II, 179 [VI.x]).

[39] Tave, p. 11. Tave quotes (pp. 3–15) several passages from Barrow, from
Hacket, and from Addison's much-admired *Spectator* No. 381, enjoining
cheerfulness as a virtue conducive to the joyful spirit of true religion.

This passage suggests that there is a vital correspondence between the spirit of temporal blessedness which invests the supper and the grace, and the kindred spirit which presides over the Lord's Supper—a correspondence illustrating Sterne's "conviction . . . that the principal spirit in the Universe is one of joy."[40]

Like Yorick's *Sermons, A Sentimental Journey* is intended to persuade the reader that, "When the affections . . . kindly break loose, Joy, is another name" for a "heavenly religion" which, "like its great author," is "universally kind and benevolent," and is "so courteous,——so good temper'd,——that every precept of it carries a balm along with it to heal the soreness of our natures, and sweeten our spirits, that we might live with such kind intercourse in this world, as will fit us to exist together in a better."[41] If we do not press the point too far, his travels may be said to combine the "seventeenth-century ideal of *pèlerinage de l'âme*" with the "eighteenth-century ideal of cosmopolitanism and sociality,"[42] for by traveling with him the reader can develop the faculties essential to participation in this joyful religion.

In this way, *A Sentimental Journey through France and Italy* —with Mr. Yorick—can lead toward a better world. And in these terms, his statement that his travels are "a quiet journey of the heart in pursuit of NATURE, and those affections which rise out of

[40] Watkins, p. 118.
[41] See *Sermons*, I, 233 (III.v), quoted pp. 283.15–284.27*n*, below (and the ref. to God as "the fountain of joy" in *Sermons*, II, 8–9, quoted p. 148.49–52*n*, below); *Sermons*, I, 129 (II.xi); I, 215 (III.iii).
[42] Maynard Mack, Introduction to Pope's *Essay on Man*, in *Poems of Alexander Pope*, Twickenham ed., Vol. III–i (London, 1950), p. lxxiv. Mack discusses the ways in which the *Essay* illustrates the "philosophical shift" between these ideals. My suggestion that *A Sentimental Journey* combines these ideals must, of course, be qualified by acknowledging that the radical differences between Yorick's travels and the various seventeenth-century conceptions of the *pèlerinage de l'âme* illustrate the divergence between the paths followed by the Sentimental Traveller and by Bunyan's pilgrim, for example: for Bunyan's Christian, "narrow is the way" (Matthew 7:14), and digressions—which for Tristram and Yorick are "the life, the soul of reading" and of living (*TS*, 1.22.73)—are disastrous. Yorick's cheerful declaration that he could "find out wherewith in [a desert] to call forth my affections" (p. 115) invites comparison with Christian's "lamentable cry" in "the wilderness of this world," at the outset of *Pilgrim's Progress*: "*What shall I do?*"

her, which make us love each other—and the world, better than
we do" (p. 219), should be taken more seriously than it has been
by many readers.[43]

But Yorick's *Journey* should not, of course, be taken solemnly,
and let us now consider its comic aspects. In traveling with him a
"man of feeling" should, ideally, have found himself participating
in a comic proof of the incongruities between his faith in his benevolence—and the realities of acting on imperfect motives in an
imperfect, though beneficent, world.

Yorick's virtues are consistently made the laughable "sport of
contingencies" (p. 70). A monk, not an orphan, appeals to him
for charity (p. 70); or, "I thought by the accent, it had been an
apostrophe to his child; but 'twas to his ass" (p. 138). The Sentimental Traveller's benevolence is warmed by wine costing two
livres a bottle (p. 68), but he has only eight sous for the beggars
who surround him in Montrieul and dispenses them with manifest
self-approval and self-gratification (pp. 132–134). And his sentimental commerce with the fair *grissette,* with the *fille de chambre* in
his hotel room, and with Maria, is subtly calculated to implicate
the reader in a demonstration that, in our imperfect state, "the
extreams of DELICACY, and the *beginnings* of CONCUPISCENCE,"—
and the extremes of charity and the beginnings of sentimentality—
are so ambiguously compounded as to be one affection.[44] However,

---

[43] Sir Herbert Read is a notable exception; see "Sterne" in his *Collected
Essays in Literary Criticism* (London, 1951), esp. p. 253. Perhaps Sterne's
reference to *A Sentimental Journey* as his *"Work of Redemption"* (see p. 18,
above) was not simply a jesting expression of his hope that the book would
redeem his reputation and fortune.

[44] *TS,* 5.1.348. Like Yorick's entire *Journey,* these scenes are characterized
by what Coleridge brilliantly described as "A sort of *knowingness,* the wit of
which depends . . . [on] the innocence and innocent ignorance over which
it triumphs; or . . . on a certain oscillation in the individual's own mind
between the remaining good and the encroaching evil of his nature, a sort of
dallying with the devil" (*Coleridge's Miscellaneous Criticism,* ed. Thomas M.
Raysor [Cambridge, Mass., 1936], Lecture IX, "Wit and Humour," pp. 121–
122; from Coleridge's MS. notes). The rhetorical strategy of these scenes is
similar to that in *Sermons,* I, 17–20 (I.ii), "The House of Feasting and the
House of Mourning Described," which has been incisively analyzed by
Traugott, pp. 99–102.

Sterne's aim in persuading the reader to participate in this kind of proof was not, I think, to satirize sentimental benevolence as a delusive sham. Though Yorick is keenly aware that Fancy is "a seduced, and a seducing slut" and "cheatest us seven times a day with thy pictures and images" (p. 92), Sterne is "not really baffled or discouraged by the threat of skepticism or solipsism."[45] Nor, heaven forbid! does Sterne wish to convert the reader to puritanical stoicism—"If nature has so wove her web of kindness, that some threads of love and desire are entangled with the piece— must the whole web be rent in drawing them out?—Whip me such stoics, great governor of nature!" (p. 237). Rather, Sterne intended that by traveling with Yorick the reader should realize that "there is nothing unmixt in this world" (p. 228), and should develop another spiritual virtue, "the gift of God" in which he had found most of his contemporaries deficient—a benignly comic sense of life, including a benevolent sense of humor about themselves.

By enabling the traveler to laugh good-humoredly at the vexations of his journey, this virtue purges his system of the splenetic vices which can deprive him of the joys of life, and it thereby helps him to reconcile the shandean paradoxes of life with the spirit of an infinitely benign Creator.[46] And by enabling him to laugh at himself with sympathetic and yet objective amusement, a comic sense of life can help him to know himself.

Commenting in the Preface to his *Journey* on "the efficient as well as the final causes of travelling" (p. 79), Yorick calls attention to the "*Novelty of my Vehicle*" and observes: "It is sufficient for my reader, if he has been a traveller himself, that with study and reflection hereupon he may be able to determine his own place and rank in the catalogue [of travellers]—it will be one step towards knowing himself" (pp. 82–83).

Arrayed in the armor of righteousness for combat against the forces of Puritanism, Stoicism, and Hobbesianism, the "man of feeling" considered it a moral imperative to love himself—indeed, " 'tis one step towards acting well, to think worthily of our na-

---

[45] McKillop, p. 195.
[46] Good-humored laughter, as Tristram points out (*TS*, 4.22.301–302), is the sovereign remedy for the spleen (see also *TS*, 4.32.337–338).

ture."[47] However, though self-love is an inducement to virtue, it
is also an incitement to pride, and can prevent us from knowing
ourselves aright.[48] In his sermon on "Self Knowledge," Yorick
considers this problem and proposes a solution which suggests a
way of correlating one aspect of the technique and of the purpose of
Yorick's *Journey*. Observing that Scripture speaks truly in pro-
nouncing the heart of man "treacherous to itself and *deceitful above
all things*,"[49] Yorick notes that man's propensity to self-deceit is
strongest when he attempts "to judge of himself—that dearest of
all parties,—so closely connected with him—so much and so long
beloved." Realizing the power of self-love to make us deceitful
casuists in our own behalf,

Some of the earliest instructors of mankind . . . saw the necessity of
laying such a stress upon this great precept of self knowledge, which
for its excellent wisdom and usefulness, many of them supposed to be
a divine direction; that it came down from Heaven, and comprehended
the whole circle both of knowledge and the duty of man. And indeed
their zeal might easily be allowed in so high an encomium upon the

-----

[47] *Sermons*, I, 82 (II.vii). Furthermore, he lived in an age when, for many,
"morality was located in goodness of heart not action" (Tave, p. 157; see also
Crane, p. 214).

[48] In his sermon on Pride (*Sermons*, II, 33–34 [IV.ix]), Yorick remarks
that, though the contention of "some satyrical pens" that "all mankind at the
bottom . . . [are] proud alike" has "more spleen than truth in it," nevertheless, it must be admitted that "Pride is a vice which grows up in society so
insensibly;—steals in unobserved upon the heart upon so many occasions;—
forms itself upon such strange pretensions, and when it has done, veils itself
under such a variety of unsuspected appearances,—sometimes even under
that of Humility itself;—in all which cases, Self-love, like a false friend, instead
of checking, most treacherously feeds this humour . . .——that upon the
whole, there is no one weakness into which the heart of man is more easily
betray'd,——or which requires greater helps of good sense and good principles to guard against." For Sterne's borrowings from Samuel Clarke in this
passage, see Hammond, p. 112.

[49] Cf. Jeremiah 17:9: "The heart is deceitful above all things, and des-
perately wicked: who can know it?"; and *Sermons*, II, 251 (VII.xvii): "who
can search the heart of man?—it is treacherous even to ourselves, and much
more likely to impose upon others." On the difficulty of knowing and judging
ourselves aright, see also "The Abuses of Conscience Considered," *Sermons*,
II, 67–80 (IV.xii), and *TS*, 2.17.123–140; and "Self-Examination," *Sermons*,
I, 160–168 (II.xiv).

attainment of a virtue, the want of which so often baffled their instructions, and rendered their endeavours of reforming the heart vain and useless. . . .

But this was a point always much easier recommended by public instructors than shewn how to be put in practice, and therefore others, who equally sought the reformation of mankind, observing that this direct road which led to it was guarded on all sides by self-love, and consequently very difficult of open access, soon found out that a different and more artful course was requisite; as they had not strength to remove this flattering passion which stood in their way and blocked up all the passages to the heart, they endeavoured by stratagem to get beyond it, and by a skilful address, if possible, to deceive it. This gave rise to the early manner of conveying their instructions in parables, fables, and such sort of indirect applications, which, tho' they could not conquer this principle of self-love, yet often laid it asleep, or at least over-reached it for a few moments, till a just judgment could be procured.[50]

Yorick's *Sentimental Journey* can, I believe, be regarded as a kind of "parable" or "fable" illustrating the perplexities, and the possibility, of fulfilling the eighteenth-century moral imperative to *Know thyself.*

---

[50] *Sermons*, I, 37–40 (I.iv). For Sterne's borrowings in this sermon from a sermon on "The Difficulty of Knowing One's Self," possibly by Swift, see Hammond, pp. 152–154.

Yorick observes in this sermon that the "prophet Nathan seems to have been a great master in this way of address" and analyzes Nathan's use of a "fable" to induce David to convict himself "out of his own mouth" (I, 37) for his crime against Uriah (II Samuel 11–12); the story of Nathan and David is also cited in *Sermons*, II, 73 (IV.xii), and *TS*, 2.17.132. Thompson (*op. cit.* [p. 27, n. 10, above], pp. 6–7) also applies Yorick's remarks (in his sermon on "Self Knowledge") on the use of parables and fables by instructors like Nathan, to the method and purpose of *A Sentimental Journey;* however, he regards Yorick primarily as a self-deluded fool unwittingly exposed and mocked by Sterne.

On the efficacy of parables as a means of instruction, see also *Sermons*, I, 25–26 (I.iii); and I, 227 (III.v), "The Prodigal Son": "I know not whether the remark is to our honour or otherwise, that lessons of wisdom have never such power over us, as when they are wrought into the heart, through the groundwork of a story which engages the passions: Is it that we are like iron, and must first be heated before we can be wrought upon? or, Is the heart so in love with deceit, that where a true report will not reach it, we must cheat it with a fable, in order to come at truth?"

His *Journey* is recounted in what Tristram apostrophized as the "Gentle Spirit of sweetest humour, who erst didst sit upon the easy pen of my beloved CERVANTES."[51] Yorick's benevolent impulses are the counterpart, in an age of sensibility, to Don Quixote's chivalric ideals, and he gives them free reign in the justified faith that they are in harmony with the great SENSORIUM of the world.[52] As a result, the Sentimental Traveller posts into quixotic dilemmas which dramatize the comic frustrations of sentimental knight-errantry. These dilemmas arise partly from the conflict between benevolent idealism and the shandean realities of an imperfect world. But they also arise from the fact that, unlike Don Quixote's exalted motives, Yorick's benevolent impulses are themselves radically equivocal and imperfect.

This aspect of Yorick's *Journey* illustrates the validity of another belief fundamental to *The Sermons of Mr. Yorick:* Man is the glory of the world—made in the image of "a Being infinitely kind" and full of "benevolent affections." But he is also its jest—living "amongst mysteries and riddles," and so perpetually baffled that he appears at times to have been sent into the world "to play the fool."[53] And he is its riddle—"a strange compound [such that]

---

[51] The spirit Tristram invokes to preside over his account of his meeting with Maria; see pp. 13–16, above.

[52] On the gradual transformation of Don Quixote from a satiric butt to an "amiable humorist" during the eighteenth century, see Tave (pp. 151–163), who points out (p. 159) that Sterne "must have been a major influence" in this transformation. (See Tristram's eulogies of Cervantes and Don Quixote in *TS,* 1.10.17–22, 3.19.191.)

[53] *Sermons,* II, 177 (VI.x); I, 82 (I.vii), 222–223 (III.iv). Yorick explains (*Sermons,* I, 223 [III.iv]) that to suppose God actually "made and sent men into the world on purpose to play the fool" would "reflect dishonour" upon Him, for God "made [man's] judgment, like his heart, upright." However, the biases "hung upon" his judgment in his imperfect state do cause him to play the fool amid the riddles of the world, particularly in attempting to know himself. See also "The Abuses of Conscience Considered," *Sermons,* II, 67–69 (IV.xii), and *TS,* 2.17.125–127; and *Sermons,* II, 254–255 (VII.xvii), "The Ways of Providence justified to Man": "have not the most obvious things that come in our way dark sides, which the quickest sight cannot penetrate into; and do not the clearest and most exalted understandings find themselves puzzled, and at a loss [cf. *TS,* 4.17.293], in every particle of matter? Go then,—proud man! . . . take a full view of thyself in this glass;—consider thy own faculties,—how narrow and imperfect;—how much they are

. . . something foreign from what charity would suspect . . . eternally twists itself" into everything he does.[54] Astride the headstrong, curvetting hobbyhorse of his sensibility, Yorick is, in Tristram's words, "as heteroclite a creature in all his declensions" as any other humorist—a laughable and an admirable fool in a universal comedy of humors.[55]

In recounting his *Journey,* however, Yorick consistently plays a double role: not only that of a benevolent humorist, but also that of a jester who observes his impulsive, quixotic counterpart with sympathetic amusement and ironic detachment. Like Tristram, Yorick is "a clown whose roles dramatize his insights,"[56] and the witty *"knowingness"* with which he plays the quixotic benevolist and the benevolent jester validates the truism that self-consciousness is essential to self-knowledge.[57] His account of his travels is written in

---

checquered with truth and falsehood;—how little arrives at thy knowledge, and how darkly and confusedly thou discernest even that little as in a glass [I Corinthians 13:12] . . ."

[54] *Sermons,* I, 197 (III.ii). See also *Sermons,* I, 230 (III.v): "Man is surely a compound of riddles and contradictions"; II, 119 (V.iv): "the best of men appear sometimes to be strange compounds of contradictory qualities . . ."

[55] *TS,* 1.11.25; on the humorist as heteroclite, see McKillop, pp. 194–195. As Coleridge observed, one of Sterne's excellences lies in "bringing forward into distinct consciousness those minutiae of thought and feeling which appear trifles, have an importance [only] for the moment, and yet almost every man feels in one way or other. Thus it has the novelty of an individual peculiarity, and yet the interest of a something that belongs to our common nature. In short, to seize happily on those points in which every man is more or less a *humorist"* (*Miscellaneous Criticism,* ed. Raysor, p. 123).

[56] Traugott, p. 119. Like Tristram (see Traugott, p. 119), Yorick is both a humorist and a man of humor, as defined by Corbyn Morris: "an HUMOURIST *is a* Person *in real Life, obstinately attached to sensible peculiar* Oddities *of his own genuine Growth, which appear in his Temper and Conduct";* a *"Man* of *Humour* is one, who can happily exhibit and expose the Oddities and Foibles of an *Humourist."* Morris remarks that "HUMOUR, in the Representation of the *Foibles* of *Persons* in *real Life,* frequently exhibits very *generous benevolent* Sentiments of Heart; And these, tho' exerted in a particular odd Manner, justly command our Fondness and Love" (*Essay Towards Fixing the True Standards of Wit, Humour, Raillery, Satire, and Ridicule* [London, 1744], ed. James L. Clifford, Augustan Reprint Society, 1947, pp. 15, 24). On Morris's theory of comedy and humor, see Tave, pp. 118–119.

[57] Like Tristram, Yorick is "both inside and outside the moment; he is not only the knower of English empirical philosophy, but the hilosopher who

a style whose subtle equivocations are the *"Vehicle"* of a complex, double awareness combining the subjective experience of the "man of feeling" and the objective vision of the man of infinite jest. The conversational intimacy and fluidity of this style[58] are calculated to persuade the reader to participate in Yorick's "travels and observations"—ideally, it should be "like reading *himself* and not the *book*."[59] For by virtue of such participation, he can learn to play the same double role Yorick plays and acquire Yorick's ability to see "himself in the true point of ridicule."[60] And he can thereby take one step towards knowing himself—as a quixotic and admirable traveler amid the paradoxes of a benign and yet shandean world.

Yorick's *Sentimental Journey* illustrates the truth of St. Paul's observation that by "professing themselves to be wise, [men become] fools,"[61] and also demonstrates that by professing themselves Fools, men can become wise.

Sterne's faith in the comic spirit rests ultimately, I think, on his faith in the benignity of a shandean world. Yorick's *Journey* is an act of faith, a creation informed by the same spirit which informs the larger Creation it represents. E. M. Forster has remarked acutely that "a god is hidden in *Tristram Shandy,* his name is Muddle, and some readers cannot accept him"[62]—but he is only partially correct. For like Tristram's "life and opinions," Yorick's "travels and observations" prove that one of the "affections" (or sentiments) arising out of NATURE "which make us love each other—and the world, better than we do" (p. 219) is a benevolent sense of

---

writes with confidence about that knower" (McKillop, p. 210). His double awareness combines Don Quixote's point of view and Cervantes', and his double role is fully consonant with his character in *Tristram Shandy*—that of a benevolent humorist with a sense of humor about himself (see *TS,* 1.10–12.17–32).

[58] "Writing, when properly managed, (as you may be sure I think mine is) is but a different name for conversation" (*TS,* 2.11.108).

[59] *Letters,* No. 229 (quoted pp. 24–25, above).

[60] *TS,* 1.10.19.

[61] Romans 1:22—Yorick's text in his sermon on "Advantages of Christianity to the world" (*Sermons,* II, 53–64 [IV.xi]).

[62] *Aspects of the Novel* (New York, 1927), p. 164.

humor about life, which enables us to reconcile the god of muddle with the God of Love, who is partially concealed and partially revealed by his Creation.[63]

Yorick is a lineal descendent of Shakespeare's Jester, whose skull is an emblem of the final VEXATION of traveling,[64] and of the ultimate muddle contrived by the God of a shandean world—the paradox that man is mortal, and yet is of infinite jest and can share the benevolent laughter and the comic perspective of his Creator. His travels are presided over by the spirit of comedy which is akin to the spirit of charity and can understand, and love, the form of the world the intellect cannot comprehend—"the comic shape of the cosmos itself."[65]

In the beginning was the Word, but we now live in a shandean babel. *A Sentimental Journey through France and Italy By Mr. Yorick* demonstrates that a comic sense of life is a "gift of God" enabling us to read the shandean parable of existence aright—as a revelation of its infinitely charitable Author. "For now we see through a glass, darkly; but then face to face: now I know in part; but then shall I know even as also I am known."

---

[63] As Walter Shandy remarks, "Every thing in this world . . . is big with jest,—and has wit in it, and instruction too,—if we can but find it out" (*TS*, 5.32.393).

[64] See p. 223.20–23*n*, below. In Yorick's travels, Sterne brought to its fullest realization the metaphor of life and of writing as a journey which is central to *Tristram Shandy* and to the *Sermons*. Death prevented Yorick from pursuing his journey into Italy, and Sterne would surely have appreciated the way time and chance (see p. 114.10*n*, below) conspired to make his own career a paradigm of his comic vision of existence: he "loved a jest in his heart" (*TS*, 1.10.19), and as Gay remarked in his own epitaph, "Life is a jest; and all things show it. I thought so once; but now I know it."

[65] Rader, "Idea and Structure in Fielding's Novels," p. 232. I am also indebted here to Cassirer, *The Platonic Renaissance in England*, pp. 170–183.

NOTE ON THE TEXT

The text of this edition of *A Sentimental Journey*, except for minor emendations recorded in the textual notes, is printed from the first edition, published in London by T. Becket and P. A. De Hondt, on 27 February 1768, in two volumes.

The first edition is clearly authoritative. Vol. I was printed from an extant manuscript in Sterne's hand, and he evidently revised the proofs. Vol. II was also apparently printed from a holograph manuscript, now lost. Sterne died on 18 March 1768, less than three weeks after the first edition appeared, and I have found no evidence that he revised the first edition before his death.[1]

The evidence that Sterne revised the proofs of Vol. I of the first edition (*A1*) is as follows. There are many, minor changes in wording between *A1* and the carefully revised holograph manuscript from which it was printed (*S1*).[2] Several of these changes can be attributed with confidence to Sterne.[3] For example, *"physical Literata"* in *S1* was altered to *"physical precieuse"* in *A1*; "Upon

---

[1] The first edition has been collated with the second edition, publ. 29 March (eleven days after Sterne's death), and with the "New Edition," which followed the second edition. See App. D, p. 319, n. 10, below.

[2] Sterne's holograph MS. of Vol. I—Egerton MS. 1610, in the British Museum. Egerton 1610, a bound volume comprising various items in addition to *S1*, and *S1* itself are described in detail in Apps. A and B. For the evidence that *S1* was the printer's copy for *A1*, see App. B, §2.

[3] He was in London while *A Sentimental Journey* was passing through the press. Sterne's concern with the printing of his works is expressed in his comments to Dodsley on the format and type of the first two volumes of *Tristram Shandy* and in his determination to "correct every proof" himself, so they would "go perfect into the world" (*Letters*, No. 39, [? Oct. 1759], pp. 80–81). See also: (1) his statement to Stephen Croft: "I have been in . . . a continual hurry since the moment I arrived here [London]—what with my books" (*Letters*, No. 70, Christmas Day [? 1760], p. 126; according to Curtis's dating of this letter, Sterne is referring to the printing of Vols. III and IV of *Tristram Shandy*, publ. 28 Jan. 1761); and (2) Sterne's comment that "I am all this week in Labour pains" with the printing of Vol. IX of *Tristram Shandy* (*Letters*, No. 177, quoted p. 12, n. 42, above). Sterne was in London during the printing of all his works (except Vols. III and IV of the *Sermons*), and both Cross and Work assume that he saw them through the press (*Life*, pp. 245, 267; *TS*, p. lxxv).

my word, said I" in *S1* was altered to "Upon my word, Madame, said I" in *A1*.[4]

The other substantive variants between *S1* and *A1* involve indifferent changes[5] and emendations of obvious errors and infelicities[6] in *S1*. I have found no way of determining, in specific instances, whether Sterne or the printing-house editor or compositor made these alterations.[7] However, since Sterne evidently revised the proofs of *A1*, I have assumed that he approved these changes even if he did not make them himself. I have therefore accepted all the indifferent variants and emendations in *A1*, and recorded the original readings in *S1* in the textual notes.

Sterne's "eloquence and . . . fame" in *A Sentimental Journey* depend greatly on "the insensible MORE or LESS" of punctuation, typography, and other formal details.[8] As we might expect, in preparing *S1* for the printer he was, in general, very careful about specifying accidentals, particularly where he intended dashes, italics, capitals, and small capitals, for example, to express nuances of style or sense. And the formal details of *S1* are usually followed very faithfully in *A1*.

---

[4] See p. 69.21*tn* (Cross [*Life*, p. 475] incorrectly states that this alteration was made in *S1*) and p. 173.61*tn*, below. See also textual notes to pp. 99.8–9, 101.40, 103.55, 117.36, 135.16, 139.29, 170.1, 171.19, 182.48, below.

[5] That is, "where one reading is not obviously superior to the other. These changes are usually small and most frequently consist in the alteration of a single word or a change in word order . . . or the addition or omission of a word . . . This kind of change is one that authors often make deliberately, but it is also one that compositors frequently make through carelessness" (Arthur Friedman, "The Problem of Indifferent Readings in the Eighteenth Century, with a Solution from *The Deserted Village*," *Studies in Bibliography*, XIII [1960], 144). See, for example, textual notes to pp. 67.20, 78.10, 132.7, below.

[6] Usually consisting in violations of grammar and idiom (Friedman, p. 144, n. 1); see, for example, textual notes to pp. 100.31, 124.17, and 148.47, below.

[7] Particularly in the case of emendations in *A1* of errors and infelicities in *S1*; for, as Friedman points out (p. 144, n. 1), the more obvious the necessity for a change, "the more impossible to assign it either to author or compositor."

[8] *TS*, 2.6.100. See especially the conclusion of Yorick's *Journey*, p. 291, below.

There are two kinds of exceptions to this general pattern. In preparing *S1*, Sterne evidently had the practice of the printing house in mind and tended to be careless or inconsistent about capitalization, pointing, and italics where he felt that his intentions were obvious and that the printer would normalize his manuscript in accord with them. For example, he frequently neglected to capitalize proper names ("france") and the first word in a sentence,[9] and occasionally failed to close quotation marks and parentheses. These and similar vagaries were usually normalized in *A1*, presumably by the printing-house editor or compositor. Such changes, which comprise most of the variants in formal details between *S1* and *A1*, have been excluded from the textual notes:[10]

---

[9] At the beginning of a paragraph, as well as after a period. This habit appears in Sterne's letters and in his other manuscripts.

[10] Several other kinds of normalization, in *A1*, of the accidentals of *S1*, have usually been excluded from the notes: (1) *Italics:* French words not italicized in *S1* are usually italicized in *A1*. (2) *Capitals:* Many nouns other than proper names are capitalized in *S1*; except for personifications, they were consistently reduced to lower case in *A1*. Bertrand Bronson has observed "a quite abrupt shift of convention" in this regard, at the midpoint of the eighteenth century: before the midcentury, most nouns were capitalized in print; in the latter half of the century, modern conventions of capitalization prevailed, and Bronson notes: "Presumably, the generation schooled to capitalize nouns would go on writing in their habitual way" (*Printing as an Index of Taste in Eighteenth Century England* [New York, 1958], p. 17). Sterne's erratic capitalization of nouns in *S1* may well reflect this habit, as modified by the shift in printing conventions. Personifications present a more difficult problem. Sterne capitalizes personifications inconsistently in *S1*, and *A1* frequently eliminates, though it almost never adds, capitals. It appears that neither Sterne's nor the printing-house editor's or compositor's sense of personification depended upon typography. I have therefore omitted variants of this kind from the notes, mainly because to include them would accord them an anachronistic significance (see Bronson, pp. 17–18). (3) *Quotation marks* are used in *S1* mainly for emphasis. *A1* follows *S1* faithfully in such instances, except that, in accord with contemporary practice, *A1* usually eliminates quotation marks where they appear in conjunction with italics (particularly where the italicized words are in French). (4) *Question marks* omitted in *S1* in direct discourse are usually supplied in *A1*. In the few instances where normalizations of the kind described above, or failures to normalize, seem to have special significance, they have been recorded in the textual notes.

The following variants have also usually been excluded: (1) in spelling, in-

they affect neither style nor sense, and from Sterne's practice in *S1*
and elsewhere, we can safely infer that he anticipated and approved
these changes.[11]

Many additional changes in the accidentals of *S1* which go
beyond mere normalization of the kind described above were made
in *A1*. Most of these alterations simply bring the capitalization
and punctuation of *S1* into closer accord with the syntax, and I
have usually excluded such variants from the textual notes.[12] A
few of these changes affect the style and (occasionally) the sense,
in minor ways. I have been unable, in specific instances, to assign
even these more significant variants with any confidence to Sterne
rather than to the printing-house editor or compositor. However,
since Sterne evidently proofread *A1*, all the changes in accidentals
between *S1* and *A1* may be regarded as generally authorized even
if not specifically authorial. It seems likely that in proofreading *A1*
he reviewed its formal aspects with the same attention that led
him to make several minor but important changes in wording.
The number of significant changes in accidentals between *S1* and
A1 is small, and he could have revised alterations made by the
printing-house editor or compositor of which he disapproved.
Moreover, Sterne's vital concern with the minutiae of punctuation
and typography suggests that he may have made at least a few

cluding corrections in *A1* of misspellings in *S1*; (2) in the use of "and" and
"&"; (3) in contractions, except for those which have a noticeable stylistic
effect, such as " 'tis" and " 'em"; (4) in hyphenated compounds, with one
exception which seems to affect the sense (see p. 68.19*tn*, below).

[11] Becket and De Hondt published Vols. V–IX of *Tristram Shandy* (1761–
1767) and Vols. III and IV of the *Sermons* (1766). Sterne was thoroughly
familiar with the normal practice of the printers they employed, and the accidentals in *A Sentimental Journey* accord closely with those in the later volumes
of *Tristram Shandy,* particularly Vol. IX, which was published in 1767 (a year
before the *Journey*).

[12] The following variants of this kind have usually not been recorded:
(1) the capitalizing of a word in *A1* to indicate the beginning of direct discourse, a shift in speakers, or a new sentence or other major syntactical unit;
(2) the addition or deletion of commas, the change of a comma to a semicolon
(and vice versa), or of a semicolon to a colon (and vice versa); (3) the correc-
tion of punctuation where Sterne revised a passage in *S1* and neglected to
revise the punctuation accordingly. I have noted a few such variants where
they affect the sense or seem to have some special significance.

changes in the accidentals of *A1* when he had the printed text before him and could weigh the effect of its formal details.[13]

As previously noted, Vol. II of the first edition (*A2*) was evidently printed from a holograph manuscript (*S2*), now lost, which comprised with *S1* a holograph of the entire *Journey*.[14] Since Sterne revised the proofs of *A1*, it seems reasonable to suppose that he proofread *A2* also. However, if he did so, he must have proofread *A2* less carefully than *A1*, for manifest errors occur much more frequently in *A2* than in *A1* (see below).

The present text of *A Sentimental Journey* is printed from my large-paper copy of the first edition.[15] I have made a few, minor changes in wording in the text, all of which have been recorded in the textual notes.[16] In Vol. I, I have emended one apparently

[13] The following kinds of variants between *S1* and *A1* have usually been noted: (1) variants in paragraphing; Sterne's paragraphing is rhetorically important, and in one instance he revised the paragraphing in *S1* (see p. 92.18–19*tn*, below); (2) instances where dashes are inserted, omitted, or replaced with other punctuation in *A1*, except where commas are substituted in *A1* for dashes in *S1* to set off attributives in direct discourse; (3) the omission or insertion in *A1* of a period before a dash, except where a period is inserted in *A1* to indicate the beginning of direct discourse or a shift in speakers. The frequent substitution of a dash in *A1* for a comma-and-dash in *S1* has usually not been noted; this change accords with the shift from the predominance of the comma-, semicolon-, and colon-and-dash in Vols. I–IV of *Tristram Shandy* to the almost exclusive use of the simple dash in Vols. V–IX (a shift which commences in Vols. III and IV, publ. by Dodsley; Vols. V–IX were publ. by Becket and De Hondt). And I have not attempted to record variations in the length of dashes between *S1* and *A1*. (4) I have noted a few other variants between the accidentals of *S1* and *A1* where the changes seemed significant enough to warrant bringing them to the reader's attention.

[14] There is some specific evidence that *S2* was the printer's copy for *A2;* see the discussion of Vol. II of the Morgan Library MS. of *A Sentimental Journey,* pp. 55–56, below.

[15] The first edition is described in App. D, §1; it was printed both on large and on ordinary paper (see App. D, §2). My large-paper copy has been collated with several additional copies in both styles. In the present edition, long "s" has been modernized, and quotation marks have been silently omitted when they are repeated at the beginning of a line.

For a list of the compound words hyphenated at the end of the line in the present edition and in the first edition, see App. D, §6. For a special problem in reprinting in the present edition dashes in the first edition, see App. D, §7.

[16] They are listed in App. D, §5.

incorrect reading, on the authority of *S1*.[17] In Vol. II, I have found it necessary to make approximately seventeen changes in wording. Many of these alterations correct the inadvertent repetition of a word in *A1*. In a few instances, I have emended what seemed to be manifest errors in grammar and idiom, usually on the basis of the Morgan Library MS. of Vol. II, which was evidently transcribed from *S2*, now lost (see below). And I have accepted one variant reading in the Morgan MS. where the reading in the first edition seemed unsatisfactory.[18] I have also made a few, minor corrections in spelling, punctuation, and other accidentals, in both volumes.[19]

In emending the first edition, I have borne in mind Sterne's warning to the printer of his *Political Romance:*

. . . at your Peril, . . . do not presume to alter or transpose one Word, nor rectify one false Spelling, nor so much as add or diminish one Comma or Tittle . . . For if you do,—In case any of the Descendents of *Curl* should think fit to invade my Copy-Right, and print it over again in my Teeth, I may not be able, in a Court of Justice, to swear strictly to my own Child, after you had *so large a Share* in the begetting it.[20]

I hope, with some trepidation, that Sterne could swear to this text as his own, my small share in begetting it notwithstanding.

MANUSCRIPTS

As previously noted, *S1* is a carefully revised fair copy. Except for two major alterations (described below), Sterne's revisions involve minor refinements and are limited to words, phrases, and a few sentences. The textual notes in the present edition record these changes in *S1*.[21]

---

[17] See p. 160.33*tn,* below.
[18] See p. 197.58*tn,* below.
[19] I have allowed the vagaries in Sterne's French to stand, as historically and individually characteristic. (In one instance, I have emended what seemed clearly to be a printer's error; see p. 77.16*tn,* below).
[20] *Letters,* No. 34, 20 Jan. 1759, p. 68.
[21] See Key to the Textual Notes, below. There is evidence that when Sterne first inscribed the last of the three chapters entitled "In the Street. Calais", it appeared at an earlier point in the text; see App. B, §6.

The other extant manuscript of *A Sentimental Journey,* in the Pierpont Morgan Library, casts additional light on the evolution of the text. This manuscript is bound in two volumes, the first (*M1*) comprising the title page and text of Vol. I and the second (*M2*) comprising the title page and text of Vol. II.[22] A comparison of *M1* with *S1* reveals that *M1* is a fair and generally accurate copy of *S1*, and that it was transcribed from *S1* before Sterne completed the revisions he made in *S1*.[23] And there is clear evidence that *M2* has the same relationship to *S2*, now lost (see below).

Because of its relationship to Sterne's holograph MS. of *A Sentimental Journey,* the Morgan MS. preserves revisions Sterne made in the text of Vol. I and Vol. II.

Vol. I. (1) After Sterne had written out *S1*, he extensively revised part of the chapter entitled "The Snuff-Box. Calais." He inserted in *S1* three new folios containing the revised version and discarded two folios containing most of the original version. *M1* was transcribed from *S1* before Sterne made this revision, and it therefore provides a transcript of the two folios he discarded from *S1*. The *M1* and *S1* versions of this portion of the text are given in Appendix C, §5. (2) Fols. 56–69 of *S1*[24] are missing, and *M1* preserves a transcript of them. There are numerous differences in wording between this portion of *M1* and the text of *A1*.[25] Some of these variants are undoubtedly the result of changes made by the *M1* copyist in transcribing *M1* from *S1*, or by the printing-house editor or compositor in printing *A1* from *S1*. But some are probably the result of changes Sterne made in the text after *M1* was transcribed from *S1*, either in *S1* or in the proofs of *A1*. I have therefore noted the differences in wording between this portion of *M1* and the text of *A1*, with certain exceptions. The *M1* copyist almost invariably emended manifest errors in *S1*, such as the inadvertent repetition of a word or the omission of a word demanded

---

[22] *M1, M2* = Morgan MS., Vols. I, II. The Morgan MS. is described in App. C. It is in two hands, neither of which, in my opinion, is Sterne's holograph (see App. C, §2).

[23] The evidence of this relationship is presented in App. C, §3.

[24] For the folio numbers in *S1* which are cited in the present edition, see App. B, §3.

[25] See p. 104.20*tn,* below.

by the sense.[26] I have therefore not recorded differences in wording
between fols. 56–69 of *M1* and the text of *A1* where the reading in
M1 is manifestly erroneous, since such readings are almost certainly scribal errors by the *M1* copyist.[27]

   Vol. II. There are many differences in wording between *M2* and
A2, ranging from single words and phrases to a paragraph. The
nature of these variants and other evidence clearly indicate that
the texts of *M2*, *S2* (now lost), and *A2* have the same relationship
as *M1*, *S1*, and *A1*,[28] and that the substantive variants between
M2 and *A2* are, therefore, the result of changes made (a) by the
copyist in transcribing *M2* from *S2;* (b) by the printing-house
editor or compositor in printing *A2* from *S2;* or (c) by Sterne,
either in *S2* or in the proofs of *A2*, after *M2* had been transcribed
from *S2*.[29] All differences in wording between *M2* and *A2* have
therefore been recorded in the textual notes to the present edition,
except for those readings in *M2* which are manifestly erroneous.[30]

   Sterne's careful revisions in the text of *A Sentimental Journey*
document the obvious fact that Tristram's disclaimer—"Ask my
pen,—it governs me,—I govern not it"[31]—is largely a rhetorical

---

   [26] See, for example, the errors in *S1* recorded p. 88.20*tn,* and p. 89.10*tn,*
below; these errors, which were corrected in *A1*, were also corrected by the
M1 copyist.

   [27] Variants in accidentals between this portion of *M1* and the text of *A1* have
also not been recorded, because *M1* does not invariably follow the accidentals
of *S1* (see App. C, p. 310, n. 12).

   [28] See App. C, §4.

   [29] To judge from the pattern of Sterne's revisions in *S1* and in the proofs of
A1, substantive variants between *M2* and *A2* involving sentences (and one
paragraph; see pp. 265.71–266.82*tn,* below) probably reflect revisions he made
in *S2*, rather than in the proofs of *A2*.

   [30] *M1* follows the accidentals of *S1* quite faithfully, but not invariably (see
App. C, p. 310, n. 12), and, as noted above, the accidentals of *S1* are extensively
changed in *A1*. I have therefore not recorded variants in accidentals between
M2 and *A2*, except: (1) where I have emended the accidentals of *A2;* (2) where
the accidentals in *A2* seemed faulty and those in *M2* seemed correct, but where
I did not feel justified in making an emendation; (3) in one instance where the
reading in *M2* is of special significance (see p. 291.153–154*tn,* below).

   [31] *TS,* 6.6.416. Cf. *Letters,* No. 213, p. 394; cf. also Sterne's claim, in Letter
No. 64 (p. 117), that he never writes a premeditated word, which is repeated
in Letter No. 66 (p. 120).

pose dramatizing the perplexities of ordering a Shandean world. Like Tristram, Sterne may have begun "with writing the first sentence——and trusting to Almighty God for the second,"[32] but he believed in lending a hand thereafter.

[32] *TS*, 8.2.540.

KEY TO THE TEXTUAL NOTES

ABBREVIATIONS

A1, A2   Vols. I and II of the first edition of *A Sentimental Journey.*

S1, S2   Sterne's holograph MS. of *A1*, and his holograph MS. (now lost) of *A2*.

M1, M2   Vols. I and II of the Morgan Library MS. of *A Sentimental Journey.*

[*M1:* u. v.]   *M1:* unrevised version—indicates that *M1* gives the unrevised version of a revised reading in *S1*.

TEXTUAL NOTES TO VOLUME I

Readings in *S1*

The textual notes to Vol. I of *A Sentimental Journey* are intended to record the following readings in *S1*, *without further identification.*

(1) All the verbal revisions Sterne made in *S1*, except for those which proved to be wholly indecipherable, and corrections of slips of the pen. The following editorial symbols are used in transcribing revisions.[1]

⟨   ⟩   Pointed brackets enclose *cancellations.* Sterne made cancellations in several ways: by running a line through a reading; by erasing a reading; by superimposing a revised reading on an initial reading (sometimes without erasing the initial reading); by altering one or more letters in a word so as to produce a revised reading.

?   An italic question mark in front of a canceled reading indicates that I am uncertain about it.

∼   ∼   Wavy lines enclose a reading which is *superimposed on* the canceled reading which immediately precedes it,

---

[1] These symbols are used in the textual notes to Vols. I and II, and in Appendices A–D.

without a space. For example: (1) "m⟨?e⟩∼y∼" = "'y'" appears to be superimposed on canceled "e" (see facsimile of fol. 52B of *S1*, after p. 320). (2) "'⟨to⟩∼I'll∼" = "I'll" is superimposed on canceled "to". (3) "vin⟨?es⟩ ∼'y∼ard" = "'y'" is superimposed on what appears to be canceled "es", and is followed by "ard"; Sterne apparently wrote "vines" initially and revised it to "vin'-yard". (4) "'⟨?p⟩∼t∼rue point of pity" = the "t" in "true" is superimposed on what appears to be a "p"; Sterne may have initially started to write "point" or "pity".

∧ ∧ Carets enclose readings which Sterne *inserted* above or below a line in *S1*. For example: "civil ⟨insolence⟩ ∧triumph∧" = Sterne canceled "insolence" and inserted "triumph" above the line.

∨ ∨ Inverted carets enclose readings which appear to have been inserted *on* a line in *S1* after the line was first inscribed. For example: "as ∨t∨he ∨Idea of him∨" = Sterne apparently wrote "as he" initially and then revised this to "as the Idea of him", by inserting "t" on the line in front of "he", and "Idea of him" above the line.

N. B.: Where the punctuation of an insertion duplicates the original punctuation, I have silently omitted the redundant punctuation in the insertion: for example, where *S1* reads "so— ∧—for∧ it", I have recorded this insertion simply as "∧for∧".

In recording insertions, I have tried to transcribe them in the order in which Sterne made them in the process of revision, which does not always correspond precisely with their physical position in *S1*. When I am uncertain about where Sterne intended an insertion to go, I have noted this fact in an editorial comment.

/ // A single slant line indicates a line division, and a double slant line a folio division, in the text of *S1*. I have indicated line and folio divisions only where I felt it would clarify Sterne's revisions by doing so.

[   ]   Square brackets enclose all editorial matter. Three spaced periods (. . .) indicate editorial omissions.

N. B.: I have tried to transcribe *S1* accurately, and I have not used "sic" to designate anomalies in *S1* such as omitted letters and misspellings.

(2) All variants in wording between *S1* and *A1* (see Note on the Text, above).

(3) A few variants in accidentals between *S1* and *A1* (see Note on the Text, above).

Readings in *M1*

Where Sterne revised *S1* after *M1* had been transcribed from it, and *M1* therefore gives the unrevised reading in *S1*, this fact is indicated in the textual notes, usually by the abbreviation [*M1:* u. v.] = *M1:* unrevised version. In a few instances where it seemed clearer to do so, I have recorded the reading in *M1* (see, e. g., p. 137.45–46*tn*).

All variants in wording between fols. 56–69 of *M1* and the text of *A1* have been recorded, except where the reading in *M1* is manifestly erroneous; see Note on the Text, *Vol. I* (2), p. 56, above.

Editorial Emendations

All editorial emendations in the text of *A1* have been recorded in the textual notes and listed in App. D, §5. In the textual notes recording emendations, both the reading in *A1* and the corresponding reading in *S1* are given.

TEXTUAL NOTES TO VOLUME II

Readings in *M2*

The textual notes to Vol. II of *A Sentimental Journey* are intended to record the following readings in *M2*, *without further identification*.

(1) All variants in wording between *M2* and *A2*, except where the reading in *M2* is manifestly erroneous (see Note on the Text, p. 56, above).

(2) A few variants in accidentals between *M2* and *A2* (see Note on the Text, p. 56, n. 30, above).

Editorial Emendations

All editorial emendations in the text of *A2* have been recorded in the textual notes and listed in App. D, §5. In the notes recording emendations, both the reading in *A2* and the corresponding reading in *M2* are given.

A

SENTIMENTAL JOURNEY

THROUGH

FRANCE AND ITALY.

BY

MR. YORICK.

VOL. I.

LONDON:

Printed for T. BECKET and P. A. DE HONDT,
in the Strand. MDCCLXVIII.

A
SENTIMENTAL JOURNEY,
&c. &c.

___THEY order, said I, this matter better in France—

—You have been in France? said my gentleman, turning quick upon me with the most civil triumph in the world.—Strange! quoth I, debating the matter with myself, That one and twenty miles sailing, for 'tis absolutely no further from Dover to Calais, 5 should give a man these rights—I'll look into them: so giving up the argument—I went straight to my lodgings, put up half a dozen shirts and a black pair of silk breeches—"the coat I have on, said I, looking at the sleeve, will do"—took a place in the Dover stage; and the packet sailing at nine the next morning—by three 10

---

3 civil ⟨insolence⟩ ∧triumph∧   5–6 Calais, ⟨should give these rights!⟩ // should . . . rights,—⟨?I'm ?determined⟩ ⟨to⟩∼I'll∼ look   10 by ⟨one⟩ ∧⟨two⟩ three∧

Title same as half-title of Vols. I and II of the first edition; see App. D, §1.

7–8. *half a dozen shirts*] Like Tristram, who also travels with only six shirts (see *TS*, 9.24.628, quoted p. 13, above), Yorick travels fast and light, unencumbered with the "mountains of baggage" with which many Englishmen journeyed (see p. 135.16*n*, below). Smollett took with him "two very large chests and a trunk, about a thousand pounds weight" (*Travels*, Letter No. 5, p. 43).

Yorick's scanty wardrobe befits a "lousy prebendary" (p. 105.32, below). Is Sterne perhaps thinking also of its appropriateness to a benevolent knight-errant? The keeper of the first inn Don Quixote stops at informs him that, although the authors of chivalric histories thought it "needless to mention Things so evidently necessary as Money and clean Shirts, . . . you may rest assur'd, that all the Knight-Errants, of whom so many Histories are full, had their purses well lined . . . and carry'd also with them some Shirts" (*Don Quixote*, 1.1.3.15; after his adventures at the inn, Don Quixote returns home to furnish himself with money and shirts [1.1.4.20, 1.1.7.42]).

8–9. *"the coat . . . will do"*] See App. E, pp. 321–322, note to p. 65.8–9.

9–10. *took . . . morning*] Cf. Smollett's description of his journey from London to Dover: "I need not tell you this is the worst road in England, with

I had got sat down to my dinner upon a fricassee'd chicken so incontestably in France, that had I died that night of an indigestion, the whole world could not have suspended the effects of the *Droits d'aubaine*—my shirts, and black pair of silk breeches—
15 portmanteau and all must have gone to the King of France—even

* All the effects of strangers (Swiss and Scotch excepted) dying in France, are seized by virtue of this law, tho' the heir be upon the spot——the profit of these contingencies being farm'd, there is no redress.

---

14 my ∧⟨six⟩∧ shirts   16–19 *All . . . redress.] [This note is on fol. 1ᵛ of *S1*, opposite *"*Droits d'aubaine"* (on fol. 2). For the fol. numbers in *S1* which are cited in the present edition, see App. B, §3.]   16 (⟨the⟩ Swiss [*M1:* u.v.] 18 the⟨se⟩ profit of these   18–19 there is no] There is ⟨can⟩ is no

---

respect to the conveniencies of travelling . . . The chambers are in general cold and comfortless, the beds paultry, the cookery execrable, the wine poison, the attendance bad, the publicans insolent, and the bills extortion" (*Travels,* Letter No. 1, p. 2). In contrast to Smollett's crabbed progress, Yorick's journey is conducted with the same good-humored *élan* as Tristram's: *"Allons!* said I; the post boy gave a crack with his whip——off I went like a cannon, and in half a dozen bounds got into *Dover*" (*TS,* 7.1.480).

14–15. *breeches . . . France*] Tristram uses the "tearing off" of his breeches at Lyons, through the indirect agency of the commissary of the royal post, to illustrate the inequities of the royal ordinances governing the post revenues and the general oppressiveness of French taxes; see *TS,* 7.33–35.525–528, and p. 262.26–30*n*, below.

15. *King of France*] See p. 68.1–3*n*, below.

16–19. *All . . . redress.*] Sterne is echoing Smollett: "France . . . piques itself on its politeness and hospitality: but the truth is, I know no country in which strangers are worse treated, with respect to their essential concerns. If a foreigner dies in France, the king seizes all his effects, *even though his heir should be upon the spot* [italics added]; and this tyranny is called the *droit d'aubaine,* founded at first upon the supposition, that all the estate of foreigners residing in France was acquired in that kingdom, and that, therefore, it would be unjust to convey it to another country. . . . The Swiss, by capitulation, are exempted from this despotism, and so are the Scots, in consequence of an ancient alliance between the two nations" (*Travels,* Letter No. 2, pp. 9–10; cited by Milic, "Sterne and Smollett's 'Travels' "). Smollett probably exaggerates the rigor with which the *droit d'aubaine* was applied (see *Travels,*

the little picture which I have so long worn, and so often have told 20
thee, Eliza, I would carry with me into my grave, would have been
torn from my neck.—Ungenerous!—to seize upon the wreck of an
unwary passenger, whom your subjects had beckon'd to their
coast—by heaven! Sire, it is not well done; and much does it
grieve me, 'tis the monarch of a people so civilized and courteous, 25
and so renown'd for sentiment and fine feelings, that I have to reason with——

But I have scarce set foot in your dominions——

---

20 often have told] often told   22 neck.—Ungenerous] neck—ungenerous
28 But]—But

---

p. xxiii, n. 1; Thicknesse, *Observations,* pp. 71–72); however, William Cole
cites, as typical, an instance in which this "inhospitable, barbarous & Gothic
Law" was strictly and harshly enforced (*Journey to Paris,* pp. 83–84).

18. *the profit . . . farm'd*] to the farmers of taxes; see p. 262.26–30*n,* below.

20–21. *the little picture . . . Eliza*] *Eliza:* Elizabeth Sclater Draper; for
Sterne's relationship with her, and its influence on *A Sentimental Journey,*
see App. E, pp. 322–326, note to p. 67.21. Sterne met Eliza after his second
trip abroad; Yorick's *Journey* coincides chronologically with Sterne's first
trip (see p. 192.7–8*n,* below). Before Eliza left for India in April 1767 (see
App. E, p. 322), she gave Sterne a miniature of herself, which serves as a
sentimental touchstone in his letters and in the *Journal to Eliza.* See, e.g.,
Journal, 13 June, p. 357: "I have a present of a portrait, (which, by the by, I
have immortalized in my Sentimental Journey)"; 17 June, p. 358: "I have
brought yʳ name *Eliza!* and Picture into my work—where they will remain—
when You & I are at rest for ever—Some Annotator or explainer of my works
in this place will take occasion, to speak of the Friendship wᶜʰ Subsisted so
long & faithfully betwixt ⟨the⟩ Yorick & the Lady he speaks of . . ." (Sterne
apparently gave Eliza a portrait of himself; see *Letters,* No. 185, London, [?
March 1767], p. 305, and *Journal,* 2 June, p. 348.) Sterne began "immortaliz-
ing" Eliza's name and picture before *A Sentimental Journey* was published;
see App. E, p. 324, n.9.

22. *torn . . . neck*] Cf. *Journal,* 14 July, pp. 379–380: "I verily think my
Eliza I shall get this Picture set, so as to wear it, as I first proposed—abᵗ my
neck—I do not like the place tis in—it shall be nearer my heart—" He also
considered having it set in a snuffbox; see p. 99.7*n,* below.

CALAIS.

WHEN I had finish'd my dinner, and drank the King of
France's health, to satisfy my mind that I bore him no spleen,
but, on the contrary, high honour for the humanity of his temper—
I rose up an inch taller for the accommodation.

5   —No—said I—the Bourbon is by no means a cruel race: they
may be misled like other people; but there is a mildness in their
blood. As I acknowledged this, I felt a suffusion of a finer kind
upon my cheek—more warm and friendly to man, than what
Burgundy (at least of two livres a bottle, which was such as I had
10 been drinking) could have produced.

—Just God! said I, kicking my portmanteau aside, what is there
in this world's goods which should sharpen our spirits, and make
so many kind-hearted brethren of us, fall out so cruelly as we do
by the way?

15   When man is at peace with man, how much lighter than a
feather is the heaviest of metals in his hand! he pulls out his purse,
and holding it airily and uncompress'd, looks round him, as if he
sought for an object to share it with—In doing this, I felt every
vessel in my frame dilate—the arteries beat all chearily together,
20 and every power which sustained life, perform'd it with so little

---

12 make⟨s⟩   16–17 purse, ⟨no matter whether tis⟩ and   19 all chearily] all-chearily

---

1–3. *King . . . temper*] Louis XV, "le Bien-Aimé" (1710–1774); during
his personal reign (1743–1774) his earlier popularity waned.
    9. *Burgundy . . . bottle*] Cf. Smollett, *Travels,* Letter No. 4, p. 24: "I
don't believe there is a drop of generous Burgundy in . . . [Boulogne]; and
the aubergistes impose upon us shamefully, when they charge it at two livres
a bottle."
    18–23. *In doing . . . machine*] A characteristic expression of Sterne's be-
lief in the interaction of benevolence and physical well-being. Cf. *Sermons,*
I, 129 (II.xi): "Should not charity and good will, like the principle of life,
circulating through the smallest vessels in every member, ought it not to
operate as regularly upon you, throughout, as well upon your words, as upon
your actions?"; I, 61–63 (I.v): "Ask the man who has a tear of tenderness

68

friction, that 'twould have confounded the most *physical precieuse* in France: with all her materialism, she could scarce have called me a machine—

I'm confident, said I to myself, I should have overset her creed.

The accession of that idea, carried nature, at that time, as high 25 as she could go—I was at peace with the world before, and this finish'd the treaty with myself—

—Now, was I a King of France, cried I—what a moment for an orphan to have begg'd his father's portmanteau of me!

---

21 *precieuse*] Literata   24 I'm] —I'm

---

always ready to shed over the unfortunate; who, withal, is ready to distribute and willing to communicate: ask him if the best things, which wits have said of pleasure, have expressed what he has felt, when by a seasonable kindness, he has *made the heart of the widow sing for joy* [Job 29:13]. Mark then the expressions of unutterable pleasure and harmony in his looks; . . . the evidence of the philosopher Epicurus is very remarkable, whose word in this matter is the more to be trusted, because a professed sensualist; who . . . still maintained, that the best way of enlarging human happiness was, by a communication of it to others. . . . exclusive of the happiness which the mind itself feels in the exercise of [charity] . . . the very body of man is never in a better state than when he is most inclined to do good offices: . . . nothing more contributes to health than a benevolence of temper . . . the very *mechanical motions* which maintain life, must be performed with more equal vigour and freedom in [a benevolent] man . . . than they can be in a poor, sordid, selfish wretch . . . What divines say of the mind, naturalists have observed of the body; that there is no passion so natural to it as love, which is the principle of doing good . . ." Cf. also *Sermons*, II, 239–240, quoted p. 162.27–29*n*, below, and Tristram's observation that "the soul and body are joint-sharers in every thing they get" (*TS*, 9.13.616).

21–23. *the most physical precieuse . . . machine*] *physical précieuse:* a woman who professed an interest in the freethinking, anti-Christian ideas currently fashionable in the Parisian salons and who subscribed to the materialist philosophy of a work like *L'Homme machine* (1748), by Julien Offray de la Mettrie (1709–1751), which analyzes all mental processes as material and mechanical (cited by Milic, p. 4, n. 1). On the *précieuses*, see also p. 181.43*n*, below.

23. *machine*] Cf. Sterne's refs. to his body as a "machine" in *Journal*, 25 April, p. 331; *Letters*, No. 198, May 1767, p. 346; No. 234, [? March 1768], p. 416.

THE MONK.
CALAIS.

I HAD scarce utter'd the words, when a poor monk of the order of St. Francis came into the room to beg something for his convent. No man cares to have his virtues the sport of contingencies —or one man may be generous, as another man is puissant—*sed*
5 *non, quo ad hanc*—or be it as it may—for there is no regular reasoning upon the ebbs and flows of our humours; they may depend upon the same causes, for ought I know, which influence the tides themselves—'twould oft be no discredit to us, to suppose it was so: I'm sure at least for myself, that in many a case I should be more
10 highly satisfied, to have it said by the world, "I had had an affair with the moon, in which there was neither sin nor shame," than have it pass altogether as my own act and deed, wherein there was so much of both.

—But be this as it may. The moment I cast my eyes upon him,
15 I was predetermined not to give him a single sous; and accordingly I put my purse into my pocket—button'd it up—set myself a little more upon my centre, and advanced up gravely to him: there was something, I fear, forbidding in my look: I have his figure this moment before my eyes, and think there was that in it
20 which deserved better.

---

title] ∧The Monk.∧ [appears to have been inserted above "Calais." after "Calais." was inscribed. The titles of the next three chapters appear to have been similarly revised.]   2 ⟨?enter'd⟩~came~ ∧into∧   4–5 puissant— ⟨?but ?not⟩~⟨?sed ?non⟩~ —*sed non*   14 may. The] may. [par.] The

---

1–2. *monk . . . St. Francis*] On his identity, see p. 102.42–48*n*, below. English travelers staying at Dessein's hotel (see p. 87.2–3*n*, below) were commonly asked for alms by a friar from the nearby Franciscan convent.

6. *ebbs and flows*] a favorite image of Sterne's: see *Sermons*, I, 44 (I.iv), 185 (III.i), 208–209 (III.iii), II, 80 (IV.xii) and *TS*, 2.17.140; *Letters*, No. 220, Nov. 1767, p. 402; *Journal*, 15 April, p. 323; *TS*, 8.11.550.

The monk, as I judged from the break in his tonsure, a few
scatter'd white hairs upon his temples, being all that remained of
it, might be about seventy—but from his eyes, and that sort of fire
which was in them, which seemed more temper'd by courtesy than
years, could be no more than sixty—Truth might lie between— 25
He was certainly sixty-five; and the general air of his countenance,
notwithstanding something seem'd to have been planting wrinkles
in it before their time, agreed to the account.

It was one of those heads, which Guido has often painted—
mild, pale—penetrating, free from all common-place ideas of fat 30
contented ignorance looking downwards upon the earth—it look'd
forwards; but look'd, as if it look'd at something beyond this world.
How one of his order came by it, heaven above, who let it fall upon a
monk's shoulders, best knows: but it would have suited a Bramin,
and had I met it upon the plains of Indostan, I had reverenced it. 35

---

26 ∧his∧   27 ∧been∧

---

27. *planting wrinkles*] Cf. *Letters,* No. 193, London, [? 30 March 1767],
p. 321, to Eliza: "May no anguish of heart plant a wrinkle upon thy face, till
I behold it again!"

29. *Guido*] Guido Reni (1575–1642), a painter of the Bolognese school,
whose works were much admired by English travelers. Commenting on a
mosaic copy of a painting by Guido of the Archangel Michael, Smollett observed: "There is a tenderness and delicacy in [Guido's] manner; and his
figures are all exquisitely beautiful, though his expression is often erroneous,
and his attitudes are always affected and unnatural. In this very piece the
archangel has all the air of a French dancing-master" (*Travels,* Letter No.
31, p. 265; see also No. 33, p. 289). (Tristram refers to "the airs of *Guido*"
in *TS,* 3.12.182.)

34. *Bramin*] Sterne and Eliza alluded to one another as the Bramin and
the Bramine, in reference to his profession and to her connections with
India (see App. E, p. 322, note to p. 67.21). Sterne's prefatory description
of the *Journal to Eliza* notes that it is "wrote under the fictitious Names of
Yorick & Draper—and sometimes of the Bramin & Bramine"; and the
Journal itself is entitled "Continuation of the Bramines [sic] Journal" (p.
322). See also, e.g., *Letters,* No. 181, p. 299; No. 201, pp. 360–363 (redirected from "Countess ******" to his "dear Bramine").

The rest of his outline may be given in a few strokes; one might put it into the hands of any one to design, for 'twas neither elegant or otherwise, but as character and expression made it so: it was a thin, spare form, something above the common size, if it lost not 40 the distinction by a bend forwards in the figure—but it was the attitude of Intreaty; and as it now stands presented to my imagination, it gain'd more than it lost by it.

When he had enter'd the room three paces, he stood still; and laying his left hand upon his breast, (a slender white staff with 45 which he journey'd being in his right)—when I had got close up to him, he introduced himself with the little story of the wants of his convent, and the poverty of his order—and did it with so simple a grace—and such an air of deprecation was there in the whole cast of his look and figure—I was bewitch'd not to have been 50 struck with it—

—A better reason was, I had predetermined not to give him a single sous.

40–41 Figure— ⟨but it was the attitude of Intreaty; and as it now stands presented⟩ // —but . . . presented

---

Since Sterne circulated the story of his affair with Eliza among his acquaintances (see App. E, p. 324, note to p. 67.21), some of them may have recognized the special significance of Yorick's reference to a "Bramin."

THE MONK.
CALAIS.

'TIS very true, said I, replying to a cast upwards with his eyes, with which he had concluded his address—'tis very true—and heaven be their resource who have no other but the charity of the world, the stock of which, I fear, is no way sufficient for the many *great claims* which are hourly made upon it.   5

As I pronounced the words *great claims*, he gave a slight glance with his eye downwards upon the sleeve of his tunick—I felt the full force of the appeal—I acknowledge it, said I—a coarse habit, and that but once in three years, with meagre diet—are no great matters; and the true point of pity is, as they can be earn'd in the 10 world with so little industry, that your order should wish to procure them by pressing upon a fund which is the property of the lame, the blind, the aged and the infirm—the captive who lies down counting over and over again the days of his afflictions, languishes also for his share of it; and had you been of the *order of* 15 *mercy*, instead of the order of St. Francis, poor as I am, continued I, pointing at my portmanteau, full chearfully should it have been open'd to you, for the ransom of the unfortunate—The monk made me a bow—but of all others, resumed I, the unfortunate of our own country, surely, have the first rights; and I have left thousands in 20 distress upon our own shore—The monk gave a cordial wave with

---

title] ∧The Monk.∧   4 which ⟨is⟩ ⟨not ["t" is doubtful]⟩∼I f∼ear, is no way
10 the ⟨?p⟩ ∼t ∼rue point of pity   18 unfortunate—] unfortunate.—

12–13. *the lame . . . the infirm*] Cf. Luke 14:21: "the poor, and the maimed, and the halt, and the blind."

13–14. *the captive . . . afflictions*] See p. 202.23–26n, below.

15–16. *order of mercy*] The Order of Our Lady of Mercy, founded in Spain, in 1218, to solicit funds for ransoming Christians captured by the Moors; the members were called Mercedarians (from Maria des Mercedes). A branch of the order was established for women in 1568. (The order is mentioned in *TS,* 5.1.346.)

his head—as much as to say, No doubt, there is misery enough in
every corner of the world, as well as within our convent—But we
distinguish, said I, laying my hand upon the sleeve of his tunick,
25 in return for his appeal—we distinguish, my good Father! betwixt
those who wish only to eat the bread of their own labour—and
those who eat the bread of other people's, and have no other plan
in life, but to get through it in sloth and ignorance, *for the love of
God.*

30   The poor Franciscan made no reply: a hectic of a moment pass'd
across his cheek, but could not tarry—Nature seemed to have had
done with her resentments in him; he shewed none—but letting
his staff fall within his arm, he press'd both his hands with resignation upon his breast, and retired.

27–29 who ⟨have no other⟩~eat the~ bread of other people's, & have no other plan
⟨in the world, but to be a ?burden ?In it, *for the love of God.*⟩ in Life . . . *God.*
32 him; ⟨at least⟩ he

27–29. *those . . . God*] Sterne's other writings contain numerous thrusts
at Catholicism and the monastic orders: see esp. *Sermons,* I, 224 (III.iv),
definition of "popery" as "a pecuniary system, well contrived to operate
upon men's passions and weakness, whilst their pockets are o'picking"
(paraphrased in II, 180 [VI.x]); II, 78–79 (IV.xii), description of the Inquisition (see *TS,* 2.17.138–139); I, 14 (I.ii); I, 207–208 (III.iii), ref. to "the
torpid Monk," quoted p. 237.8–11*n*, below; *Tristram Shandy,* ridicule of Dr.
Slop, Abbess of Andoüillets (7.20–25.503–510), Walter's and Toby's visit to
the Abbey of St. Germain (7.27.513–515) and Tristram's remark that Walter
"hated a monk and the very smell of a monk worse than all the devils in hell"
(7.27.514).
    28–29. *for . . . God*] a translation of "pour l'amour de Dieu," a standard
appeal for alms (see p. 133.43, below).

THE MONK.
CALAIS.

MY heart smote me the moment he shut the door—Psha! said
I with an air of carelessness, three several times—but it would
not do: every ungracious syllable I had utter'd, crouded back into
my imagination: I reflected, I had no right over the poor Franciscan,
but to deny him; and that the punishment of that was enough to the 5
disappointed without the addition of unkind language—I consider'd his grey hairs—his courteous figure seem'd to re-enter and
gently ask me what injury he had done me?—and why I could use
him thus—I would have given twenty livres for an advocate—I
have behaved very ill; said I within myself; but I have only just set 10
out upon my travels; and shall learn better manners as I get along.

---

title] ∧The Monk.∧   1 psha!— ⟨psha!⟩ said   7 re-enter] re- / -enter *A1,*
reenter *S1* [cf. *A1* "re-establishment", p. 150.30, below]   8 ask ⟨me⟩ ∧me∧ what
9 given] give

1–11. *My heart . . . along.*] Commenting on the philanthropy of the
Good Samaritan, Parson Yorick remarks that, because of "an old religious
grudge—the worst of all grudges," the Samaritans and the Jews "held themselves mutually discharged not only from all offices of friendship and kindness, but even from the most common acts of courtesy and good manners"
(*Sermons,* I, 31 [I.iii]).
    Yorick's remorse over his ill treatment of the monk and his resolve to
"learn better manners" typify the cosmopolitan benevolence of the Sentimental Traveller, in contrast to the attacks on Catholicism in the *Sermons*
and *Tristram Shandy* (see p. 74.27–29*n*, above), and in the observations of the
average English traveler. Smollett vented his spleen on the ceremonies and
festivals of the Roman Church as "a perpetual comedy" intended to divert a
populace reduced to miserable poverty, partly by the impositions of the
Church; see *Travels,* Letters No. 4, pp. 28–29; No. 20, pp. 174–175; No. 27,
pp. 229–230.

THE DESOBLIGEANT.
CALAIS.

WHEN a man is discontented with himself, it has one advantage however, that it puts him into an excellent frame of
mind for making a bargain. Now there being no travelling through
France and Italy without a chaise—and nature generally prompt-
5 ing us to the thing we are fittest for, I walk'd out into the coach
yard to buy or hire something of that kind to my purpose: an old
*Desobligeant in the furthest corner of the court, hit my fancy at

* A chaise, so called in France, from its holding but one person.

---

title] ∧The Desobligeant.∧ [appears to have been inserted above "Calais." after
"Calais." was inscribed]   3 bargain. Now] bargain: now   4 ∧without a
chaise∧   7 *Desobligeant] [not italicized in *S1* here and at pp. 85.132, 87.6,
88.21, below]   8 *A chaise . . . person.] [This note is at the bottom of fol. 17
of *S1* and is separated from the text by a line running the width of the folio. Sterne's
holograph in this note is markedly smaller than it is in the text above it, and the note
appears to have been inserted after fol. 17 was first inscribed.]

3–4. *Now . . . chaise*] English travelers were generally agreed that a
post-chaise was the most expeditious, convenient, and comfortable means of
travel in France (see Mead, pp. 52–59). Millard observed (pp. 21–22) that
"There is what they call a stage coach from Calais to Paris; . . . but by no
means think of entering into this disingenious French invention, which is
more like to Noah's Ark, than any thing else I can compare it, and is seven
days on its journey to Paris."

6–7. *an old *Desobligeant*] See Plate 5, following p. 292, below.

8. **A chaise . . . but one person.*] Although some *desobligéantes* may have
been capable of holding only one person, this type of chaise was apparently
so called primarily because it was too narrow to hold two persons comfort-
ably, and the occupant could not conveniently offer to accommodate another
person. See *La Grande encyclopédie* (Paris: Lamirant, n.d.); *Dictionnaire
nationale ou . . . universel de la langue Française* (Paris, 1874); *Dictionnaire
générale de la langue Française* (Paris, 1920).

76

first sight, so I instantly got into it, and finding it in tolerable
harmony with my feelings, I ordered the waiter to call Monsieur 10
Dessein the master of the hôtel—but Monsieur Dessein being gone
to vespers, and not caring to face the Franciscan whom I saw on the
opposite side of the court, in conference with a lady just arrived,
at the inn—I drew the taffeta curtain betwixt us, and being determined to write my journey, I took out my pen and ink, and wrote 15
the preface to it in the *Desobligeant.*

---

13 ∧side of the Court∧   15 journey ⟨thro' France and Italy ⟩, I
16 *Desobligeant*] *Disobligeant A1, Desobligeant S1*

10–11. *Monsieur Dessein . . . hôtel*] See p. 87.2–3*n*, below.

PREFACE
In the DESOBLIGEANT.

IT must have been observed by many a peripatetic philosopher, That nature has set up by her own unquestionable authority certain boundaries and fences to circumscribe the discontent of man: she has effected her purpose in the quietest and easiest
5 manner by laying him under almost insuperable obligations to work out his ease, and to sustain his sufferings at home. It is there only that she has provided him with the most suitable objects to partake of his happiness, and bear a part of that burden which in all countries and ages, has ever been too heavy for one pair of
10 shoulders. 'Tis true we are endued with an imperfect power of spreading our happiness sometimes beyond *her* limits, but 'tis so ordered, that from the want of languages, connections, and dependencies, and from the difference in education, customs and habits, we lie under so many impediments in communicating our
15 sensations out of our own sphere, as often amount to a total impossibility.

It will always follow from hence, that the balance of sentimental commerce is always against the expatriated adventurer: he must buy what he has little occasion for at their own price—his con-
20 versation will seldom be taken in exchange for theirs without a large discount—and this, by the by, eternally driving him into the

---

5 under almost insuperable] under almost under insuperable   10 'Tis] it is
10 ∧with∧   12 languages] language   14–15 our ⟨pleasurable⟩ sensations
17 ∧always∧

Pages 78–85. *Preface*] Yorick's observations on travel in the Preface are partially anticipated in Yorick's sermon on the Prodigal Son; see App. E, pp. 326–330, note to pp. 78–85. The Preface to *Tristram Shandy* also appears *in medias res* (3.20.192 ff.).

17–18. *sentimental commerce*] Cf. *Sermons*, I, 18 (I.ii), "benevolent . . . commerce"; II, 175 (VI.x), ref. to saints and hermits who " 'fled unnaturally from all commerce with their fellow creatures' "; II, 224 (VII.xiv), the virtues of carrying on "peaceable commerce" and "social intercourse" with our fellowmen.

hands of more equitable brokers for such conversation as he can find, it requires no great spirit of divination to guess at his party—

This brings me to my point; and naturally leads me (if the see-saw of this *Desobligeant* will but let me get on) into the efficient as 25 well as the final causes of travelling—

Your idle people that leave their native country and go abroad for some reason or reasons which may be derived from one of these general causes—

Infirmity of body,   *30*
Imbecility of mind, or
Inevitable necessity.

The first two include all those who travel by land or by water, labouring with pride, curiosity, vanity or spleen, subdivided and combined *in infinitum.*   35

The third class includes the whole army of peregrine martyrs; more especially those travellers who set out upon their travels with the benefit of the clergy, either as delinquents travelling under the direction of governors recommended by the magistrate— or young gentlemen transported by the cruelty of parents and *40* guardians, and travelling under the direction of governors recommended by Oxford, Aberdeen and Glasgow.

---

29 causes—] causes   37 those ⟨who⟩ Travellers who   40 transported ⟨of
[i.e., "off"]⟩ by

---

30. *Infirmity of body*] Both Sterne and Smollett were driven abroad by infirmity of body; see pp. 2, 12, and p. 33, n. 28, above.

37–41. *those travellers . . . governors*] See Bunbury's satirical print, Plate 7, following p. 000, below: the young English gentleman (in the center) travels "with the benefit of" an English clerical governor, who is standing behind him (see *Catalogue of Prints and Drawings in the British Museum,* IV, 798–799). The practice of sending young men abroad with a governor, or tutor, was a favorite target for ridicule: see Smollett's strictures on Mr. Jolter as a typical specimen of "those animals who lead raw boys about the world, under the denomination of travelling governors" (*Peregrine Pickle,* ch. 39) and on young Englishmen who return from abroad "finished connoisseurs and coxcombs" (*Travels,* Letter No. 29, p. 251); the description by a "lac'd Governor" of his pupil's triumphant progress through Europe, in the *Dun-*

There is a fourth class, but their number is so small that they
would not deserve a distinction, was it not necessary in a work of
45 this nature to observe the greatest precision and nicety, to avoid
a confusion of character. And these men I speak of, are such as
cross the seas and sojourn in a land of strangers with a view of
saving money for various reasons and upon various pretences:
but as they might also save themselves and others a great deal of
50 unnecessary trouble by saving their money at home—and as their
reasons for travelling are the least complex of any other species of
emigrants, I shall distinguish these gentlemen by the name of
Simple Travellers.

---

46 ⟨T⟩∼A∼nd these

---

ciad, IV, 282–334; the comments on the folly of sending young men on the
Grand Tour under the direction of "some poor Scholar," in *Spectator* No.
364 (III, 368–370), and in Yorick's sermon on the Prodigal Son (App. E,
p. 329, note to pp. 78–85); and in Tristram's promise to give a "delectable" account of his experiences as a traveling governor (see p. 1, above).

Sterne considered the possibility of leading "a bear round Europe" on
his two trips abroad: see *Letters,* No. 77, Coxwold, June 1761, p. 140; No.
149, Coxwold, [? Sept.] 1765, p. 257; see also No. 132, Coxwold, Sept. 1764,
p. 228, ref. to the possibility of traveling with "some *gros* my Lord" to Paris:
"I'll try if I can make him relish the joys of the *Tuileries, Opera Comique,* &c."
He contemplated making a third trip to Paris in December 1766 as traveling
companion to a "young nobleman" (*Letters,* No. 172, Coxwold, Sept. 1766,
p. 288).

41–42. *governors . . . Glasgow*] probably a gibe at the low standards pre-
vailing in British universities (see Mead, pp. 119–120).

43–53. *fourth class . . . Simple Travellers*] See Yorick's satiric portrait
of the traveling governor who takes pride in teaching his pupil to travel as
cheaply as possible, in the sermon on the Prodigal Son (pp. 329–330, below).
On the title page of *The Gentleman's Guide,* Millard announced that he had
traveled through France "on a Principle which he most sincerely recom-
mends to his Countrymen, viz. Not to spend more Money in the Country of
our natural Enemy, than is requisite to support, with Decency, the Character
of an ENGLISHMAN."

Smollett, of necessity a Simple Traveller who had to spend money con-
servatively abroad (see p. 33, n. 28, above), was continually exasperated by
the "flagrant imposition" to which he was subjected (*Travels,* Letter No. 6,
p. 44), mainly as a result of the extravagance of many English travelers, whose

Thus the whole circle of travellers may be reduced to the following *Heads.*   55

> Idle Travellers,
> Inquisitive Travellers,
> Lying Travellers,
> Proud Travellers,
> Vain Travellers,   60
> Splenetic Travellers.

Then follow the Travellers of
Necessity.
The delinquent and felonious Traveller,

---

54 whole ⟨Body⟩ ∧circle∧   62–71 Then follow . . . class.] [For the exact format in *A1* of this portion of the text, which has often been reprinted in a misleading
form, see facsimiles of pp. 27 and 28 of *A1,* facing p. 320, below.]

---

readiness to pay exorbitant prices was the subject of much scornful comment
(see Mead, pp. 186 ff.). He observed that the high cost of living in Montpellier "is owing to the concourse of English who come hither, and, like
simple birds of passage, allow themselves to be plucked by the people of the
country, who know their weak side, and make their attacks accordingly.
They affect to believe, that all the travellers of our country are grand seig-
neurs, immensely rich and incredibly generous; and we are silly enough to
encourage this opinion, by submitting quietly to the most ridiculous extortion, as well as by committing acts of the most absurd extravagance" (*Travels,*
Letter No. 10, p. 91). His attempts to travel inexpensively cost him endless
trouble with postilions and landlords, and he advised "every traveller who
consults his own ease and convenience, to be liberal of his money to all that
sort of people; and even to wink at the imposition of aubergistes on the road,
unless it be very flagrant. So sure as you enter into disputes with them, you
will be put to a great deal of trouble, and fret yourself to no manner of purpose" (*Travels,* Letter No. 12, p. 113). However, as Tristram's comments on
his *Travels* suggest, Smollett seldom followed his own good advice: see *TS,*
9.24.628–629, quoted p. 15, above.

    47. *sojourn . . . strangers*] possibly an echo of the many Biblical refs. to
sojourning strangers; cf., e.g., Leviticus 19:33: "if a stranger sojourn with
thee in your land, ye shall not vex him."

    64. *The delinquent and felonious Traveller*] In Boulogne (a gathering-place
for "delinquent and felonious" Britishers compelled to flee abroad), Tristram encounters "a jolly set" of "debtors and sinners" who assume that he is
pursued by the authorities for debt, murder, treason, or some other crime
(*TS,* 7.7.487–488).

65   The unfortunate and innocent Traveller,
      The simple Traveller,
      And last of all (if you please) The

      Sentimental Traveller (meaning thereby myself) who have
      travell'd, and of which I am now sitting down to give an account—
70 as much out of *Necessity*, and the *besoin de* Voyager, as any one in
      the class.

      I am well aware, at the same time, as both my travels and observa-
      tions will be altogether of a different cast from any of my fore-
      runners; that I might have insisted upon a whole nitch entirely to
75 myself—but I should break in upon the confines of the *Vain*
      Traveller, in wishing to draw attention towards me, till I have some
      better grounds for it, than the mere *Novelty of my Vehicle.*

      It is sufficient for my reader, if he has been a traveller himself,
      that with study and reflection hereupon he may be able to deter-

---

66 Traveller,] Traveller—   70 *besoin de* Voyager] [*S1* also reads *"besoin d
Voyager"*]   72 a⟨s⟩~t~ . . . time, ⟨That⟩ ∧as∧   74–76 nitch . . . at-
tention] ⟨nitch entirely to myself—but my title page forbids to draw attention,⟩
[This canceled reading appears upside down at the bottom of fol. 25ᵛ; fol. 25 begins with "nitch . . . attention", ll. 74–76, above. Sterne evidently began what is
now fol. 25ᵛ with this canceled reading, and then turned the sheet over and began
what is now fol. 25 with the final version. He made similar revisions elsewhere in *S1*:
see App. B, p. 298, n. 3.]   77 *Vehicle*] vehicle

      67–71. *The Sentimental Traveller . . . class*] Sterne had to travel of neces-
sity—partly to flee Death, and partly to seek fresh literary inspiration (see pp.
2, 12, above).

      77. *Novelty of my Vehicle*] In dedicating his "Charity Sermon" on Elijah
and the Widow of Zarephath to the Dean of York, Sterne begged his indulgence, *"being afraid there can be little left to be said upon the subject of* Charity,
which has not been often thought, and much better expressed [cf. Pope, *Essay on
Criticism*, ii, 298] *by many who have gone before: and indeed, it seems so beaten
and common a path, that it is not an easy matter for a new comer to distinguish
himself in it, by any thing except the novelty of his* Vehicle" (*Sermons*, I, 51 [I.v];
first publ. York, 1747 [*Life*, pp. 597–598; *Letters*, No. 8, July 1747, p. 23]).
See also Sterne's ref. to his *Political Romance* as a "*Vehicle*" in *Letters*, No. 35,
Jan. 1759, p. 73; his ref. to *Tristram Shandy* as a "vehicle" in *Letters*, No. 77,
June 1761, p. 140; and Walter Shandy's ref. to man as a "curious vehicle,"
quoted p. 101.39–40n, below.

mine his own place and rank in the catalogue—it will be one step 80
towards knowing himself; as it is great odds, but he retains some
tincture and resemblance, of what he imbibed or carried out, to the
present hour.

The man who first transplanted the grape of Burgundy to the
Cape of Good Hope (observe he was a Dutch man) never dreamt 85
of drinking the same wine at the Cape, that the same grape produced upon the French mountains—he was too phlegmatic for
that—but undoubtedly he expected to drink some sort of vinous
liquor; but whether good, bad, or indifferent—he knew enough
of this world to know, that it did not depend upon his choice, but 90
that what is generally called *chance* was to decide his success:
however, he hoped for the best; and in these hopes, by an intemperate confidence in the fortitude of his head, and the depth
of his discretion, *Mynheer* might possibly overset both in his new
vineyard; and by discovering his nakedness, become a laughing- 95
stock to his people.

Even so it fares with the poor Traveller, sailing and posting
through the politer kingdoms of the globe in pursuit of knowledge
and improvements.

Knowledge and improvements are to be got by sailing and post- 100
ing for that purpose; but whether useful knowledge and real im-

---

83 ⟨?t⟩~h~our   92 however, he hoped] however ⟨He⟩ ∧⟨Mynheer⟩∧ hoped
95 vin⟨?es⟩~'y~ard   98 in ⟨quest⟩ ∧pursuit∧

84–96. *The man . . . people.*] On the vineyards and wines of the Dutch
colony at the Cape of Good Hope and the identity of the Dutchman who
planted the first vineyard there, see App. E, pp. 331–332, note to p. 83.84-
96.

92–96. *by an intemperate confidence . . . people*] Cf. Noah's experience in
his (the first) vineyard, in Genesis 9:20–22: "And Noah began to be an
husbandman, and he planted a vineyard: And he drank of the wine, and was
drunken; and he was uncovered within his tent. And Ham . . . saw the
nakedness of his father . . ." There are many refs. in the Bible to the discovering of nakedness, e.g., Exodus 20:26, Ezekiel 16:36–37, 22:10, 23:18.

100–126. *Knowledge . . . going*—] This paragraph is largely adapted from
Bishop Joseph Hall's *Quo Vadis?* See App. E, pp. 332–336, note to pp. 83.-
100–85.126.

provements, is all a lottery—and even where the adventurer is
successful, the acquired stock must be used with caution and
sobriety to turn to any profit—but as the chances run prodigiously
105 the other way both as to the acquisition and application, I am of
opinion, That a man would act as wisely, if he could prevail upon
himself, to live contented without foreign knowledge or foreign
improvements, especially if he lives in a country that has no absolute want of either—and indeed, much grief of heart has it oft and
110 many a time cost me, when I have observed how many a foul step
the inquisitive Traveller has measured to see sights and look into
discoveries; all which, as Sancho Pança said to Don Quixote, they
might have seen dry-shod at home. It is an age so full of light, that
there is scarce a country or corner of Europe whose beams are not
115 crossed and interchanged with others—Knowledge in most of its
branches, and in most affairs, is like music in an Italian street,
whereof those may partake, who pay nothing—But there is no
nation under heaven—and God is my record, (before whose
tribunal I must one day come and give an account of this work)—
120 that I do not speak it vauntingly—But there is no nation under
heaven abounding with more variety of learning—where the
sciences may be more fitly woo'd, or more surely won than here—
where art is encouraged, and will so soon rise high—where Nature
(take her all together) has so little to answer for—and, to close all,

---

104 ∧as∧   104–105 ⟨?t⟩~p~rodigiously the   105–106 of ⟨an⟩ opinion
117 th⟨ey⟩~ose~   122 won∧then here∧   123 high— ⟨and⟩∧⟨?further,—⟩∧
⟨?nature⟩~where~ Nature [the process of revision here is unclear]

112–113. *all which, as Sancho Pança . . . home*] a ref. to Sancho's lament
in parting with his wife: "wou'd Heaven but be pleas'd to let me live at home
dry-shod, in Peace and Quietness, without gadding over Hill and Dale,
thro' Brambles and Briars" (*Don Quixote*, 2.3.5.472; cited by Vrooman, p.
149, n. 2). However, the reflection Yorick attributes to Sancho is adapted
from *Quo Vadis?*: cf. "*that . . . dryshod*" in the excerpts quoted from *Quo
Vadis?* in App. E, p. 334, note to pp. 83.100–85.126. In *TS*, 7.4.482–483,
Addison's learned *Remarks on Several Parts of Italy* (1705) is ridiculed as the
kind of pedantic travel book that could have been written "dry shod."
118. *God . . . record*] See App. E, p. 333, n. 2.

where there is more wit and variety of character to feed the mind *125*
with—Where then, my dear countrymen, are you going—

—We are only looking at this chaise, said they—Your most
obedient servant, said I, skipping out of it, and pulling off my hat—
We were wondering, said one of them, who, I found, was an *inquisi-*
tive traveller—what could occasion its motion.—'Twas the agita- *130*
tion, said I coolly, of writing a preface—I never heard, said the
other, who was a *simple traveller*, of a preface wrote in a *Desobli-*
geant.—It would have been better, said I, in a *Vis a Vis*.

—*As an English man does not travel to see English men*, I retired
to my room.   *135*

129–130 ∧I found∧ was ⟨?i⟩~a~n *inquisitive*   131–132 heard ⟨of a preface⟩,
said . . . preface   133 *Vis a Vis*] Vis a Vis   134 ∧*man*∧   134 *men,*]
men—

---

126. *Where . . . going*—] See App. E, p. 335, n. 8.

129–131. *We . . . writing a preface*] See the refs. in Sterne's writings to the
interaction between the traveler's emotions and the motions of his vehicle
cited p. 142*n*, below.

133. *Vis a Vis*] a light carriage in which two (or four) persons sit face to
face.

134. *As . . . English men*] Smollett reflected, after being rebuffed by an
English traveler to whom he had offered his services (as a physician): "This
sort of reserve seems peculiar to the English disposition. When two natives
of any other country chance to meet abroad, they run into each other's
embrace like old friends, even though they have never heard of one another
till that moment; whereas two Englishmen in the same situation maintain a
mutual reserve and diffidence, and keep without the sphere of each other's
attraction, like two bodies endowed with a repulsive power" (*Travels*, Letter
No. 41, pp. 342–343). Of an Englishman who traveled three days with two of
his countrymen without exchanging a word with them, he observed: "This
is a character truly British" (*Travels*, Letter No. 35, p. 304). For similar
comments see Mead, pp. 130–132.

Yorick's remark may also be intended as an ironic thrust at English travelers who seemed to have traveled *only* to see other Englishmen, and congregated with their countrymen (particularly in Paris), having become bored
with viewing "pictures, statues, and churches" (p. 218, below), and frustrated by their inability to speak the native language and failure to meet men
of rank and cultivation (see Yorick's comments on this head in the

sermon on the Prodigal Son, App. E, p. 330, note to pp. 78–85). Sharp observed: "I have not seen one young [English] gentleman on his travels, who does not appear more eager than I am to return to his friends and country. I had always figured to myself, that they were in the highest delight, when making the Grand Tour; but I find by experience, that when they are here, they consider it as a kind of apprenticeship for qualifying a gentleman, and would often return back abruptly, did they not feel themselves ashamed to indulge the inclination: Indeed, were it not, that in the great cities they meet with numbers of their countrymen, the hours would lye too heavy on their hands; for few men can spend their whole life in the pursuit of virtú, and some have not the qualifications of birth to recommend them to persons of high rank, where only is to be found what little society there is in *Italy*" (*Letters from Italy*, Letter No. 38, pp. 170–171).

CALAIS.

I Perceived that something darken'd the passage more than myself, as I stepp'd along it to my room; it was effectually Mons.
Dessein, the master of the hôtel, who had just return'd from
vespers, and, with his hat under his arm, was most complaisantly
following me, to put me in mind of my wants. I had wrote myself *5*
pretty well out of conceit with the *Desobligeant*; and Mons. Dessein
speaking of it, with a shrug, as if it would no way suit me, it immediately struck my fancy that it belong'd to some *innocent traveller*, who, on his return home, had left it to Mons. Dessein's honour
to make the most of. Four months had elapsed since it had finish'd *10*
its career of Europe in the corner of Mons. Dessein's coachyard;
and having sallied out from thence but a vampt-up business at the
first, though it had been twice taken to pieces on Mount Sennis, it
had not profited much by its adventures—but by none so little
as the standing so many months unpitied in the corner of Mons. *15*

---

1 ∧that∧   2 ⟨?c⟩∼r∼oom   7 ⟨?n⟩∼w∼ould no way   9 it ⟨at⟩ // to
10 four ⟨long⟩ months   10 elapsed] lapsed

2–3. *Mons. Dessein, the master of the hôtel*] In 1762, the year of Yorick's
Journey (see p. 192.7–8*n*, below), Dessein was master of the Lyon d'Argent in
Calais, and Sterne probably stopped there in January 1762 on his first trip to
Paris (see p. 89.11*n*, below). (The Lyon d'Argent burned down in 1764,
and when Sterne went abroad for the second time, in October 1765, he put
up at Dessein's new establishment in Calais, the Hôtel d'Angleterre.) For
Dessein's career, his reputation among English travelers, and the fame and
prosperity he gained from Sterne's allusions to him in *A Sentimental Journey*,
see App. E, pp. 336–338, note to p. 87.2–3.

13. *it . . . Mount Sennis*] a ref. to the method of crossing the Alps at Mt.
Cenis, on the French-Italian border, southwest of Turin: "The passage into
Italy is composed of a very steep ascent, . . . the descent on the *Italian* side
is not so steep as that on the side of *Savoy*. . . . Both going and returning,
when you arrive at the foot of the mountain, your coach, or chaise, is taken
to pieces, and carried upon mules to the other side, and you yourself are
transported by two men, on a common straw elbow chair . . . fixed upon
two poles, like a sedan-chair" (Sharp, *Letters from Italy*, No. 53, p. 287; see
also Mead, p. 62).

Dessein's coachyard. Much indeed was not to be said for it—but
something might—and when a few words will rescue misery out
of her distress, I hate the man who can be a churl of them.

—Now was I the master of this hôtel, said I, laying the point of
20 my fore-finger on Mons. Dessein's breast, I would inevitably make
a point of getting rid of this unfortunate *Desobligeant*—it stands
swinging reproaches at you every time you pass by it—

Mon Dieu! said Mons. Dessein—I have no interest—Except the
interest, said I, which men of a certain turn of mind take, Mons.
25 Dessein, in their own sensations—I'm persuaded, to a man who
feels for others as well as for himself, every rainy night, disguise
it as you will, must cast a damp upon your spirits—You suffer,
Mons. Dessein, as much as the machine—

I have always observed, when there is as much *sour* as *sweet* in a
30 compliment, that an Englishman is eternally at a loss within himself, whether to take it, or let it alone: a Frenchman never is: Mons.
Dessein made me a bow.

C'est bien vrai, said he—But in this case I should only exchange
one disquietude for another, and with loss: figure to yourself,
35 my dear Sir, that in giving you a chaise which would fall to pieces
before you had got half way to Paris—figure to yourself how much
I should suffer, in giving an ill impression of myself to a man of
honour, and lying at the mercy, as I must do, *d'un homme d'esprit.*

The dose was made up exactly after my own prescription; so
40 I could not help taking it—and returning Mons. Dessein his bow,
without more casuistry we walk'd together towards his Remise,
to take a view of his magazine of chaises.

17–18 few ⟨little ∧words∧ will set the post chaise of an innocent traveller a going, I⟩
words . . . I   20 make] make make   23 *Mon*] —Mon   24–25 ∧Mons.ͬ
Dessein∧   25 persuaded, ⟨that,⟩ to   27–28 damp, ⟨Mons.ͬ Dessein,⟩ upon
. . . suffer, ^Mon.^ / ∧Dessein,∧   30–31 ∧within himself∧   33 ∧in this
case∧   34–36 and with loss . . . figure to] ⟨and with loss— / —for in giving
Monsieur a chaise wᶜʰ will not answer it's destination—figure to⟩ [This canceled
reading appears upside down at the bottom of fol. 34ᵛ of *S1;* fol. 34 begins with "and
with loss . . . figure to", ll. 34–36, above (see p. 82.74–76*tn,* above).]   36 had
got] got   37 suffer, ⟨both by⟩ ∧in∧   38 mercy, ⟨*?encore,*⟩ ∧as . . . do,∧
42 to ⟨see⟩ ∧take a View of∧

---

41. *Remise*] coach-house.

IN THE STREET.

CALAIS.

IT must needs be a hostile kind of a world, when the buyer (if it be but of a sorry post-chaise) cannot go forth with the seller thereof into the street to terminate the difference betwixt them, but he instantly falls into the same frame of mind and views his conventionist with the same sort of eye, as if he was going along 5 with him to Hyde-park corner to fight a duel. For my own part, being but a poor sword's-man, and no way a match for Monsieur *Dessein,* I felt the rotation of all the movements within me, to which the situation is incident—I looked at Monsieur *Dessein* through and through—ey'd him as he walked along in profile— 10 then, *en face*—thought he look'd like a Jew—then a Turk—disliked his wig—cursed him by my gods—wished him at the devil—

—And is all this to be lighted up in the heart for a beggarly account of three or four louisd'ors, which is the most I can be overreach'd in?—Base passion! said I, turning myself about, as a 15 man naturally does upon a sudden reverse of sentiment—base, ungentle passion! thy hand is against every man, and every man's hand against thee—heaven forbid! said she, raising her hand up

---

5–6 ∧along with him∧ . . . ∧corner∧ . . . duel. ⟨with him.⟩ for   8 *Desseinɹ* Dessein [never italicized in *S1*]   10 as he walked along] ∧as walk'd along∧ 15 overreach∧'d∧   18–19 She ⟨laying her hand across her eyes,⟩ ∧raising . . . forehead,∧

---

11. *thought . . . Jew*] possibly a ref. to the fact that Dessein made a tidy profit by converting English currency into French for his English clients; see App. E, p. 337, note to p. 87.2–3.

11. *a Turk*] In a letter advising his wife about arrangements for her journey to France in 1762, Sterne added a postscript on Dessein: ". . . at Calais at the Lyon D'Argent—the master a Turk in grain" (*Letters,* No. 95, Paris, June 1762, p. 177). Cross (*Life,* p. 382) erroneously cites this as an allusion to Mons. Grandsire, from whom Dessein leased the Lyon d'Argent; see App. E, p. 336, note to p. 87.2–3.

17–18. *thy . . . thee*] a paraphrase of Genesis 16:12: Cain's "hand will be against every man, and every man's hand against him." This verse is paraphrased also in *Sermons,* I, 108 (II.ix); II, 88 (V.i).

to her forehead, for I had turned full in front upon the lady whom
20 I had seen in conference with the monk—she had followed us unperceived—Heaven forbid indeed! said I, offering her my own—
she had a black pair of silk gloves open only at the thumb and two
fore-fingers, so accepted it without reserve—and I led her up to
the door of the Remise.

25   Monsieur *Dessein* had *diabled* the key above fifty times before he
found out he had come with a wrong one in his hand: we were as
impatient as himself to have it open'd; and so attentive to the obstacle, that I continued holding her hand almost without knowing
it; so that Monsieur *Dessein* left us together with her hand in mine,
30 and with our faces turned towards the door of the Remise, and
said he would be back in five minutes.

      Now a colloquy of five minutes, in such a situation, is worth one
of as many ages, with your faces turned towards the street: in the
latter case, 'tis drawn from the objects and occurrences without—
35 when your eyes are fixed upon a dead blank—you draw purely
from yourselves. A silence of a single moment upon Monsieur
Dessein's leaving us, had been fatal to the situation—she had infallibly turned about—so I begun the conversation instantly.—

      —But what were the temptations, (as I write not to apologize
40 for the weaknesses of my heart in this tour,—but to give an account
of them)—shall be described with the same simplicity, with which
I felt them.

---

20 monk, ⟨and⟩~—~ ∧She∧   28 ⟨?I⟩~t~hat I   32 situation, ⟨(which, ∧by
the way,∧ is one of those wᶜʰ can happen to a man but once in his life)⟩ is
35 upon ⟨the door of a remise,⟩ ∧a dead Blank—∧   38 ⟨?a⟩~t~he   38 instantly.—] instantly—   39 what ⟨?was⟩~⟨?were⟩~ ∧were∧ the temptation VsV

THE REMISE DOOR.

CALAIS.

WHEN I told the reader that I did not care to get out of the *Desobligeant*, because I saw the monk in close conference with a lady just arrived at the inn—I told him the truth; but I did not tell him the whole truth; for I was full as much restrained by the appearance and figure of the lady he was talking to. Suspicion 5 crossed my brain, and said, he was telling her what had passed: something jarred upon it within me—I wished him at his convent.

When the heart flies out before the understanding, it saves the judgment a world of pains—I was certain she was of a better order of beings—however, I thought no more of her, but went on and 10 wrote my preface.

---

7 with∧in∧ [*M1*: u.v.]

---

7. *something . . . me*] Cf. Sterne's statement to Eliza that his wife's presence in Coxwold will prevent him from continuing the *Journal:* "She will be ever present—& if I take up my pen for thee—something will jarr within me as I do it" (*Journal*, 4 Aug., p. 387); cf. also *Sermons*, I, 200 (III.ii): "something jars, and will for ever jar in these cases: imposture is all dissonance."

8–9. *the heart . . . judgment*] One of Sterne's many refs. to the interplay between "heart" and "head": see esp. *Letters*, No. 10, Nov. 1750, p. 27; No. 236, March 1768, p. 419; *Journal*, 25 June, pp. 364–365 (quoted p. 100.15*n*, below); 18 July, p. 380; *TS*, 6.17.436; *Sermons*, I, 173 (II.xv). See also the refs. to "heart" and "head" with respect to the *Sermons*, in *Sermons*, I, viii (I, Preface); *Letters*, No. 180, to Eliza, [? Jan. 1767], p. 298; *TS*, 4.26.317.

Yorick observes in one of his sermons that the "judgments of the more disinterested and impartial of us, receive no small tincture from our affections: we generally consult them in all doubtful points, and it happens well if the matter in question is not almost settled, before the arbitrator is called into the debate" (*Sermons*, I, 223–224 [III.iv]).

8–15. *When . . . her*] Cf. the rapid progress of Yorick's sentimental commerce with the lady, with Sterne's explanation to Elizabeth Vesey for his having written her "upon so short an Acquaintance—*short*, did I say—I unsay it again: I have had the happiness to be acquainted with Mrs Vesey almost time immemorial—surely the most penetrating of her sex need not be

91

The impression returned, upon my encounter with her in the
street; a guarded frankness with which she gave me her hand,
shewed, I thought, her good education and her good sense; and as
15 I led her on, I felt a pleasurable ductility about her, which spread
a calmness over all my spirits—

—Good God! how a man might lead such a creature as this
round the world with him!—

I had not yet seen her face—'twas not material; for the drawing
20 was instantly set about, and long before we had got to the door of
the Remise, *Fancy* had finished the whole head, and pleased herself as much with its fitting her goddess, as if she had dived into
the TIBER for it—but thou art a seduced, and a seducing slut; and
albeit thou cheatest us seven times a day with thy pictures and
25 images, yet with so many charms dost thou do it, and thou deckest
out thy pictures in the shapes of so many angels of light, 'tis a
shame to break with thee.

---

14 good ⟨?manner⟩~educa~tion   18–19 him!—┼I [bracket in *S1* indicates par.
M1: no par.]   21 *Fancy*] Fancy

---

told that intercourses of this kind are not to be dated by hours, days or
months, but by the slow or rapid progress of our intimacies which can be
measured only by the degrees of penetration by wch we discover Characters
at first sight, or by the openess and *frankness* [italics added] of heart wch lets
the by-stander into it, *without the pains of reflection* [italics added]; either of
these spares us, what a short life can ill afford and that is, that Long and un-
conscionable time in forming Connections, which had much better be spent
in tasting the fruits of them—now, I maintain, that of this frame & contexture
is the fair Mrs Vesey—her character is to be read at once; I saw it before I had
walk'd ten paces besides ⟨you⟩ her.—I believe in my Conscience, dear Lady,
that you have absolutely no inside at all" (*Letters,* No. 76, June [? 1761],
pp. 137–138).
      21–23. *Fancy . . . for it*] Cf. Tristram's invitation to the reader, to pic-
ture the Widow Wadman according to his own fancy, on the blank page he
has provided (*TS,* 6.38.470), and his description of the working of the
Fancy (8.5.543).
      Milic points out (p. 16, n. 1) that Yorick is comparing the operations of
Fancy to the archaeologists' practice of searching for the missing heads of
statues of gods and goddesses at the bottom of the Tiber.

When we had got to the door of the Remise, she withdrew her hand from across her forehead, and let me see the original—it was a face of about six and twenty—of a clear transparent brown, simply *30* set off without rouge or powder—it was not critically handsome,

---

31 without ⟨either⟩ rouge

30–34. *a face . . . widow'd look*] This description may have been partly inspired by Eliza, who was twenty-two when Sterne met her. In a letter to her (*Letters,* No. 189, London, March 1767, pp. 312–313), Sterne praised his picture of her (see p. 67.20–21*n,* above) as "calculated only to please . . . [a] sentimental philosopher," for in it she appeared unadorned, "simple as a vestal . . . the good girl nature made you . . . When I first saw you, I beheld you as an object of compassion, and as a very plain woman. . . . You are not handsome, Eliza, nor is yours a face that will please the tenth part of your beholders,—but are something more; . . . I never saw so intelligent, so animated, so good a countenance; nor was there, (nor ever will be), that man of sense, tenderness, and feeling, in your company three hours, that was not (or will not be) your admirer, or friend, in consequence of it; that is, if you assume, or assumed, no character foreign to your own, but appeared the artless being nature designed you for. . . . [you possess] that bewitching sort of nameless excellence, that men of nice sensibility alone can be touched with.

Were your husband in England, I would freely give him five hundred pounds . . . to let you only sit by me two hours in a day, while I wrote my Sentimental Journey. I am sure the work would sell so much the better for it, that I should be re-imbursed the sum more than seven times told.—I would not give nine pence for the picture of you, the Newnham's have got executed —It is the resemblance of a conceited, made-up coquette. Your eyes, and the shape of your face . . . [are] finer than any I beheld in all my travels . . ."

30–31. *simply . . . powder*] in contrast to the heavy make-up fashionable among Frenchwomen of rank, which dismayed English travelers. Smollett fulminated against "the manner in which the faces of the ladies are primed and painted" as carrying "human affectation to the very farthest verge of folly and extravagance," and observed: "the *fard,* or *white,* with which their necks and shoulders are plaistered, . . . may be in some measure excusable, as their skins are naturally brown, or sallow; but the *rouge,* which is daubed on their faces, from the chin up to the eyes, without the least art or dexterity, . . . renders the aspect really frightful, or at best conveys nothing but ideas of disgust and aversion. You know, that without this horrible masque no married lady is admitted at court, or in any polite assembly" (*Travels,* Letter No. 7, p. 56). Thicknesse insisted that the beauty of many Frenchwomen was

but there was that in it, which in the frame of mind I was in, which attached me much more to it—it was interesting; I fancied it wore the characters of a widow'd look, and in that state of its declension,
35 which had passed the two first paroxysms of sorrow, and was quietly beginning to reconcile itself to its loss—but a thousand other distresses might have traced the same lines; I wish'd to know what they had been—and was ready to enquire, (had the same *bon ton* of conversation permitted, as in the days of Esdras)—

33–34 interesting; ⟨I fancyd, I discernd the ?traces of⟩ // I . . . of a   37–38 know
⟨her story,⟩ ∧what . . . been—∧

---

apparent "in spite of the singularity of the *paint, pomatum and powder, so much complained of*" (*Observations*, p. 79; this book was written partly to vindicate the French against the strictures of other writers, particularly Smollett, and Thicknesse may have Smollett's comments in mind). See also Cole's description of Frenchwomen at the opera "painted most frightfully without any Art, on their Cheeks with red" (*Journey to Paris*, p. 266).

Shortly before Lydia left France to visit him in Coxwold in 1767, Sterne wrote her: "I must desire . . . [that you] throw all your rouge pots into the Sorgue before you set out—I will have no rouge put on in England" (*Letters*, No. 210, Coxwold, Aug. 1767, pp. 391–392).

33–34. *I fancied . . . widow'd look*] As Don Quixote frequently points out, "the order of Knighthood-Errant was instituted . . . [to] protect Widows, relieve Orphans [see p. 69.28–29, above], and assist all the Distress'd in general" (*Don Quixote*, 1.2.3.64; see also 2.3.16.538–539, 2.3.17.552 [quoted p. 116.19–27n, below], 2.4.36.689, 2.4.72.921).

Widows are frequently mentioned in the *Sermons* as natural objects of compassion: see esp. I, 48–70, on Elijah and the Widow of Zarephath (I.v); I, 61–63, quoted p. 68.18–23n, above; II, 152, 156 (VI.vii); II, 221 (VII.xiv).

Sterne several times expressed his hopes that Eliza, his "wife elect" (*Letters*, No. 192, quoted in App. E, p. 325, note to p. 67.21), would be widowed: see esp. *Journal*, 17 June, p. 359; 28 June, p. 366.

39. *bon ton*] Cf. Sterne's remarks on the "*bon ton*" of French conversation in *Letters*, No. 87, quoted p. 159.25–26n, below.

39–41. *Esdras . . . troubled?*"] paraphrased from II Esdras 10:31: "What aileth thee? and why art thou so disquieted? and why is thine understanding troubled, and the thoughts of thine heart?"

"*What aileth thee? and why art thou disquieted? and why is thy under-* 40 *standing troubled?*"—In a word, I felt benevolence for her; and resolved some way or other to throw in my mite of courtesy—if not of service.

Such were my temptations—and in this disposition to give way to them, was I left alone with the lady with her hand in mine, and 45 with our faces both turned closer to the door of the Remise than what was absolutely necessary.

---

46 with ⟨both⟩ our faces both

---

42. *throw . . . mite*] Cf. Mark 12:42: "And there came a certain poor widow, and she threw in two mites" (cf. also Luke 21:2).

THE REMISE DOOR.
CALAIS.

THIS certainly, fair lady! said I, raising her hand up a little lightly as I began, must be one of Fortune's whimsical doings: to take two utter strangers by their hands—of different sexes, and perhaps from different corners of the globe, and in one moment
5 place them together in such a cordial situation, as Friendship herself could scarce have atchieved for them, had she projected it for a month—

—And your reflection upon it, shews how much, Monsieur, she has embarassed you by the adventure.—

10 When the situation is, what we would wish, nothing is so ill-timed as to hint at the circumstances which make it so: you thank Fortune, continued she—you had reason—the heart knew it, and was satisfied; and who but an English philosopher would have sent notices of it to the brain to reverse the judgment?

15 In saying this, she disengaged her hand with a look which I thought a sufficient commentary upon the text.

It is a miserable picture which I am going to give of the weakness of my heart, by owning, that it suffered a pain, which worthier occasions could not have inflicted.—I was mortified with the loss

---

6 could ⟨but⟩ ∧scarse∧   8 much, ⟨my good Chevalier!⟩ ∧Mons.ʳ∧   10 what ⟨a ?man⟩ ∧we∧   15 she ⟨withdrew⟩ ∧disengaged∧   18 pain, ∧⟨by it,⟩∧ which   19 inflicted.—] inflicted—   19 was ⟨hurt⟩ ∧mortified∧

---

12. *you had reason*] a translation of "vous aviez raison."
13–14. *who but an English philosopher . . . judgment?*] The English were popularly regarded by the French as a philosophical, serious people: for characteristic expressions of this view, see Minnie M. Miller, "The English People as Portrayed in Certain French Journals, 1700–1760," *Modern Philology,* XXXIV (1937), 365–376. On the French reputation for levity, see p. 248.67–70*n*, below.

of her hand, and the manner in which I had lost it carried neither 20
oil nor wine to the wound: I never felt the pain of a sheepish in-
feriority so miserably in my life.

The triumphs of a true feminine heart are short upon these
discomfitures. In a very few seconds she laid her hand upon the
cuff of my coat, in order to finish her reply; so some way or other, 25
God knows how, I regained my situation.

—She had nothing to add.

I forthwith began to model a different conversation for the lady,
thinking from the spirit as well as moral of this, that I had been
mistaken in her character; but upon turning her face towards me, 30
the spirit which had animated the reply was fled—the muscles
relaxed, and I beheld the same unprotected look of distress which
first won me to her interest—melancholy! to see such sprightliness
the prey of sorrow.—I pitied her from my soul; and though it may
seem ridiculous enough to a torpid heart,—I could have taken her 35
into my arms, and cherished her, though it was in the open street,
without blushing.

The pulsations of the arteries along my fingers pressing across
hers, told her what was passing within me: she looked down—a
silence of some moments followed.   40

23–24 these ⟨?overthrows⟩ discomfitures   28 a ⟨?n⟩~d~ifferent   34 sorrow— ⟨?fresh ?fuel to the benevolence wch was ?stird up!⟩ —I   40 silence ⟨of
?several⟩ of some

20–21. *neither oil . . . wound*] Cf. Luke 10:33–34, quoted p. 276.12–15n,
below.

31–32. *the spirit . . . distress*] Cf. *Sermons,* I, 229 (III.v): "Nothing so
powerfully calls home the mind as distress: the tense fibre then relaxes,——
the soul retires to itself,——sits pensive and susceptible of right impressions"
(cf. "lax'd . . . fibre," *Letters,* No. 129, quoted p. 225.15–16n, below).

34. *I . . . soul*] Cf. *Letters,* No. 123, Paris, May 1764, p. 214: "I pity him
from my soul . . ."

38–39. *The pulsations . . . me*] The Widow Wadman compels Toby to
travel the lines on his map with his finger, rather than with his pipe, "For
as there was no arterial or vital heat in the end of the tobacco-pipe, it could
excite no sentiment——it could neither give fire by pulsation——or receive

I fear, in this interval, I must have made some slight efforts towards a closer compression of her hand, from a subtle sensation I felt in the palm of my own—not as if she was going to withdraw hers—but, as if she thought about it—and I had infallibly lost it a
45 second time, had not instinct more than reason directed me to the last resource in these dangers—to hold it loosely, and in a manner as if I was every moment going to release it, of myself; so she let it continue, till Monsieur *Dessein* returned with the key; and in the mean time I set myself to consider how I should undo the ill im-
50 pressions which the poor monk's story, in case he had told it her, must have planted in her breast against me.

---

41 fear, ⟨during⟩ ∧in∧   45 ∧directed me∧   46 resoure ⟨?I ?had⟩∼in these∼ dangers— ⟨I⟩ ∧to∧ h⟨e⟩∼o∼ld [Sterne apparently wrote "I held" initially]

---

it by sympathy . . . Whereas, in following my uncle *Toby*'s forefinger with hers, . . . pressing sometimes against the side of it . . . it set something at least in motion" (*TS*, 8.16.555; cited by Vrooman, p. 217, n. 3).

THE SNUFF-BOX.
CALAIS.

THE good old monk was within six paces of us, as the idea of him cross'd my mind; and was advancing towards us a little out of the line, as if uncertain whether he should break in upon us or no.—He stopp'd, however, as soon as he came up to us, with a world of frankness; and having a horn snuff-box in his hand, he 5 presented it open to me—You shall taste mine—said I, pulling out my box (which was a small tortoise one) and putting it into his hand—'Tis most excellent, said the monk; Then do me the favour, I replied, to accept of the box and all, and when you take a pinch out of it, sometimes recollect it was the peace-offering of a man who 10 once used you unkindly, but not from his heart.

---

title] The ⟨?Remise ?Door⟩~Snuff Box.~   1 The ⟨?good⟩ ∧good∧ old m⟨?a⟩~o~n∨k∨ was with∧in∧ [m⟨?a⟩~o~n∨k∨": Sterne apparently wrote "man" initially and then altered it to "monk" by superimposing "o" on "a" and inserting "k" on the line.]   1-2 as ∨t∨he ∧Idea of him∧ [Sterne apparently wrote "he" initially]   2 ∧us∧   4 no.—He] no—he   5 frankness, ⟨in⟩ ∧⟨his⟩∧ and 8-9 favour, I replied, to] favour to   10-11 a ⟨fellow-labourer⟩ ∧man∧ who ∨once∨

---

7. *my box*] As Vrooman suggests (pp. 204–206), the exchange of snuff-boxes between Yorick and the monk may have been indirectly inspired by Eliza's gift to Sterne of a snuffbox, which he associated with her picture (see p. 67.20–21*n*, above): anticipating Mrs. Sterne's visit from France, to make a financial settlement with him, Sterne complained to Eliza, "I shall be . . . pluck'd bare—all but of y^r Portrait & Snuff Box & y^r other dear Presents" (*Journal*, 2 June, p. 348; see also *Letters*, No. 208, p. 389); and in a later entry in the *Journal*, he wrote: "Ten in the morning, with my Snuff open at the Top of this sheet,—& your gentle sweet face opposite to mine" (27 June, p. 365). While he was writing *A Sentimental Journey* Sterne was given another snuff-box, which he also associated with Eliza's picture: "I have just rec^d as a present from a right Honble—a most elegant gold Snuff [box] fabricated for me at Paris—I wish Eliza was here—I would lay it at her feet—however I will enrich my gold Box, with her picture" (*Letters*, No. 208, to Mrs. James, Coxwold, Aug. 1767, p. 388; the same snuffbox is mentioned, together with Eliza's picture, in the *Journal*, 13 June, p. 357). For his proposal to wear her picture about his neck, see p. 67.22*n*, above.

99

The poor monk blush'd as red as scarlet. *Mon Dieu!* said he,
pressing his hands together—you never used me unkindly.—I
should think, said the lady, he is not likely. I blush'd in my turn;
15 but from what movements, I leave to the few who feel to analyse—
Excuse me, Madame, replied I—I treated him most unkindly; and
from no provocations—'Tis impossible, said the lady.—My God!
cried the monk, with a warmth of asseveration which seemed not
to belong to him—the fault was in me, and in the indiscretion of
20 my zeal—the lady opposed it, and I joined with her in maintaining
it was impossible, that a spirit so regulated as his, could give
offence to any.

I knew not that contention could be rendered so sweet and
pleasurable a thing to the nerves as I then felt it.—We remained
25 silent, without any sensation of that foolish pain which takes place,
when in such a circle you look for ten minutes in one another's
faces without saying a word. Whilst this lasted, the monk rubb'd
his horn box upon the sleeve of his tunick; and as soon as it had
acquired a little air of brightness by the friction—he made a low
30 bow, and said, 'twas too late to say whether it was the weakness or
goodness of our tempers which had involved us in this contest—

---

15 what ⟨motions⟩ movements   15 analyze—] analyse.—   16 [For
an earlier version, in *M1*, of the text from "Excuse me" (l. 16, above) through
"took his leave." (p. 101.35, below), see App. C, §5, pp. 311–315.]   19 the
⟨?pros⟩ indiscretion   20 ⟨?him⟩~it~   20–21 maintaining ⟨That a heart so
goo⟩ ∧it was impossible,∧ That . . . regulated   24 ∧a thing∧   24–25 it—
⟨it begot a silence⟩ We remain'd silent   28–35 [For a canceled version in *S1*
of the text from "upon" through "leave." (ll. 28–35, above), see App. C, §5, p. 314,
transcript of fol. 52B of *S1*.]   31 goodness of our] goodness our

---

15. *but . . . analyse*] Cf. Sterne's exclamation to Eliza: "What a stupid,
selfish, unsentimental set of Beings are the Bulk of our Sex! by Heaven! not
one man out of 50, informd ⟨either⟩ with feelings—or endow'd either with
heads or hearts able to possess & fill the mind . . . of such a Being as thee,
with one Vibration [see p. 274.39n, below] like its own" (*Journal,* 25 June,
pp. 364–365); cf. also his complaint to Dr. John Eustace about the lack of
"true feeling in the *herd* of the *world,*" in *Letters,* No. 229, quoted p. 24, above.

but be it as it would—he begg'd we might exchange boxes—In saying this, he presented his to me with one hand, as he took mine from me in the other; and having kiss'd it—with a stream of good nature in his eyes he put it into his bosom—and took his leave. 35

I guard this box, as I would the instrumental parts of my religion, to help my mind on to something better: in truth, I seldom go abroad without it; and oft and many a time have I called up by it the courteous spirit of its owner to regulate my own, in the justlings of the world; they had found full employment for his, as I 40 learnt from his story, till about the forty-fifth year of his age, when

---

32 exchange] exchanges following p. 320, below] for it

37 m⟨?e⟩~y~ ∧mind∧ [see facsimile of fol. 52B of *S1*, 40 found full . . . for his] found ⟨him⟩ full . . .

36–37. *the instrumental . . . religion*] Cf. Tristram's ref. to the "instrumental parts of [St. Hilarion's] religion" (*TS*, 8.31.583); and the refs. to the "instrumental duties" of religion in *Sermons*, I, 80 (I.vi), II, 77 (IV.xii).

38–39. *have . . . own*] Cf. *Sermons*, II, 41 (IV.x): "The great business of man, is the regulation of his spirit; the possession of such a frame and temper of mind, as will lead us peaceably through this world, and in the many weary stages of it, afford us, what we shall be sure to stand in need of,——*Rest unto our souls*" (cf. Jeremiah 6:16). Cf. also Yorick's reflections in *Sermons*, I, 178, 177 (II.xv) on "the subject of a contented mind——and the duty in man of regulating his spirit, in our way through life" and on "the aids which religion offers us towards the regulation of our spirit under the evils of life."

39–40. *the justlings . . . world*] a favorite expression with Sterne. Cf. *Sermons*, I, 123 (II.x): "How many justlings and hard struggles do we undergo, in making our way in the world?"; I, 14–15 (I.ii), II, 177–179 (VI.x), refs. to "the many hard justlings" and to the "shocks and hard jostlings" we experience in this "journey of life"; *Letters*, No. 129, Aug. 1764, p. 224, to Sarah Tuting, in which Sterne advised her that, in her journey to Italy for her health, "no hard jostlings . . . must disturb either body or mind" (this letter is also cited p. 225.15–16*n*, below). Cf. also Walter Shandy's observation that, "Though man is of all others the most curious vehicle . . . yet at the same time 'tis of so slight a frame and so totteringly put together, that the sudden jerks and hard jostlings it unavoidably meets with in this rugged journey, would overset and tear it to pieces a dozen times a day—was it not . . . that there is a secret spring within us . . . that great and elastic power within us of counterbalancing evil, which like a secret spring in a well-

upon some military services ill requited, and meeting at the same
time with a disappointment in the tenderest of passions, he abandon'd the sword and the sex together, and took sanctuary, not so
45 much in his convent as in himself.

I feel a damp upon my spirits, as I am going to add, that in my
last return through Calais, upon inquiring after Father Lorenzo, I
heard he had been dead near three months, and was buried, not in
his convent, but, according to his desire, in a little cimetiery be-
50 longing to it, about two leagues off: I had a strong desire to see
where they had laid him—when, upon pulling out his little horn
box, as I sat by his grave, and plucking up a nettle or two at the
head of it, which had no business to grow there, they all struck

---

42 services ⟨not h⟩ ill   47 Lorenzo, ∧⟨for so⟩∧ I   50 it, ⟨a⟩ ∧about two∧
league∨s∨ [Sterne apparently wrote "a league" initially]

---

ordered machine, though it can't prevent the shock—at least it imposes upon
our sense of it" (*TS*, 4.8.278–279); several phrases in this passage appear
also in *Sermons*, II, 147–148 (VI.vii).

42–48. *some military . . . months*] Cross (*Life*, pp. 384–385) makes the
rather dubious assumption that Father Lorenzo is the same person as the
"Father Felix" Mrs. Thrale encountered while in Calais with her husband
and Dr. Johnson in 1775. When she returned to Calais in Sept. 1784, as Mrs.
Piozzi, she "enquired of the Franciscan friar who attended us at the inn, what
was become of Father Felix, who did the duties of the quête . . . about a
dozen years ago, when I recollect minding that his manners and story struck
Dr. Johnson exceedingly, who said that so complete a character could
scarcely be found in romance. He had been a soldier, it seems, and was no
incompetent or mean scholar . . . I was glad to hear he was well" (Hester
L. Piozzi, *Observations and Reflections Made in the Course of a Journey Through
France, Italy, and Germany* [London, 1789], I, 2–3). According to a traveler
who claimed to have "enquired particularly of Monsieur Dessein about Pere
Lorenzo" in 1776, Dessein assured him "that no monk any way answering to
that description, ever in his time, lived at Calais" (see *Letters*, No. 91, n. 2,
pp. 170–171).

46–47. *my last . . . Calais*] Sterne returned from his second, and last,
trip to the Continent in early June 1766 (see *Letters*, p. 278, n. 3).

52–55. *his grave . . . tears*] The letter Sterne redirected from the "Countess ******" to Eliza contains the following sentimental exchange with

together so forcibly upon my affections, that I burst into a flood of
tears—but I am as weak as a woman; and I beg the world not to 55
smile, but pity me.

54–55 affections, / ⟨that I wept over him, as a widow—but⟩ / that . . . tears— // 'I
am . . . woman [*M1:* "affections that I wept over him, as a widow—but // I am as
weak as a woman". The following reading appears upside down at the bottom of fol.
54ᵛ of *S1:* "I am as weak as a woman:—"; fol. 54 begins with "I . . . woman",
l. 55, above (see p. 82.74–76*tn* above).]   55 tears—but I] tears— // 'I [see
prec. *tn*]

"Cordelia," one of the ghostly nuns Sterne imagined himself visiting in the
ruins of Byland Abbey, near Coxwold: ". . . and will not you, Yorick, mix
your ashes with us too?—for ever my Cordelia! and some kind hearted Swain
shall come and weed our graves, as I have weeded thine . . . I can ⟨lay⟩ lie
besides thy grave, and drop tears of tenderness upon the Turf wᶜʰ covers
thee" (*Letters,* No. 201, Coxwold [? June 1767], p. 361). See also Tristram's
injunction to all "men of goodness" to "Weed [Trim's] grave clean, . . . for
he was your brother" (*TS,* 6.25.451). (In the *Journal,* 12 June, p. 356, Sterne
told Eliza that on "a delicious Walk of Romance" to Byland Abbey he
"pluckd up a score Bryars by the roots wᶜʰ grew ⟨up⟩ near the edge of the
foot way, that they might not scratch or incommode you—")

THE REMISE DOOR.
CALAIS.

I HAD never quitted the lady's hand all this time; and had held it
so long, that it would have been indecent to have let it go, without first pressing it to my lips: the blood and spirits, which had
suffer'd a revulsion from her, crouded back to her, as I did it.

5   Now the two travellers who had spoke to me in the coach-yard,
happening at that crisis to be passing by, and observing our communications, naturally took it into their heads that we must be *man
and wife* at least; so stopping as soon as they came up to the door of
the Remise, the one of them, who was the inquisitive traveller,
10 ask'd us, if we set out for Paris the next morning?—I could only
answer for myself, I said; and the lady added, she was for Amiens.
—We dined there yesterday, said the simple traveller—You go
directly through the town, added the other, in your road to Paris.
I was going to return a thousand thanks for the intelligence, *that
15 Amiens was in the road to Paris*; but, upon pulling out my poor
monk's little horn box to take a pinch of snuff—I made them a
quiet bow, and wishing them a good passage to Dover—they left
us alone—

—Now where would be the harm, said I to myself, if I was to beg
20 of this distressed lady to accept of half of my chaise?—and what
mighty mischief could ensue?

Every dirty passion, and bad propensity in my nature, took the
alarm, as I stated the proposition—It will oblige you to have a

---

7 ⟨?were⟩~must~ ∧be∧   13 ⟨?Amiens⟩~the Town~ ∧added the other∧
17 wish⟨'d⟩~ing~ them ∧⟨both⟩∧ a   20 [Fols. 56–69 of *S1*, comprising the
text from "-tressed lady" (l. 20, above) through "all this while." (p. 112.36, below),
are missing; see App. B, §3, p. 300. The variants in wording between *M1* and this
portion of *A1* (see the following textual notes) are discussed in the Note on the Text,
Vol. I (2), p. 55, above.]   20 half of my] half my *M1*

third horse, said AVARICE, which will put twenty livres out of your pocket.—You know not who she is, said CAUTION—or what scrapes 25 the affair may draw you into, whisper'd COWARDICE—

Depend upon it, Yorick! said DISCRETION, 'twill be said you went off with a mistress, and came by assignation to Calais for that purpose—

—You can never after, cried HYPOCRISY aloud, shew your face 30 in the world—or rise, quoth MEANNESS, in the church—or be any thing in it, said PRIDE, but a lousy prebendary.

---

32 it, said PRIDE, but] it but *M1*

---

24. *third horse*] As Millard points out (p. 18), the regulations governing travel by post-chaise in France required that a chaise occupied by one person had to have two horses, and one occupied by two persons had to have a third horse.

27. *Discretion*] Cf. *Letters,* No. 64, [? June 1760], pp. 117–118, to Mary Macartney: "god bless you . . . for what you say upon *Discretion* (or Reflection I forget w^{ch}—but I verily believe you take a delight in recommending these two prudent old gentlewomen to me, merely because you know they are not entirely to my taste—I'm sure with regard to Discretion, tho' I have no great communications with her—I had always a regard for her at the bottome—She is a very honest Woman; & I should be a brute to use her ill—only I insist upon it, she must not spoil good company." Cf. also *Sermons,* I, 201 (III.ii): "Discretion generally shakes her head" at "a man of a real open and generous integrity,——who carries his heart in his hand,——who says the thing he thinks; and does the thing he pretends"; and *TS,* 1.12.28–30, Eugenius' lecture to Yorick on his lack of discretion, which destroys his career in the church (see next note) and leads to his death.

31–32. *or rise . . . prebendary*] one of many refs. in Sterne's writings to his failure to receive the preferment he had hoped for in the church (see p. 200.99–100n, below). In 1762, when Yorick's *Journey* takes place (see p. 192.7–8n, below), Sterne was prebendary of North Newbald (see *Letters,* p. 9, n. 23). On Sterne's early career in the church and the destruction of his hopes for preferment, see Lewis P. Curtis, *The Politicks of Laurence Sterne* (Oxford, 1929); *Life,* pp. 36–110; *Letters,* esp. No. 12, pp. 32–34. While he was writing *A Sentimental Journey,* Sterne received offers of preferment: see *Journal,* 2 Aug., p. 384; 3 Aug., p. 386; *Letters,* No. 217, Coxwold, Oct. 1767, pp. 397–398; No. 224, Coxwold, Dec. 1767, p. 406.

—But 'tis a civil thing, said I—and as I generally act from the
first impulse, and therefore seldom listen to these cabals, which
35 serve no purpose, that I know of, but to encompass the heart with
adamant—I turn'd instantly about to the lady—

—But she had glided off unperceived, as the cause was pleading,
and had made ten or a dozen paces down the street, by the time I
had made the determination; so I set off after her with a long
40 stride, to make her the proposal with the best address I was master
of; but observing she walk'd with her cheek half resting upon the
palm of her hand—with the slow, short-measur'd step of thought-
fulness, and with her eyes, as she went step by step, fix'd upon
the ground, it struck me, she was trying the same cause herself.—
45 God help her! said I, she has some mother-in-law, or tartufish
aunt, or nonsensical old woman, to consult upon the occasion, as
well as myself: so not caring to interrupt the processe, and deem-
ing it more gallant to take her at discretion than by surprize, I
faced about, and took a short turn or two before the door of the
50 Remise, whilst she walk'd musing on one side.

---

39 set off after] set after *M1*

33–34. *as . . . impulse*] like Tristram: "A sudden impulse comes across
me——drop the curtain, *Shandy*—I drop it——Strike a line here across the
paper, *Tristram*—I strike it" (*TS*, 4.10.281).
45. *tartufish*] Cf. Tristram's scornful reference to "Prudes and Tartufs"
(*TS*, 5.1.343).

IN THE STREET.
CALAIS.

HAVING, on first sight of the lady, settled the affair in my fancy, "that she was of the better order of beings"—and then laid it down as a second axiom, as indisputable as the first, That she was a widow, and wore a character of distress—I went no further; I got ground enough for the situation which pleased me—and had 5 she remained close beside my elbow till midnight, I should have held true to my system, and considered her only under that general idea.

She had scarce got twenty paces distant from me, ere something within me called out for a more particular inquiry—it brought on 10 the idea of a further separation—I might possibly never see her more—the heart is for saving what it can; and I wanted the traces thro' which my wishes might find their way to her, in case I should never rejoin her myself: in a word, I wish'd to know her name— her family's—her condition; and as I knew the place to which she 15 was going, I wanted to know from whence she came: but there was no coming at all this intelligence: a hundred little delicacies stood in the way. I form'd a score different plans—There was no such thing as a man's asking her directly—the thing was impossible.

A little French *debonaire* captain, who came dancing down the 20 street, shewed me, it was the easiest thing in the world; for popping in betwixt us, just as the lady was returning back to the door of the Remise, he introduced himself to my acquaintance, and before he had well got announced, begg'd I would do him the honour to present him to the lady—I had not been presented my- 25 self—so turning about to her, he did it just as well by asking her, if she had come from Paris?—No: she was going that rout, she

---

11 might possibly never] might never *M1*   26 did it just] did just *M1*

11–12. *I . . . more*] Cf. *Letters,* No. 187, March 1767, p. 309, to Eliza: "I probably shall never see you more."

said.—*Vous n'etez pas de Londre?*—She was not, she replied.—Then Madame must have come thro' Flanders.—*Apparamment vous etez*
30 *Flammande?* said the French captain.—The lady answered, she was.—*Peutetre, de Lisle?* added he—She said, she was not of Lisle.—Nor Arras?—nor Cambray?—nor Ghent?—nor Brussels? She answered, she was of Brussels.

He had had the honour, he said, to be at the bombardment of it
35 last war—that it was finely situated, *pour cela*—and full of noblesse when the Imperialists were driven out by the French (the lady made a slight curtsy)—so giving her an account of the affair, and of the share he had had in it—he begg'd the honour to know her name—so made his bow.

40 —*Et Madame a son Mari?*—said he, looking back when he had made two steps—and without staying for an answer—danced down the street.

Had I served seven years apprenticeship to good breeding, I could not have done as much.

35–36. *last war . . . French*] presumably the War of the Austrian Succession (1740–1748), during which Brussels, held by the English, Dutch, and Austrians ("Imperialists"), was captured by the French after a month's siege. The Seven Years War did not officially end until 1763, and Yorick's journey takes place in 1762; see p. 192.7–8*n*, below.

43. *Had . . . good breeding*] Cf. Smollett on the "good breeding" of Frenchmen: "Of all the coxcombs on the face of the earth, a French *petit maitre* is the most impertinent: and they are all *petit maitres . . .* vanity is the great and universal mover among all ranks and degrees of people in this nation . . . they are the greatest *egotists* in the world; and the most insignificant individual talks in company with the same conceit and arrogance, as a person of the greatest importance. Neither conscious poverty nor disgrace will restrain him in the least either from assuming his full share of the conversation, or making his addresses to the finest lady, whom he has the smallest opportunity to approach: nor is he restrained by any other consideration whatsoever. It is all one to him whether he himself has a wife of his own, or the lady a husband; . . . He takes it for granted that his addresses cannot but be acceptable" (*Travels*, Letter No. 7, pp. 59–60, 66; see also p. 110.5–36*n*, below).

THE REMISE.
CALAIS.

A S the little French captain left us, Mons. Dessein came up with the key of the Remise in his hand, and forthwith let us into his magazine of chaises.

The first object which caught my eye, as Mons. Dessein open'd the door of the Remise, was another old tatter'd *Desobligeant:* 5 and notwithstanding it was the exact picture of that which had hit my fancy so much in the coach-yard but an hour before—the very sight of it stirr'd up a disagreeable sensation within me now; and I thought 'twas a churlish beast into whose heart the idea could first enter, to construct such a machine; nor had I much more char- 10 ity for the man who could think of using it.

I observed the lady was as little taken with it as myself: so Mons. Dessein led us on to a couple of chaises which stood abreast, telling us as he recommended them, that they had been purchased by my Lord A. and B. to go the *grand tour*, but had gone no further 15 than Paris, so were in all respects as good as new—They were too good—so I pass'd on to a third, which stood behind, and forthwith began to chaffer for the price—But 'twill scarce hold two, said I, opening the door and getting in—Have the goodness, Madam, said Mons. Dessein, offering his arm, to step in—The lady hesitated 20 half a second, and stepp'd in; and the waiter that moment beckoning to speak to Mons. Dessein, he shut the door of the chaise upon us, and left us.

---

14 us as he] us he *M1*   18 'twill] ⌄it⌄ will *M1*

THE REMISE.
CALAIS.

C'EST bien comique, 'tis very droll, said the lady smiling, from the reflection that this was the second time we had been left together by a parcel of nonsensical contingencies—*c'est bien comique,* said she—

5 —There wants nothing, said I, to make it so, but the comick use which the gallantry of a Frenchman would put it to—to make love the first moment, and an offer of his person the second.

'Tis their *fort:* replied the lady.

It is supposed so at least—and how it has come to pass, con-
10 tinued I, I know not; but they have certainly got the credit of understanding more of love, and making it better than any other nation upon earth: but for my own part I think them errant bunglers, and in truth the worst set of marksmen that ever tried Cupid's patience.

---

1 *comique* . . . said] comique, said *M1*   10–11 [Cf. "they . . . love" (ll. 10–11, above) and "What . . . commerce" (p. 111.27–28, below) with the following canceled reading on fol. 89ᵛ of *S1:* "⟨they have got the credit of understanding this branch of commerce,⟩". See App. B, §5, pp. 301–302.]

5–36. —*There . . . while.*] In castigating Frenchmen as "petit maitres" (see p. 108.43n, above), Smollett observes that a Frenchman "piques himself upon being polished above the natives of any other country by his conversation with the fair sex. In the course of this communication, with which he is indulged from his tender years, he learns like a parrot, by rote, the whole circle of French compliments, which you know are a set of phrases, ridiculous even to a proverb; and these he throws out indiscriminately to all women, without distinction, in the exercise of that kind of address, which is here distinguished by the name of gallantry: it is no more than his making love to every woman who will give him the hearing. It is an exercise, by the repetition of which he becomes very pert, very familiar, and very impertinent. Modesty, or diffidence, I have already said, is utterly unknown among them, and therefore I wonder there should be a term to express it in their language" (*Travels,* Letter No. 7, pp. 60–61).

—To think of making love by *sentiments!*   15

I should as soon think of making a genteel suit of cloaths out of remnants:—and to do it—pop—at first sight by declaration—is submitting the offer and themselves with it, to be sifted, with all their *pours* and *contres*, by an unheated mind.

The lady attended as if she expected I should go on.   20

Consider then, madam, continued I, laying my hand upon hers—

That grave people hate Love for the name's sake—

That selfish people hate it for their own—

Hypocrites for heaven's—   25

And that all of us both old and young, being ten times worse frighten'd than hurt by the very *report*—What a want of knowledge in this branch of commerce a man betrays, whoever lets the

---

27-28 What . . . commerce] [see p. 110.10–11*tn,* above]

15-17. —*To think . . . remnants*] Cf. Tristram's condemnation of "an error which the bulk of the world lie under——but the *French,* every one of 'em to a man, who believe in it, almost as much as the REAL PRESENCE [i.e., transubstantiation], '*That talking of love, is making it.*' ———I would as soon set about making a black-pudding by the same receipt" (*TS,* 9.25[18].634). Cf. also Sterne's remark that he carries on his love affairs "in the French way, sentimentally" (*Letters,* No. 148, quoted pp. 128.17–25*n,* below); and Tristram's recommendation of "the pure and sentimental parts of the best *French* Romances" (*TS,* 1.18.49).

23. *grave . . . name's sake*] Sterne may be echoing *The Anatomy of Melancholy:* in the Preface to the Third Partition of the *Anatomy,* on Love-Melancholy (6th ed. [London, 1651], p. 406), Burton observes that some readers will undoubtedly complain that this subject is "*too light for a Divine, too Commical,*" because "by the naughtiness of men it is so come to pass . . . [that] the very name of love is odious to *chaster* ears; And therefore some again out of an affected gravity, will dislike all for the names sake before they read a word; . . . so they may be admired for grave Philosophers, and staid carriage." (For a major borrowing in *A Sentimental Journey* from Burton's reflections on Love-Melancholy in the *Anatomy,* see p. 130.6–18*n,* below.)

word come out of his lips, till an hour or two at least after the time,
30 that his silence upon it becomes tormenting. A course of small,
quiet attentions, not so pointed as to alarm—nor so vague as to
be misunderstood,—with now and then a look of kindness, and
little or nothing said upon it—leaves Nature for your mistress,
and she fashions it to her mind.—

35 Then I solemnly declare, said the lady, blushing—you have
been making love to me all this while.

30–31 small, quiet] small, and quiet *M1*

THE REMISE.

CALAIS.

MONSIEUR *Dessein* came back to let us out of the chaise, and acquaint the lady, the Count de L—— her brother was just arrived at the hotel. Though I had infinite good will for the lady, I cannot say, that I rejoiced in my heart at the event—and could not help telling her so—for it is fatal to a proposal, Madam, 5 said I, that I was going to make you—

—You need not tell me what the proposal was, said she, laying her hand upon both mine, as she interrupted me.—A man, my good Sir, has seldom an offer of kindness to make to a woman, but she has a presentiment of it some moments before— 10

Nature arms her with it, said I, for immediate preservation —But I think, said she, looking in my face, I had no evil to apprehend—and to deal frankly with you, had determined to accept it.—If I had—(she stopped a moment)—I believe your good will would have drawn a story from me, which would have made pity 15 the only dangerous thing in the journey.

In saying this, she suffered me to kiss her hand twice, and with a look of sensibility mixed with a concern she got out of the chaise— and bid adieu.

[*S1* recommences with this chapter; see p. 104.20*tn*, above.]   2 L———] L----
5 ∧for∧   7 tell ⟨it⟩ me what ⟨it⟩ ∧the proposal∧   8 me.—A] me—a
9 good ⟨Cavalier!⟩ ∧Sir∧   14 it.—] it—   14 ∧I believe∧   17 ⟨As she
said this⟩ ∧In saying this∧   17–18 with a look of] with of   19 and ⟨we⟩ bid

---

2. *the Count de L——, her brother*] See p. 145.13*n*, below.

IN THE STREET.
CALAIS.

I NEVER finished a twelve-guinea bargain so expeditiously in my life: my time seemed heavy upon the loss of the lady, and knowing every moment of it would be as two, till I put myself into motion—I ordered post horses directly, and walked towards the
5 hotel.

Lord! said I, hearing the town clock strike four, and recollecting that I had been little more than a single hour in Calais—

—What a large volume of adventures may be grasped within this little span of life by him who interests his heart in every thing, and
10 who, having eyes to see, what time and chance are perpetually holding out to him as he journeyeth on his way, misses nothing he can *fairly* lay his hands on.—

---

8 —What] [*S1:* no par.]   12 on.—] on—

6–12. *Lord!* . . . *on.*—] a characteristic example of Sterne's interest in the problematic relationship between clock time and our sense of duration; see, e.g., p. 241.4*n*, below; *TS*, 2.8.103–104; 3.18.188–191. For a penetrating discussion of Sterne's indebtedness to Locke's analysis of duration (*Essay Concerning Human Understanding*, Bk. II, ch. xiv), see Traugott, pp. 34 ff.

10. *having eyes to see*] Cf. Mark 8:18: "Having eyes, see ye not?"; Matthew, 13:13: "Therefore speak I to them in parables: because they seeing see not"; Luke 8:10: "Unto you it is given to know the mysteries of the kingdom of God: but to others in parables; that seeing they might not see . . ."

10. *time and chance*] Cf. Ecclesiastes 9:11: "time and chance happeneth to them all." In his sermon on this text, Yorick argues that the "secret and unseen workings in human affairs" of time and chance, which so often "baffle all our endeavours," are actually the "wisdom and contrivance" of "the secret and over-ruling providence of . . . Almighty God" (*Sermons*, I, 93–100 [II.viii]; for Sterne's borrowings from John Tillotson in this sermon, see Hammond, pp. 164–165). On this same theme, see *Sermons*, II, 20–21 (IV.viii); and II, 254–255, quoted p. 44, n. 53, above. The ref. to "time and chance" in Ecclesiastes 9:11 is paraphrased also in *Sermons*, II, 225 (VII.xiv); and in *Journal*, 13 July, p. 379.

10–12. *what time . . . hands on*] Cf. Tristram's description of "seizing

—If this won't turn out something—another will—no matter—
'tis an assay upon human nature—I get my labour for my pains
—'tis enough—the pleasure of the experiment has kept my senses, 15
and the best part of my blood awake, and laid the gross to sleep.

I pity the man who can travel from *Dan* to *Beersheba*, and cry,
'Tis all barren—and so it is; and so is all the world to him who will
not cultivate the fruits it offers. I declare, said I, clapping my
hands chearily together, that was I in a desert, I would find out 20
wherewith in it to call forth my affections—If I could not do better,

---

13-15 another . . . enough— // ⟨—another will—no matter—I get / my Labour
for my pains—'tis enough:⟩ / the pleasure [When Sterne first inscribed the text of
this chapter from "⟨—another will . . ." through the conclusion (p. 120, below), it
may have appeared much earlier in *S1;* see App. B, §6, pp. 302–307.]   18 'Tis]
'tis   19-20 offers. ⟨for my own part was I⟩ ∧I declare . . . was I∧
20-21 out ⟨something⟩ ∧wherewith∧

---

every handle . . . which chance held out to [him] in [his] journey" through
Languedoc, quoted p. 268.1–10*n*, below.
14. *my labour for my pains*] This proverbial phrase is used also in *Letters,*
No. 213, Sept. 1767, p. 394.
16. *the best . . . blood*] Cf. "the best . . . blood" in *Sermons,* I, 207–208,
quoted p. 237.8–11*n*, below.
17. *from Dan to Beersheba*] a paraphrase of the Biblical formula, "from Dan
even to Beer-sheba" (Judges 20:1; II Samuel 24:2); Dan and Beersheba lay
at the northern and southern extremities of Canaan. (The expression is used
also in *TS,* 8.16.555).
17-21. *I pity . . . affections*] Cf. Smollett: "we . . . descended into the
Campania of Rome, which is almost a desert. The view of this country, in
its present situation, cannot but produce emotions of pity and indignation in
the mind of every person who retains any idea of its antient cultivation and
fertility. It is nothing but a naked withered down, desolate and dreary, almost without inclosure, corn-field, hedge, tree, shrub, house, hut, or habitation" (*Travels,* Letter No. 29, p. 245).
19-20. *clapping . . . together*] Cf. *TS,* 7.29.517: "With what velocity, continued I, clapping my two hands together, shall I fly down the rapid *Rhone.*"
19-21. *the fruits . . . affections*] Cf. Tristram's comment that his father's
"researches" on the Grand Tour "would have found fruit even in a desert,"
quoted in App. E, p. 346, note to p. 176.27–37; cf. also his boast (*TS,*
7.43.536) that his journey through the "barren" plains of Languedoc was the
"most fruitful" period of his life, quoted p. 268.1–10*n*, below. See p. 116.23*n*,
below.

I would fasten them upon some sweet myrtle, or seek some melancholy cypress to connect myself to—I would court their shade, and greet them kindly for their protection—I would cut my name upon
25 them, and swear they were the loveliest trees throughout the desert: if their leaves wither'd, I would teach myself to mourn, and when they rejoiced, I would rejoice along with them.

The learned SMELFUNGUS travelled from Boulogne to Paris—from Paris to Rome—and so on—but he set out with the spleen
30 and jaundice, and every object he pass'd by was discoloured or distorted—He wrote an account of them, but 'twas nothing but the account of his miserable feelings.

25–26 them,— ⟨and think they were my own⟩, and . . . desert　　　28 Smel⟨d⟩~ f~ungus [This revision was also made in *S1* at pp. 117.33, 118.40, below. *S1* reads "Smelfungus" on p. 120, ll. 57, 61, 63, below.]　　　31 wrote ⟨the⟩ an 31 ∧*nothing but*∧

19–27. *I declare . . . them.*] Yorick's sentimental knight-errantry in a desert recalls Don Quixote's conduct in the desert of the Sierra Morena, where, in the manner of a true knight-errant, he mourns over imaginary cruelties inflicted on him by Dulcinea (*Don Quixote,* 1.3.11.188 ff.). Cf. also Don Quixote's praise (2.3.17.552) of the nobility of the "Knight-Errant, who fir'd with the Thirst of a glorious Fame, wanders through Desarts, through solitary Wildernesses, . . . in Quest of perilous Adventures, resolv'd to bring them to a happy Conclusion. Yes, I say, a nobler Figure is a Knight-Errant succouring a Widow [see p. 94.33–34*n*, above] in some depopulated Place, than the Court-Knight making his Addresses to the City Dames."
22. *myrtle*] held sacred to Venus by the ancients and emblematic of love. Cf. *Letters,* No. 4 [? 1739/40], p. 19 (written to his wife during their courtship?—see *Letters,* pp. 12–15): "Thou wilt leave thy name upon the myrtle-tree.—If trees, and shrubs, and flowers, could compose an elegy, I should expect a very plaintive one upon this subject."
23. *connect*] Cf. Sterne's remark about "tasting the fruits" of "Connections," in *Letters,* No. 76, to Elizabeth Vesey, quoted p. 91.8–15*n*, above.
28. *Smelfungus*] Tobias Smollett; see pp. 32–38, above.
32. *the account . . . feelings*] Cf. Sterne's description of the *Journal* as "a Diary of the miserable feelings of a person separated from a Lady for . . . whose Society he languish'd" (p. 322); and his statement to Eliza that "at present all I can write would be but the History of my miserable feelings" (*Journal,* 4 Aug., p. 387).

I met Smelfungus in the grand portico of the Pantheon—he
was just coming out of it—*'Tis nothing but a huge cock-pit**, said
he—I wish you had said nothing worse of the Venus of Medicis, *35*

* Vide S——'s Travels.

34–35 *cock-pit**, . . . he] *cock pit* . . . he*   36 *Vide S———'s Travels.] Vide
his Travels [on fol. 74ᵛ of *S1*, opposite " '*Tis* . . . said he" (ll. 34–35, above), on fol.
75. *M1* does not have this note.]

---

33. *I met . . . Pantheon*] When Sterne reached Italy in November 1765,
on his second trip abroad, Smollett had returned to England (*Letters*, p. 267,
n. 8). Smollett met Mrs. Sterne and, almost certainly, Sterne himself, in
Montpellier, in November 1763 (see *Travels*, Letter No. 11, p. 102; and
Knapp, *Tobias Smollett*, pp. 252–253).
    Cf. *Letters*, No. 156, Florence, Dec. 1765, p. 266: "in 5 days shall tread
the Vatican, and be introduced to all the Saints in the Pantheon—"
    33–35. *the Pantheon . . . said he*] Cf. Smollett, *Travels*, Letter No. 31,
pp. 268–269: "I was much disappointed at sight of the Pantheon, which,
after all that has been said of it, looks like a huge cock pit, open at top. . . .
Within side it has much the air of a mausoleum. It was this appearance
which, in all probability, suggested the thought to Boniface IV. to transport
hither eight and twenty cart-loads of old rotten bones, dug from different
burying-places, and then dedicate it as a church to the blessed Virgin and
all the holy martyrs. I am not one of those who think it is well lighted by
the hole at the top, which is about nine and twenty feet in diameter, although
the author of the Grand Tour [Thomas Nugent] calls it but nine. . . . I
visited it several times, and each time it looked more and more gloomy and
sepulchral."
    35–39. *I wish . . . nature.*] Cf. Smollett, *Travels*, Letter No. 28, pp. 235–
236: "With respect to the famous Venus Pontia, commonly called *de Medicis*,
. . . I believe I ought to be intirely silent, or at least conceal my real sentiments, which will otherwise appear equally absurd and presumptuous. It
must be want of taste that prevents my feeling that enthusiastic admiration
with which others are inspired at sight of this statue: . . . I cannot help
thinking that there is no beauty in the features of Venus; . . . Without all
doubt, the limbs and proportions of this statue are elegantly formed, and
accurately designed, according to the nicest rules of symmetry and proportion; and the back parts especially are executed so happily, as to excite the
admiration of the most indifferent spectator."
    36. **Vide . . . Travels.*] See ll. 33–35*n*, above.

replied I—for in passing through Florence, I had heard he had
fallen foul upon the goddess, and used her worse than a common
strumpet, without the least provocation in nature.

40   I popp'd upon Smelfungus again at Turin, in his return home;
and a sad tale of sorrowful adventures had he to tell, "wherein he
spoke of moving accidents by flood and field, and of the cannibals
which each other eat: the Anthropophagi"—he had been flea'd
alive, and bedevil'd, and used worse than St. Bartholomew, at
45 every stage he had come at—

—I'll tell it, cried Smelfungus, to the world. You had better tell
it, said I, to your physician.

---

37 I,—⟨for on seeing the grand Dukes gallery⟩ // ⟨in⟩~—~ for in . . . Florence
37 ∧he had∧   39 strumpet ⟨?upon ?no⟩~without~   42 field ⟨"of hair
breadth scapes, & imminent⟩ "and   44 ∧& used . . . Bartholomew—∧ [*M1:*
u.v.]   44 Bartholomew,] Bartholomew— [see prec. *tn*]

40–45. *I popp'd . . . come at*—] Cf. Smollett's account of his journey from
Turin to Nice "over frightful mountains covered with snow" (*Travels,* Letter
No. 38, pp. 315 ff.); Yorick exaggerates Smollett's description of the dangers
of the trip.
    41–43. "*wherein . . . Anthropophagi*"] a paraphrase of *Othello,* I.iii.134–
145. Referring to Eliza's journey to India, Sterne paraphrased another line
of Othello's speech (I.iii.167): see *Journal,* 27 July, p. 381. (Sterne also
quotes *Othello* in *Letters,* No. 142, [? May 1765], p. 245.)
    43–44. *flea'd . . . St. Bartholomew*] St. Bartholomew was one of the
twelve apostles in the first century A.D.; according to tradition, he was flayed
to death in Armenia. Milic notes ("Sterne and Smollett's 'Travels' ") that
the reference may have been suggested to Sterne by Smollett's description
of the "frightful" pictures of the Christian martyrs in the basilica of St.
Peter's in Rome, including "Bartholomew fleaed alive" (*Travels,* Letter No.
31, pp. 266–267).
    46–47. *You . . . physician.*] Like Sterne, Smollett was driven abroad by
ill-health (see p. 33, above). Yorick's advice to him here may be a sarcastic
thrust at his failure as a practicing physician (with "Physician, heal thyself"
[Luke 4:23] in mind?). Tristram alludes to Smollett's incompetence as a
physician in *TS,* 6.11.428–429 (see p. 429, n. 4). (For Smollett's observations
as a "medical traveller," see, e.g., p. 175.22–27*n,* below.)

Mundungus, with an immense fortune, made the whole tour; going on from Rome to Naples—from Naples to Venice—from Venice to Vienna—to Dresden, to Berlin, without one generous 50 connection or pleasurable anecdote to tell of; but he had travell'd straight on looking neither to his right hand or his left, lest Love or Pity should seduce him out of his road.

48–51. *Mundungus . . . tell of*] Mundungus has traditionally been identified as Dr. Samuel Sharp (1700?–1778), whose *Letters from Italy* were published in 1766, the year Smollett's *Travels* appeared. Like Smollett, Sharp was ill, and critical of the Italians (see p. 173.58n, below). However, as Milic (p. 31, n. 13) points out, the identification is very doubtful. Sharp did not have "an immense fortune," and he did not travel from Venice to Berlin. Mundungus' travels do coincide almost exactly with the itinerary of a trip Sterne intended to take with Henry Errington, a wealthy young Englishman, in returning to England from Italy in 1765–66: see *Letters*, No. 162, Rome, 30 March 1766, p. 275; No. 158, Naples, 5 Feb. 1766, p. 269.

Although it seems unlikely that Sterne had Sharp in mind in characterizing Mundungus, it is worth noting that the *OED* gives "offal" as a possible (though rare) meaning for *mundungus*, and that Sharp proposes, in some detail, a more efficient way of transporting dung out of Naples (*Letters from Italy*, No. 33, pp. 143–144).

51–53. *but . . . road*] Cf. *Sermons*, I, 29 (I.iii), on the Good Samaritan: "Look into the world—how often do you behold a sordid wretch, whose straight heart is open to no man's affliction, taking shelter behind an appearance of piety . . . Take notice with what sanctity he goes to the end of his days, in the same selfish track in which he at first set out—turning neither to the right hand nor to the left—but plods on—pores all his life long upon the ground, as if afraid to look up, lest peradventure he should see aught which might turn him one moment out of that straight line where interest is carrying him—or if, by chance, he stumbles upon a hapless object of distress, . . . *devoutly* passing by on the other side, as if unwilling to trust himself to the impressions of nature, or hazard the inconveniences which pity might lead him into upon the occasion."

Unlike Mundungus, Tristram allows himself to be seduced out of his road by the sight of Maria, whom the postilion describes as the "love and pity of all the villages around us" (see *TS*, 9.24.630, and pp. 15–16, above). Tristram elsewhere (*TS*, 1.14.36–37) remarks: "Could a historiographer drive on his history, as a muleteer drives on his mule,—straight forward;—— for instance, from *Rome* all the way to *Loretto*, without ever once turning his head aside either to the right hand or to the left,—he might venture to fore-

Peace be to them! if it is to be found; but heaven itself, was it
55 possible to get there with such tempers, would want objects to give
it—every gentle spirit would come flying upon the wings of Love
to hail their arrival—Nothing would the souls of Smelfungus and
Mundungus hear of, but fresh anthems of joy, fresh raptures of
love, and fresh congratulations of their common felicity—I heartily
60 pity them: they have brought up no faculties for this work; and
was the happiest mansion in heaven to be allotted to Smelfungus
and Mundungus, they would be so far from being happy, that the
souls of Smelfungus and Mundungus would do penance there to all
eternity.

---

58 hear ∧of∧   60 this ⟨enjoyment⟩ work   61–63 allotted ⟨them, they⟩ ∧to
Smelfungus & Mundungus, they∧ would . . . happy that the⟨y⟩ ∧Souls of Smelfungus & Mundungus∧ would [*M1:* u.v.]   64 eternity.] eternity.—

---

tell you to an hour when he should get to his journey's end;——but the
thing is, morally speaking, impossible: For, if he is a man of the least spirit,
he will have fifty deviations from a straight line to make with this or that
party as he goes along, which he can no ways avoid. He will have views and
prospects to himself perpetually solliciting his eye . . ."

54. *Peace . . . them!*] Cf. Luke 24:36, John 20:19: "Peace be unto you."
54–64. *Peace . . . eternity.*] This paragraph is partially adapted from the
Sermons; see App. E, pp. 338–342, note to p. 120.54–64.

Cf. *TS,* 7.13.494: "REASON is, half of it, SENSE; and the measure of heaven
itself is but the measure of our present appetites and concoctions."

MONTRIUL.

I HAD once lost my portmanteau from behind my chaise, and twice got out in the rain, and one of the times up to the knees in dirt, to help the postilion to tie it on, without being able to find out what was wanting—Nor was it till I got to Montriul, upon the landlord's asking me if I wanted not a servant, that it occurred to 5 me, that that was the very thing.

A servant! That I do most sadly, quoth I—Because, Monsieur, said the landlord, there is a clever young fellow, who would be very proud of the honour to serve an Englishman—But why an English one, more than any other?—They are so generous, said 10 the landlord—I'll be shot if this is not a livre out of my pocket, quoth I to myself, this very night—But they have wherewithal to be so, Monsieur, added he—Set down one livre more for that, quoth I—It was but last night, said the landlord, *qu'un my Lord Anglois presentoit un ecu a la fille de chambre—Tant pis, pour Mad^{lle}* 15 *Janatone*, said I.

---

4 was ⟨?the ?matter⟩~wanting~   8 fellow, ⟨un joli garçon,⟩ who [*M1:* u.v.]
12 this ⟨?night⟩ very night   15 *anglois* ⟨*donnoit*⟩ ∧*presentoit*∧

1–3. *I . . . on*] Tristram makes the "national reflection . . . *That something is always wrong in a French post-chaise upon first setting out.* Or the proposition may stand thus. *A French postilion has always to alight before he has got three hundred yards out of town.* What's wrong now?——Diable!—— a rope's broke!——a knot has slipt! . . ." (*TS,* 7.8.488–489).

8. *the landlord*] identified as Mons. Varennes, master of the Hôtel de la Cour de France, by John Poole (1786?–1872), the dramatist, in "Sterne at Calais and Montreuil," *London Magazine and Review,* Jan. 1825, pp. 38–46 (see *Life,* p. 381*n*). Poole retraced Yorick's route and attempted to identify the persons and places referred to in the *Journey,* in the belief that "every incident [Sterne] relates is founded in fact" (p. 39). Poole notes (p. 44) that Varennes' inn was "the only one of any importance" in Montreuil at the time of Yorick's journey (1762; see p. 192.7–8*n*, below).

9–13. *But why . . . added he*] On the foolish extravagance of many English travelers, see p. 80.43–53*n*, above.

16. *Janatone*] Cf. Tristram's encounter with Janatone, whom he considers the only object in Montreuil worth describing (*TS,* 7.9.489–491).

Now Janatone being the landlord's daughter, and the landlord supposing I was young in French, took the liberty to inform me, I should not have said *tant pis*—but, *tant mieux. Tant mieux,* 20 *toujours, Monsieur,* said he, when there is anything to be got— *tant pis,* when there is nothing. It comes to the same thing, said I. *Pardonnez moi,* said the landlord.

I cannot take a fitter opportunity to observe once for all, that *tant pis* and *tant mieux* being two of the great hinges in French 25 conversation, a stranger would do well to set himself right in the use of them, before he gets to Paris.

A prompt French Marquis at our ambassador's table demanded of Mr. H——, if he was H—— the poet? No, said H—— mildly— *Tant pis,* replied the Marquis.

30 It is H—— the historian, said another—*Tant mieux,* said the Marquis. And Mr. H——, who is a man of an excellent heart, return'd thanks for both.

20–21 be ⟨[at least one illegible word deleted] ?by ?it⟩~got—*tant*~   28 H$^{\underline{ume}}$, if . . . H$^{\underline{ume}}$ the [The identifying letters are in pencil and are not in Sterne's hand; dashes, rather than solid lines, are used in *S1* after the third "H" in this line and after the "H" in ll. 30, 31, below.]

---

28. *Mr. H*——] David Hume (1711–1776), philosopher and historian; from 1763 to 1765 he was secretary to the Earl of Hertford, Ambassador to the Court of France, and was lionized in Paris. In 1773 Hume pronounced *Tristram Shandy* the "best Book . . . that has been writ by any Englishman these thirty Years . . . bad as it is" (see *Letters,* p. 220, n. 2).

28. *H*—— *the poet*] John Home, pron. "Hume" (1722–1808), author of the popular tragedy *Douglas* (produced at Covent Garden, 1757) and of several other tragedies.

For an amusing and somewhat similar incident in which Sterne failed to recognize Louis Dutens at a dinner in Paris, see *Letters,* pp. 251–252, n. 9.

31. *Mr. H*—— . . . *heart*] Denying a rumor that he and Hume had quarreled in Paris at the table of Lord Hertford, the English ambassador, Sterne observed: "I should be most exceedingly surprized to hear that *David* ever had an unpleasant contention with any man; . . . for, in my life, did I never meet with a being of a more placid and gentle nature; and it is this amiable turn of his character, that has given more consequence and force to his scepticism, than all the arguments of his sophistry. . . . We had, I remem-

When the landlord had set me right in this matter, he called in La Fleur, which was the name of the young man he had spoke of— saying only first, That as for his talents, he would presume to say 35 nothing—Monsieur was the best judge what would suit him; but for the fidelity of La Fleur, he would stand responsible in all he was worth.

The landlord deliver'd this in a manner which instantly set my mind to the business I was upon—and La Fleur, who stood waiting 40 without, in that breathless expectation which every son of nature of us have felt in our turns, came in.

---

39 ∧instantly∧   41 ∧that∧   42 turns— ⟨directly⟩ came

---

ber well, a little pleasant sparring at Lord *Hertford*'s table at *Paris;* but there was nothing in it that did not bear the marks of good-will and urbanity on both sides.—I had preached that very day at the Ambassador's Chapel, and *David* was disposed to make a little merry with the *Parson;* and, in return, the Parson was equally disposed to make a little mirth with the *Infidel*" (*Letters,* No. 126, [? July 1764], p. 218; although this letter appeared in William Combe's volume of forgeries of Sterne, I think Curtis is right in considering it substantially genuine).

34. *La Fleur*] See App. E, pp. 342–343, note to p. 123.34.

MONTRIUL.

I AM apt to be taken with all kinds of people at first sight; but
never more so, than when a poor devil comes to offer his service
to so poor a devil as myself; and as I know this weakness, I always
suffer my judgment to draw back something on that very account—
5 and this more or less, according to the mood I am in, and the case
—and I may add the gender too, of the person I am to govern.

When La Fleur enter'd the room, after every discount I could
make for my soul, the genuine look and air of the fellow determined the matter at once in his favour; so I hired him first—and
10 then began to inquire what he could do: But I shall find out his
talents, quoth I, as I want them—besides, a Frenchman can do
every thing.

Now poor La Fleur could do nothing in the world but beat a
drum, and play a march or two upon the fife. I was determined to
15 make his talents do; and can't say my weakness was ever so insulted
by my wisdom, as in the attempt.

La Fleur had set out early in life, as gallantly as most Frenchmen do, with *serving* for a few years; at the end of which, having

---

1 ∧kinds of∧   3 th⟨?e⟩~i~s   5 this more or less, according] this, more or
less according   5 in; ⟨?or⟩~&~ the case   7 L⟨?e⟩~?a~∧a∧ Fleur [Sterne
changed "Le" to "La" here, apparently by superimposing "a" on "e" and then, because the change was unclear, writing an "a" in above the line. The appearance of *S1*
and the fact that *M1* reads "Le Fleur" throughout (see App. C, §4 (4), p. 311) indicates that Sterne wrote "Le" throughout *S1* initially and then changed it to "La"
(usually by superimposing "a" on "e"), except in a few places (e.g., *S1* reads "Le
Fleur" at pp. 123.34, 123.37, 123.40, above; 128.17, 136.19, 136.26, 136.36, below).
Where he failed to make this change in *S1*, "Le Fleur" was changed to "La Fleur"
in *A1*.]   8 look, ⟨of⟩ // and air of   8-9 and air . . . determined] ⟨and air
of the fellow ?struck ?me ?determind⟩ [This canceled reading appears upside down
at the bottom of fol. 83ᵛ of *S1*; fol. 83 begins with "and air . . . determined", ll.
8-9, above (see p. 82.74-76*tn*, above). Fol. 83ᵛ is numbered 85 in Sterne's hand
(the number is upside down in the lower left-hand corner), and fol. 83 bears the
canceled number ⟨85⟩ in Sterne's hand. On the foliation of *S1*, see App. B, §4, pp.
300-301.]   17 had ⟨gallantly⟩ set . . . as ∧gallantly∧ most   17 gallantly
as most] ∧gallantly∧ most [see prec. *tn*]

satisfied the sentiment, and found moreover, That the honour of
beating a drum was likely to be its own reward, as it open'd no 20
further track of glory to him—he retired *a ses terres*, and lived
comme il plaisoit a Dieu—that is to say, upon nothing.

—And so, quoth *Wisdome*, you have hired a drummer to attend
you in this tour of your's thro' France and Italy! Psha! said I, and
do not one half of our gentry go with a hum-drum *compagnon du* 25
voiage the same round, and have the piper and the devil and all to
pay besides? When man can extricate himself with an *equivoque*
in such an unequal match—he is not ill of—But you can do something else, La Fleur? said I—*O qu'oui!*—he could make spatterdashes, and play a little upon the fiddle—Bravo! said Wisdome— 30
Why, I play a bass myself, said I—we shall do very well.—You
can shave, and dress a wig a little, La Fleur?—He had all the dispositions in the world—It is enough for heaven! said I, interrupting him—and ought to be enough for me—So supper coming in,
and having a frisky English spaniel on one side of my chair, and a 35
French valet, with as much hilarity in his countenance as ever
nature painted in one, on the other—I was satisfied to my heart's
content with my empire; and if monarchs knew what they would
be at, they might be as satisfied as I was.

21–22 he . . . nothing] ⟨pour Sortir le jours de fêtes, pour faire le Galant vis a vis sa
Maitresse—s'adoniser—⟩ [This canceled reading appears on fol. 83ᵛ of *S1,* opposite
"he . . . nothing" (ll. 21–22, above), on fol. 84. Sterne may have initially intended
to insert this canceled reading after *"terres"* (l. 21, above). See pp. 246.5, 247.36–37,
below, where portions of this canceled reading appear in slightly different form.]
22 a⟨?u⟩ dieu   26–27 *voiage* ⟨&⟩~the~ ⟨have the piper to pay besides?—⟩ same
. . . besides?   26 and all] an all   27 ∧can∧   29 ∧O qu'oui!∧
31 ∧said I∧ . . . ⟨?w⟩~v~ery well; ⟨quoth I⟩.—you   33 heaven!] heaven!—
37 —⟨I⟩~on~ the . . . I   37–38 ∧to . . . content∧

---

21. *he retired a ses terres*] i.e., he deserted.
29–30. *spatterdashes*] "A kind of long gaiter or legging of leather, cloth,
etc., to keep the trousers or stockings from being spattered, esp. in riding"
(*OED*).
31. *I play a bass myself*] Sterne's interest in music is evident throughout
Tristram Shandy; see esp. 5.15.371–372.

MONTRIUL.

A S La Fleur went the whole tour of France and Italy with me,
and will be often upon the stage, I must interest the reader a
little further in his behalf, by saying, that I had never less reason
to repent of the impulses which generally do determine me, than
5 in regard to this fellow—he was a faithful, affectionate, simple
soul as ever trudged after the heels of a philosopher; and notwithstanding his talents of drum-beating and spatterdash-making,
which, tho' very good in themselves, happen'd to be of no great
service to me, yet was I hourly recompenced by the festivity of his
10 temper—it supplied all defects—I had a constant resource in his
looks in all difficulties and distresses of my own—I was going to
have added, of his too; but La Fleur was out of the reach of every
thing; for whether 'twas hunger or thirst, or cold or nakedness, or
watchings, or whatever stripes of ill luck La Fleur met with in our
15 journeyings, there was no index in his physiognomy to point them

---

1–2 me ⟨?in ?quality of ?drumstick⟩, and   4 ∧do∧ determine⟨d⟩   8 ∧no∧
10 temper ∧—⟨?wᶜʰ⟩~It~ . . . defects∧   11 all ⟨my⟩ difficulties and distresses
⟨?whatever⟩ of my own

1–10. *As . . . defects*] Yorick's affectionate benevolence toward La Fleur
is reminiscent of Uncle Toby's relationship with Trim. Smollett's opinion of
valets, though characteristically sour, typifies the feelings of many English
travelers: "Nothing gives me such chagrin, as the necessity I am under to
hire a *valet de place* . . . you cannot conceive with what eagerness and
dexterity those rascally valets exert themselves in pillaging strangers. There
is always one ready in waiting on your arrival, who . . . interests himself
in your affairs with such artful officiousness that you will find it difficult to
shake him off, even though you are determined beforehand against hiring
any such domestic. He produces recommendations from his former masters,
and the people of the house vouch for his honesty. The truth is, those fel-
lows are very handy, useful, and obliging; and so far honest, that they will
not steal in the usual way . . . but they fleece you without mercy in every
other article of expence" (*Travels*, Letter No. 6, pp. 46–47).
13–15. *hunger . . . journeyings*] paraphrased from St. Paul's description
of his sufferings in II Corinthians 11:23–27: "in stripes above measure . . .
In journeyings often, . . . in watchings often, in hunger and thirst, . . . in
cold and nakedness . . ."

126

out by—he was eternally the same; so that if I am a piece of a philosopher, which Satan now and then puts it into my head I am —it always mortifies the pride of the conceit, by reflecting how much I owe to the complexional philosophy of this poor fellow, for shaming me into one of a better kind. With all this, La Fleur 20 had a small cast of the coxcomb—but he seemed at first sight to be more a coxcomb of nature than of art; and before I had been three days in Paris with him—he seemed to be no coxcomb at all.

---

19 complexion∧al∧

MONTRIUL.

THE next morning La Fleur entering upon his employment, I delivered to him the key of my portmanteau with an inventory of my half a dozen shirts and silk pair of breeches; and bid him fasten all upon the chaise—get the horses put to—and desire 5 the landlord to come in with his bill.

C'est un garçon de bonne fortune, said the landlord, pointing through the window to half a dozen wenches who had got round about La Fleur, and were most kindly taking their leave of him, as the postilion was leading out the horses. La Fleur kissed all their 10 hands round and round again, and thrice he wiped his eyes, and thrice he promised he would bring them all pardons from Rome.

The young fellow, said the landlord, is beloved by all the town, and there is scarce a corner in Montriul where the want of him will not be felt: he has but one misfortune in the world, continued 15 he, "He is always in love."—I am heartily glad of it, said I,—'twill save me the trouble every night of putting my breeches under my head. In saying this, I was making not so much La Fleur's eloge, as my own, having been in love with one princess or another almost all my life, and I hope I shall go on so, till I die, 20 being firmly persuaded, that if ever I do a mean action, it must be

---

1 enter⟨?d⟩~ing~   2 ∧to∧ [*M1*: u.v.]   3 ∧my∧   8 ∧most kindly∧

17-25. *In . . . again*] Cf. Sterne's assurance to a friend that "I am glad that you are in love—'twill cure you (at least) of the spleen, which has a bad effect on both man and woman—I myself must ever have some dulcinea in my head—it harmonises the soul—and in those cases I first endeavour to make the lady believe so, or rather I begin first to make myself believe that I am in love—but I carry on my affairs quite in the French way, sentimentally —*l'amour* (say they) *n'est rien sans sentiment*'—Now notwithstanding they make such a pother about the *word,* they have no precise idea annex'd to it —and so much for that same subject called love—" (*Letters*, No. 148, 1765, p. 256). Cf. also *TS,* 8.26.578: "I call not love a misfortune, from a persuasion, that a man's heart is ever the better for it——Great God! what must my uncle *Toby*'s have been, when 'twas all benignity without it."

in some interval betwixt one passion and another: whilst this interregnum lasts, I always perceive my heart locked up—I can scarce find in it, to give Misery a sixpence; and therefore I always get out of it as fast as I can, and the moment I am rekindled, I am all generosity and good will again; and would do any thing in the 25 world either for, or with any one, if they will but satisfy me there is no sin in it.

—But in saying this—surely I am commending the passion— not myself.

A FRAGMENT.

————THE town of Abdera, notwithstanding Democritus lived there trying all the powers of irony and laughter to reclaim it, was the vilest and most profligate town in all Thrace. What for poisons, conspiracies and assassinations—libels, pasquinades and 5 tumults, there was no going there by day—'twas worse by night.

Now, when things were at the worst, it came to pass, that the Andromeda of Euripides being represented at Abdera, the whole

---

1 ⟨T⟩ ————the town

---

1. *Abdera . . . Democritus*] Known as "the laughing philosopher," Democritus (ca. 460–ca. 357 B.C.) was an inhabitant of Abdera, Thrace. In *The Anatomy of Melancholy,* from which Sterne borrowed extensively in *Tristram Shandy* and in this "Fragment" (see the next note), Robert Burton, who published the *Anatomy* under the name of "Democritus Jr.," frequently refers to Democritus' ironic laughter at the follies of his fellow-Abderites (see esp. *Anatomy,* 6th ed. [London, 1651], "Democritus Junior to the Reader," p. 2, where Burton cites the tradition that Democritus was the town clerk of Abdera; see also Tristram's ref. to this tradition in *TS,* 7.4.483).

Richard Griffith, to whom Sterne showed part of the MS. of *A Sentimental Journey* in September 1767, referred to Sterne as "the modern Democritus, Tristram Shandy" in recounting their conversations (see *Letters,* pp. 398–399, n. 3).

6–18. *the Andromeda . . . men*"] As Ferriar (I, 118–120) and others have noted, this anecdote is adapted from *The Anatomy of Melancholy,* 6th ed. (London, 1651), Third Partition, on Love-Melancholy (sect. 2, memb. 3, subsect. 4, p. 485; Burton's source is Lucian's *De historia scribenda*). Burton observes that there is

> *no stronger engine* [to induce love] *then to hear or read of love toyes, fables and discourses . . . and many by this means are quite mad.* At *Abdera* in *Thrace* (*Andromeda* one of *Euripedes* Tragedies being played) the spectators were so much moved with the object, and those pathetical love speeches of *Perseus,* amongst the rest, *O Cupid, Prince of Gods and men, &c.* that every man almost a good while after spake pure Iambicks, and raved still on *Perseus* speech *O Cupid, Prince of Gods and men.* As Car-men, Boyes and Prentises, when a new song is published with us, go singing that new tune still in the streets; they continually acted that Tragical part of *Perseus,* and in every mans mouth was *O Cupid,* in every street, *O Cupid,* in every house almost, *O Cupid, Prince of Gods and men,* pro-

130

orchestra was delighted with it: but of all the passages which delighted them, nothing operated more upon their imaginations,
than the tender strokes of nature which the poet had wrought up 10
in that pathetic speech of Perseus,

O Cupid, prince of God and men, &c.

Every man almost spoke pure iambics the next day, and talk'd of
nothing but Perseus his pathetic address—"O Cupid! prince of
God and men"—in every street of Abdera, in every house—"O 15
Cupid! Cupid!"—in every mouth, like the natural notes of some
sweet melody which drops from it whether it will or no—nothing
but "Cupid! Cupid! prince of God and men"—The fire caught—
and the whole city, like the heart of one man, open'd itself to
Love.   20

No pharmacopolist could sell one grain of helebore—not a
single armourer had a heart to forge one instrument of death—
Friendship and Virtue met together, and kiss'd each other in the
street—the golden age return'd, and hung o'er the town of Abdera
—every Abderite took his oaten pipe, and every Abderitish woman 25
left her purple web, and chastly sat her down and listen'd to the
song—

'Twas only in the power, says the Fragment, of the God whose
empire extendeth from heaven to earth, and even to the depths of
the sea, to have done this.   30

---

11 ⟨?th⟩~in~ that ∧pathetic∧   12 -O- *Cupid*   13 [The following rejected
reading appears upside down at the bottom of fol. 93ᵛ of *S1:* "—every man in
Abdera"; fol. 93 begins with "Every man almost", l. 13, above (see p. 82.74–76*tn,*
above). Cf. "every man almost" in the passage quoted from *The Anatomy of Melancholy,* p. 130.6–18*n,* above.]   14–15 "O Cupid! . . . men"] *"O Cupid /
"Prince of God* & men"   18 Cupid! prince] Cupid Prince   28 'Twas]—
'twas   28 Fragment, ⟨of the⟩ ⟨?G⟩~⟨P~rince⟩ / of ∧the∧ God ⟨& men⟩ whose
[Sterne apparently wrote initially: "of the God"; then changed this to "of the Prince
of God & men"; and then changed this to "of the God whose".]   29 from ⟨the⟩
heaven   30 the ⟨ocean⟩ ∧Sea∧ [*M1:* u.v.]

---

nouncing still like stage-players, *O Cupid;* they were so possessed all with
that rapture, and thought of that pathetical love speech, they could not
a long time after forget, or drive it out of their minds, but *O Cupid, Prince
of Gods and men,* was ever in their mouths.

MONTRIUL.

WHEN all is ready, and every article is disputed and paid for in the inn, unless you are a little sour'd by the adventure, there is always a matter to compound at the door, before you can get into your chaise; and that is with the sons and daughters of 5 poverty, who surround you. Let no man say, "let them go to the devil"—'tis a cruel journey to send a few miserables, and they have had sufferings enow without it: I always think it better to take a few sous out in my hand; and I would counsel every gentle traveller to do so likewise: he need not be so exact in setting down 10 his motives for giving them—they will be register'd elsewhere.

For my own part, there is no man gives so little as I do; for few that I know have so little to give: but as this was the first publick act of my charity in France, I took the more notice of it.

A well-a-way! said I. I have but eight sous in the world, shewing 15 them in my hand, and there are eight poor men and eight poor women for 'em.

A poor tatter'd soul without a shirt on instantly withdrew his claim, by retiring two steps out of the circle, and making a disqualifying bow on his part. Had the whole parterre cried out, 20 *Place aux dames*, with one voice, it would not have conveyed the sentiment of a deference for the sex with half the effect.

Just heaven! for what wise reasons hast thou order'd it, that beggary and urbanity, which are at such variance in other countries, should find a way to be at unity in this?

---

5 ∧who surround you∧   7 sufferings] suffering   8–9 every ∧gentle∧ traveller ⟨gentle & simple⟩ // do so   9 to do] do [see prec. *tn*]   14 but] but / but
14–16 but ⟨six⟩ ∧eight∧ sous . . . are ⟨six⟩ ∧eight∧ poor men and ⟨six⟩ ∧eight∧ poor
women for ⟨th⟩'em   21 sex . . . effect] ⟨sex with more sweetness—⟩ [This
canceled reading appears upside down at the bottom of fol. 96ᵛ of *S1*. The number
99 appears upside down in the lower left-hand corner of fol. 96ᵛ; this number indicates that this canceled reading is probably an earlier version of "sex . . . effect"
(l. 21, above) on fol. 97, which bears the canceled number ⟨99⟩ in Sterne's hand.
On the foliation of *S1*, see App. B, §4, pp. 300–301.]

—I insisted upon presenting him with a single sous, merely for 25 his *politesse*.

A poor little dwarfish brisk fellow, who stood over-against me in the circle, putting something first under his arm, which had once been a hat, took his snuff-box out of his pocket, and generously offer'd a pinch on both sides of him: it was a gift of conse- 30 quence, and modestly declined—The poor little fellow press'd it upon them with a nod of welcomeness—*Prenez en—prenez*, said he, looking another way; so they each took a pinch—Pity thy box should ever want one! said I to myself; so I put a couple of sous into it—taking a small pinch out of his box, to enhance their value, 35 as I did it—He felt the weight of the second obligation more than that of the first—'twas doing him an honour—the other was only doing him a charity—and he made me a bow down to the ground for it.

—Here! said I to an old soldier with one hand, who had been 40 campaign'd and worn out to death in the service—here's a couple of sous for thee—*Vive le Roi!* said the old soldier.

I had then but three sous left: so I gave one, simply *pour l'amour de Dieu*, which was the footing on which it was begg'd—The poor woman had a dislocated hip; so it could not be well, upon any other 45 motive.

Mon cher et tres charitable Monsieur—There's no opposing this, said I.

My Lord Anglois—the very sound was worth the money—so I gave *my last sous for it*. But in the eagerness of giving, I had over- 50 look'd a *pauvre honteux*, who had no one to ask a sous for him, and who, I believed, would have perish'd, ere he could have ask'd one for himself: he stood by the chaise a little without the circle, and wiped a tear from a face which I thought had seen better days—

---

25 ∧sous merely∧   31 fellow ⟨?of⟩ press'd ["⟨?of⟩": Sterne may have started to write "offered"]   32 them ⟨?again⟩~with~   32 ∧*en*∧   45 hip; ⟨was extreme old, & extreme ugly, & but one eye left in her head,⟩ so [*M1:* u.v.] 48 I.] I—   49 *My*] —''*My*   51 to ⟨beg⟩ ∧ask a sous∧   52–53 could ∧have∧ ask∨d∨ ∧one∧

55 Good God! said I—and I have not one single sous left to give him—
But you have a thousand! cried all the powers of nature, stirring
within me—so I gave him—no matter what—I am ashamed to say
how much, now—and was ashamed to think, how little, then: so if
the reader can form any conjecture of my disposition, as these two
60 fixed points are given him, he may judge within a livre or two
what was the precise sum.

   I could afford nothing for the rest, but, *Dieu vous benisse—Et
le bon Dieu vous benisse encore*—said the old soldier, the dwarf, &c.
The *pauvre honteux* could say nothing—he pull'd out a little hand-
65 kerchief, and wiped his face as he turned away—and I thought he
thank'd me more than them all.

---

60 ∧or two∧   63 ∧encore∧   63–64 &c. . . ⟨and⟩ the *pauvre*
64 ∧out∧   65 his ⟨eyes,⟩ ∧face . . . away—∧

THE BIDET.

HAVING settled all these little matters, I got into my post-chaise with more ease than ever I got into a post-chaise in my life; and La Fleur having got one large jack-boot on the far side of a little *bidet**, and another on this (for I count nothing of his legs) —he canter'd away before me as happy and as perpendicular as a 5 prince.—

—But what is happiness! what is grandeur in this painted scene of life! A dead ass, before we had got a league, put a sudden stop to La Fleur's career—his bidet would not pass by it—a contention arose betwixt them, and the poor fellow was kick'd out of his jack- 10 boots the very first kick.

La Fleur bore his fall like a French christian, saying neither more or less upon it, than, Diable! so presently got up and came to the charge again astride his bidet, beating him up to it as he would have beat his drum. 15

* Post horse.

---

5 and ∧as∧   6 prince.—] prince—   16 *Post horse.] [This note and the asterisk following *"bidet"* (l. 4, above) are not in *S1*.]

---

3. *jack-boot*] a very large, strong boot (extending above the knee), worn by postilions to protect their legs. The enormous size of the jackboots used by French postilions (on which English travelers commented: see Mead, p. 53) is illustrated by those worn by the figure at the extreme left in Bunbury's satirical print of the Grand Tour, Plate 7, following p. 292, below.

16. **Post horse.*] *A bidet* (l. 4, above) is a small horse, and I suspect this note may have been added by Sterne as a humorous reference to the small size of French post-horses compared with English ones. This fact was often commented on with exasperation by English travelers (see Mead, pp. 52–53), for reasons which Tristram makes clear in his journey through France: "Now I hate to hear a person, especially if he be a traveller, complain that we do not get on so fast in *France* as we do in *England*; whereas we get on much faster, *consideratis considerandis*; thereby always meaning, that if you weigh their vehicles with the mountains of baggage which you lay both before and behind upon them—and then consider their puny horses, with the very little

The bidet flew from one side of the road to the other, then back
again—then this way—then that way, and in short every way but
by the dead ass.—La Fleur insisted upon the thing—and the bidet
20 threw him.

What's the matter, La Fleur, said I, with this bidet of thine?
—*Monsieur*, said he, *c'est un cheval le plus opiniatré du monde*—
Nay, if he is a conceited beast, he must go his own way, replied
I—so La Fleur got off him, and giving him a good sound lash, the
25 bidet took me at my word, and away he scamper'd back to Montriul.
—*Peste!* said La Fleur.

It is not *mal a propos* to take notice here, that tho' La Fleur
availed himself but of two different terms of exclamation in this
encounter—namely, *Diable!* and *Peste!* that there are nevertheless
30 three, in the French language; like the positive, comparative, and
superlative, one or the other of which serve for every unexpected
throw of the dice in life.

Le Diable! which is the first, and positive degree, is generally
used upon ordinary emotions of the mind, where small things
35 only fall out contrary to your expectations—such as—the throwing
once doublets—La Fleur's being kick'd off his horse, and so forth—
cuckoldom, for the same reason, is always—*Le Diable!*

---

18 then ⟨?side⟩~this~ way⟨s⟩ — then ⟨?every⟩~that~ way . . . every way
19 ass. —] asse—   21 matter, ⟨?with⟩~La~ Fleur, ∧said I∧ with ["La" appears
to read "L⟨e⟩~a~"; see p. 124.7*tn*, above.]   27 to ⟨?obs⟩~ta~ke notice ["⟨?obs⟩":
Sterne may have started to write "observe"]   30 ∧like∧   33 first ∧& positive degree∧   34 ∧small∧   35 only . . . out ∧⟨only⟩∧ contrary   35–
36 as ⟨Le Fleur's fall⟩ —the . . . doublets ⟨& ?so ?forth.—⟩~——Le Fleur's~ ⟨?kick'd⟩
/ ⟨[at least one illegible word deleted]⟩~being~ kick'd . . . & so forth—

---

they give them—'tis a wonder they get on at all" (*TS*, 7.20.503). In a letter
to his wife describing their projected trip in France, Sterne wrote: "sometimes I shall take a bidet—(a little post horse) and scamper before" the
chaise (*Letters*, No. 93, Paris, 1762, p. 173).
36. *once doublets*] a gaming term for a throw of two dice which turns up a
pair ("doublets") of ones ("once" or "ones" = "of one," signifying the
ace), in a game where the object is to make as high a score as possible (Milic,
p. 45, n. 7).

But in cases where the cast has something provoking in it, as in that of the bidet's running away after, and leaving La Fleur aground in jack-boots—'tis the second degree. 40

'Tis then *Peste!*

And for the third—

—But here my heart is wrung with pity and fellow-feeling, when I reflect what miseries must have been their lot, and how bitterly so refined a people must have smarted, to have forced them upon 45 the use of it.—

Grant me, O ye powers which touch the tongue with eloquence in distress!—whatever is my *cast*, Grant me but decent words to exclaim in, and I will give my nature way.

—But as these were not to be had in France, I resolved to take 50 every evil just as it befell me without any exclamation at all.

La Fleur, who had made no such covenant with himself, followed the bidet with his eyes till it was got out of sight—and then, you may imagine, if you please, with what word he closed the whole affair. 55

As there was no hunting down a frighten'd horse in jack-boots, there remained no alternative but taking La Fleur either behind the chaise, or into it.—

I preferred the latter, and in half an hour we got to the post-house at Nampont. 60

---

42 And] [no par. in *S1*]   45–46 smarted ⟨under them ?as ?they⟩ to have forced them ⟨to it⟩~upon~ ⟨it.⟩ ⋀the use of it—⋀ [*M1:* "upon it."]   48 but ⟨religious and⟩ decent [*M1:* u.v.]   50 as ⟨neither the one or the other⟩ ⋀these⋀ were ⋀not⋀ to [*M1:* u.v.]   57 ⋀either⋀   58 it.—] it—

42–50. *And . . . France*] Cf. Tristram's mock reluctance about telling the reader the two French words used to make a post-horse get on, which he reveals in the story of the Abbess of Andoüillets (*TS*, 7.20.503 ff.).

54–55. *you may imagine . . . affair*] See Sterne's complaints about the cleanliness of his readers' imaginations, cited p. 289.123–128*n*, below.

NAMPONT.
THE DEAD ASS.

—AND this, said he, putting the remains of a crust into his wallet—and this, should have been thy portion, said he, hadst thou been alive to have shared it with me. I thought by the accent, it had been an apostrophe to his child; but 'twas to his ass, 5 and to the very ass we had seen dead in the road, which had occasioned La Fleur's misadventure. The man seemed to lament it much; and it instantly brought into my mind Sancho's lamentation for his; but he did it with more true touches of nature.

The mourner was sitting upon a stone bench at the door, with 10 the ass's pannel and its bridle on one side, which he took up from time to time—then laid them down—look'd at them and shook his head. He then took his crust of bread out of his wallet again, as if to eat it; held it some time in his hand—then laid it upon the bit of his ass's bridle—looked wistfully at the little arrangement he 15 had made—and then gave a sigh.

6–7 misadventure. ⟨?The ?man⟩~?He ⟨seem'd⟩~ ∧seem'd to∧ lament⟨?ed⟩ it ⟨with ?great ?passion⟩~much—~ ; ["?passion" may read "feeling"] [Sterne may have written initially: "The man lamented it with great passion (or "feeling")".] 6 The man] ?He [see prec. *tn*]

NAMPONT. THE DEAD ASS.] Cf. Tristram's encounter with the ass at Lyons (*TS*, 7.32.522 ff.).

3. *hadst . . . alive*] See p. 140.46–47*n*, below.

7. *Sancho's lamentation*] a ref. to Sancho's lament, after his beloved ass Dapple had been stolen in the Sierra Morena: "finding himself depriv'd of that dear Partner of his Fortunes, and best Comfort in his Peregrinations, he broke out into the most pitiful and sad Lamentations in the World; insomuch that he wak'd Don *Quixote* with his Moans. O dear Child of my Bowels, cry'd he, born and bred under my Roof, my Childrens Play-fellow, the Comfort of my Wife, the Envy of my Neighbours, the Ease of my Burdens, the Staff of my Life, and in a Word, half my Maintenance; for with Six and twenty *Maravedis,* which were daily earn'd by thee, I made shift to keep half my Family"

The simplicity of his grief drew numbers about him, and La Fleur amongst the rest, whilst the horses were getting ready; as I continued sitting in the post-chaise, I could see and hear over their heads.

—He said he had come last from Spain, where he had been from the furthest borders of Franconia; and had got so far on his return home, when his ass died. Every one seem'd desirous to know what business could have taken so old and poor a man so far a journey from his own home.

It had pleased heaven, he said, to bless him with three sons, the finest lads in all Germany; but having in one week lost two of the eldest of them by the small-pox, and the youngest falling ill of the same distemper, he was afraid of being bereft of them all; and made a vow, if Heaven would not take him from him also, he would go in gratitude to St. Iago in Spain.

When the mourner got thus far on his story, he stopp'd to pay nature her tribute—and wept bitterly.

He said, Heaven had accepted the conditions; and that he had set out from his cottage with this poor creature, who had been a patient partner of his journey—that it had eat the same bread with him all the way, and was unto him as a friend.

---

20 —He said] He said   22 one ⟨?ask'd ?what⟩∼seem'd desi∼rous to know what
24 ⟨country⟩∼Home∼   28–31 all; / ⟨and, promised heaven, if he recoverd, he
wᵈ go to Sᵗ Iago de Compostella to return thanks— / [par.] —When the ⟨⟨?old⟩⟩∼
M∼ourner got to / this part of his story—he stop'd to pay⟩ // and made a vow . . .
Spain / ⟨[par.] Upon getting ⟨⟨?thus⟩⟩∼to∼ this point of / of⟩ / [par.] When the
Mourner . . . story [⟨⟨ ⟩⟩ = deletion within deletion]   29 him also, he] him,
he   33 the conditions] th⟨?i⟩∼e∼ condition⟨?s⟩

(*Don Quixote*, 1.3.9.163–164). Tristram also refers to Sancho's lamentation for his ass (*TS*, 7.36.529).

30. *St. Iago in Spain*] the shrine of the apostle St. James (the greater) in Santiago de Compostela (see ll. 28–31*tn*, above), in northwest Spain; the supposed site of St. James's tomb and one of the chief shrines of Christendom.

35–36. *it . . . friend*] paraphrased from II Samuel 12:3, quoted p. 275.9–11*n*, below.

Every body who stood about, heard the poor fellow with concern
—La Fleur offered him money.—The mourner said, he did not
want it—it was not the value of the ass—but the loss of him.—
40 The ass, he said, he was assured loved him—and upon this told
them a long story of a mischance upon their passage over the
Pyrenean mountains which had separated them from each other
three days; during which time the ass had sought him as much as
he had sought the ass, and that they had neither scarce eat or
45 drank till they met.

Thou hast one comfort, friend, said I, at least in the loss of thy
poor beast; I'm sure thou hast been a merciful master to him.—
Alas! said the mourner, I thought so, when he was alive—but now
that he is dead I think otherwise.—I fear the weight of myself and
50 my afflictions together have been too much for him—they have

---

38 him ⟨a sous.⟩ ∧money—∧ ⟨towards his loss.⟩ The Mourner   40 said ⟨loved⟩
he . . . loved ⟨?it⟩ ∧him∧   46 one ⟨?consolation⟩ ∧comfort∧ , ⟨?at⟩~fr~iend
∧said I∧ at least   47–49 him.—Alas! said the mourner, I thought so . . . otherwise.—I fear] ∧I thought so . . . otherwise—I fear &c- —∧ [This inserted passage
is written on fol. 109ᵛ of *S1*, opposite "him.—alas! said the Mourner I fear", on fol.
110; there is a large caret between "Mourner" and "I" in *S1*, indicating where
the passage on fol. 109ᵛ should be inserted. A smaller caret below the dash after
"him.—∧" (sic) in *S1* (see "him.—", l. 47, above) may indicate that Sterne considered
inserting the passage on fol. 109ᵛ there. *M1:* "alas! said the Mourner, I fear"]
49 otherwise.—] otherwise—

46–47. *Thou . . . him.*] Yorick's remark and the mourner's words, "hadst
thou been alive" (p. 138.3, above), may possibly echo the comment of the
alderman in *Don Quixote* upon finding the dead body of his ass: "Had he
been alive, as sure as he was an Ass he would have Bray'd again. But let him
go, this Comfort I have at least Brother; though I have lost him, I've found
out that rare Talent of yours [for braying]" (2.3.25.605–606). (Sterne's
remarkable capacity for echoing the phrasing and idiom of the Motteux-
Ozell translation of *Don Quixote* is indicated by some of the examples cited
in my article, "Some Borrowings in Sterne from Rabelais and Cervantes,"
English Language Notes, III [1965], 111–118; see esp. p. 114, the first borrowing from *Don Quixote.*)

shortened the poor creature's days, and I fear I have them to answer for.—Shame on the world! said I to myself—Did we love each other, as this poor soul but loved his ass—'twould be something.—

---

52 ⟨If ?we⟩~Did~ we   53–54 something.—] something—

NAMPONT.
THE POSTILLION.

THE concern which the poor fellow's story threw me into, required some attention: the postillion paid not the least to it, but set off upon the *pavè* in a full gallop.

The thirstiest soul in the most sandy desert of Arabia could not
5 have wished more for a cup of cold water, than mine did for grave and quiet movements; and I should have had an high opinion of the postillion had he but stolen off with me in something like a pensive pace.—On the contrary, as the mourner finished his lamentation, the fellow gave an unfeeling lash to each of his beasts,
10 and set off clattering like a thousand devils.

---

4 ⟨?traveller⟩~Soul~   6 an] a   7 ∧he∧   7 ∧me∧   8 pace.—On]
pace—on

NAMPONT. THE POSTILLION.] As Vrooman points out (pp. 191–192), this incident illustrates one of Sterne's favorite themes—the relationship between motion and emotion, which he often expresses in terms of the interaction between a traveler's motions and his feelings. See, e.g., in *Tristram Shandy* (cited by Vrooman, p. 191, n. 5): Yorick's belief that "brisk trotting and slow argumentation, like wit and judgment, were two incompatible movements" (1.10.20); Tristram's description of the effect on his imagination of the successively fast and slow movements of the vehicles in which he rides (5.1.342); his remark that, "When the precipitancy of a man's wishes hurries on his ideas ninety times faster than the vehicle he rides in—woe be to truth!" (7.8.488); his statement that, "being very thin," he finds motion "so much of joy——and . . . to stand still, or get on but slowly, . . . death and the devil" (7.13.493); and esp. his description of the harmony between his kindly emotions and the oscillations of his chaise when he encounters Maria (9.24.629, quoted p. 15, above). See also Yorick's explanation that the motions of the *Desobligeant* in which he was sitting were caused by the "agitation" of writing the preface to his *Journey* (p. 85, above).

4–5. *The thirstiest . . . water*] Cf. *Letters,* No. 64, Coxwold, [? June 1760], p. 117: "An urn of cold water in the driest stage of the driest Desert in Arabia,

I called to him as loud as I could, for heaven's sake to go slower —and the louder I called the more unmercifully he galloped.— The deuce take him and his galloping too—said I—he'll go on tearing my nerves to pieces till he has worked me into a foolish passion, and then he'll go slow, that I may enjoy the sweets of it. 15

The postillion managed the point to a miracle: by the time he had got to the foot of a steep hill about half a league from Nampont,—he had put me out of temper with him—and then with myself, for being so.

My case then required a different treatment; and a good rattling 20 gallop would have been of real service to me.—

—Then, prithee get on—get on, my good lad, said I.

The postillion pointed to the hill—I then tried to return back to the story of the poor German and his ass—but I had broke the clue—and could no more get into it again, than the postillion 25 could into a trot.—

---

15 the ⟨full⟩ sweets   21 me.—] me—   26 trot.—] trot—

---

pour'd out by an angel's hand to a thirsty Pilgrim, could not have been more gratefully received than Miss Macartny's Letter——pray is that Simile too warm? or conceived too orientally)?" As Curtis notes (*Letters,* p. 118, n. 2), here and in *A Sentimental Journey* Sterne is echoing Proverbs 25:25: "As cold waters to a thirsty soul, so is good news from a far country."

11–15. *I called . . . it.*] Yorick's difficulties with the postilion typify the frustrations of other travelers. Smollett characterized French postilions as "lazy, lounging, greedy, and impertinent. If you chide them for lingering, they will continue to delay you the longer: if you chastise them with sword, cane, cudgel, or horse-whip, they will either disappear entirely, and leave you without resource; or they will find means to take vengeance by overturning your carriage. . . . [They may] drive at a waggon pace, with a view to provoke your impatience" (*Travels,* Letter No. 41, pp. 341, 340).

25. *clue*] orig., a ball of thread or yarn; hence, "that which guides or threads a way through a maze, perplexity, difficulty" (*OED*).

—The deuce go, said I, with it all! Here am I sitting as candidly disposed to make the best of the worst, as ever wight was, and all runs counter.

30   There is one sweet lenitive at least for evils, which nature holds out to us; so I took it kindly at her hands, and fell asleep; and the first word which roused me was *Amiens.*

—Bless me! said I, rubbing my eyes—this is the very town where my poor lady is to come.

---

28 was,] was—   33 ⟨?G⟩∼B∼less [Sterne may have started to write "God Bless"]

AMIENS.

THE words were scarce out of my mouth, when the Count de
L***'s post-chaise, with his sister in it, drove hastily by: she
had just time to make me a bow of recognition—and of that particular kind of it, which told me she had not yet done with me.
She was as good as her look; for, before I had quite finished my 5
supper, her brother's servant came into the room with a billet, in
which she said, she had taken the liberty to charge me with a letter,
which I was to present myself to Madame R*** the first morning
I had nothing to do at Paris. There was only added, she was sorry,
but from what *penchant* she had not considered, that she had been 10
prevented telling me her story—that she still owed it me; and if my
rout should ever lay through Brussels, and I had not by then forgot
the name of Madame de L***—that Madame de L*** would be
glad to discharge her obligation.

Then I will meet thee, said I, fair spirit! at Brussels—'tis only 15
returning from Italy through Germany to Holland, by the rout of
Flanders, home—'twill scarce be ten posts out of my way; but were
it ten thousand! with what a moral delight will it crown my journey,

---

9 added, ⟨that⟩ she   12 and I had] & had   15 Then] —then
15 Brussels—] Brussels.—

---

13. *Madame de L***]* identified as "the Marquise Lamberti" on p. 347 of
the account of La Fleur published in the *European Magazine* (see App. E,
p. 342, note to p. 123.34). The account is apparently fictitious, and the identification (cited in Ferriar, II, 52*n; Life,* p. 386) seems to be without authority.

15-22. *Then . . . cheeks]* In commenting on Toby's affair with the Widow
Wadman, Tristram observes that for a woman "in sorrow or distress . . .
infinite was [Toby's] pity; nor would the most courteous knight of romance
have gone further, at least upon one leg, to have wiped away a tear from a
woman's eye" (*TS,* 9.3.602–603).

17. *ten posts]* about sixty miles.

18. *a moral delight]* Cf. *Sermons,* II, 25, ref. to "that moral delight arising
in the mind from the conscience of a humane action," quoted in App. E,
p. 339, n. 6; II, 85 (V.i), ref. to "that moral delight, arising from the conscience of well-doing," e.g., comforting "the broken-hearted."

145

in sharing in the sickening incidents of a tale of misery told to me
20 by such a sufferer? to see her weep! and though I cannot dry up
the fountain of her tears, what an exquisite sensation is there still
left, in wiping them away from off the cheeks of the first and fairest
of women, as I'm sitting with my handkerchief in my hand in
silence the whole night besides her.

25 There was nothing wrong in the sentiment; and yet I instantly
reproached my heart with it in the bitterest and most reprobate of
expressions.

It had ever, as I told the reader, been one of the singular blessings of my life, to be almost every hour of it miserably in love with
30 some one; and my last flame happening to be blown out by a whiff

---

20 sufferer? ⟨to sit besides a friendless / friendless Being as she weeps!⟩ ∧to see her
weep! ∧   22 ∧off∧   23 women] woman

---

22. *wiping . . . cheeks*] probably an echo of Isaiah 25:8: "the Lord God
will wipe away tears from off all faces." Sterne paraphrases this passage twice
in the *Sermons:* in a description of Heaven as "that happier country, . . .
where God will wipe away all tears from off our faces for ever and ever" (I,
125 [II.x]); and in a comment that the man who lifts his eyes to the joys of
Heaven "wipes away all tears from off his eyes for ever and ever" (I, 17
[II.xv]). Sterne echoes these paraphrases of Isaiah in the *Journal* (3 Aug.,
p. 386): after telling Eliza that without her a mitre would not sit easy on his
brow (see p. 200.99–100n, below), he remarks: "I want kindly to smooth
thine, & not only wipe away thy tears but dry up the Sourse of them for
ever—"
    22–23. *the first . . . women*] Cf. Sterne's descriptions of Eliza as "the
best and fairest of all [Nature's] . . . works" (*Letters,* No. 193, to Eliza,
[? March 1767], p. 321), and as the "first and best of woman kind" (*Journal,*
31 July, p. 384).
    23–24. *as . . . her*] Cf. *Journal,* 28 April, p. 334: "I was not deceived
Eliza! by my presentiment that I should find thee out in my dreams; for I
have been with thee almost the whole night, alternately soothing ⟨Y⟩ Thee,
or telling thee my sorrows"; 15 June, p. 358: "would I was at the feet of yʳ
Bed—fanning breezes to You, in yʳ Slumbers."
    28–30. *It . . . some one*] See pp. 128.17–25n, above.
    30. *my last flame*] In a letter in which he wittily asserts that he is sexually
virtuous, Sterne remarks: "I had rather raise a gentle flame, than have a

of jealousy on the sudden turn of a corner, I had lighted it up afresh at the pure taper of Eliza but about three months before— swearing as I did it, that it should last me through the whole journey—Why should I dissemble the matter? I had sworn to her eternal fidelity—she had a right to my whole heart—to divide my 35 affections was to lessen them—to expose them, was to risk them: where there is risk, there may be loss—and what wilt thou have, Yorick! to answer to a heart so full of trust and confidence—so good, so gentle and unreproaching?

—I will not go to Brussels, replied I, interrupting myself—but 40 my imagination went on—I recall'd her looks at that crisis of our separation when neither of us had power to say Adieu! I look'd at the picture she had tied in a black ribband about my neck—and blush'd as I look'd at it—I would have given the world to have kiss'd it,—but was ashamed—And shall this tender flower, said I, 45 pressing it between my hands—shall it be smitten to its very root—

36–37 them; ⟨and⟩ where / ∧-terrupting myself∧ 45 ashamed—And] ashamed.—and   39 unreproaching ⟨as Eliza's⟩ [*M1:* u.v.]   43 tied ⟨trembling⟩ in   45 ∧it∧ [*M1:* u.v.]   40∨ in-∨

---

different one raised in me.—Now, I take heav'n to witness, after all this *badinage* my heart is innocent" (*Letters,* No. 213, Sept. 1767, p. 394).

31–34. *I had . . . journey*] Sterne met Eliza in January 1767; Yorick's *Journey* takes place in 1762 (see p. 192.7–8*n,* below).

34–35. *I had . . . fidelity*] In the *Journal,* Sterne asks Eliza to "Remember my Truth . . . to thee and eternal fidelity" (29–30 May, p. 346); for similar vows that he will remain faithful to her, see *Journal,* 21 April, p. 326; 25 April, p. 332; 2 June, p. 348.

41–42. *I recall'd . . . Adieu!*] Cf. *Journal,* 6 July, p. 374: "Three long Months and three long days are pass'd & gone, since my Eliza sighed on taking her Leave of Albions cliffs, & of all in Albion, which was dear to her —How oft have I smarted at the Idea, of that last longing Look by wch thou badest adieu to all thy heart ⟨flutter'd⟩ Sufferd ⟨on⟩ at that dismal Crisis— twas the Separation of Soul & Body—& equal to nothing but what passes on that tremendous Moment.—& like it in one Consequence, that thou art in another World." Cf. also his refs. to the "Crisis" of their separation and to the "Anguish" it caused him, in *Journal,* 28 June, p. 366; 10 June, p. 355.

42–43. *I look'd . . . neck*] See p. 67.22*n,* above.

and smitten, Yorick! by thee, who hast promised to shelter it in thy breast?

Eternal fountain of happiness! said I, kneeling down upon the 50 ground—be thou my witness—and every pure spirit which tastes it, be my witness also, That I would not travel to Brussels, unless Eliza went along with me, did the road lead me towards heaven.

In transports of this kind, the heart, in spite of the understanding, will always say too much.

47–48 thee who has promised . . . in ⟨his⟩~thy~ breast [*M1:* "in his breast"] [The following canceled reading appears upside down at the bottom of fol. 119ᵛ of *S1:* "⟨in his b⟩"; and fol. 119 begins with "in ⟨his⟩~thy~ breast" (see p. 82.74–76*tn*, above). The number 121 appears upside down in the lower left-hand corner of fol. 119ᵛ, and fol. 119 bears the canceled number ⟨121⟩ in Sterne's hand. On the foliation of *S1,* see App. B, §4, pp. 300–301.]   47 hast] has [see prec. *tn*] 50–51 tastes ⟨?thee⟩ it

---

49–52. *Eternal fountain . . . heaven.*] Cf. *Sermons,* II, 8–9 (IV.vii): "Grant me, gracious GOD! to go chearfully on, the road which thou hast marked out . . . continue the light of this dim taper thou hast put into my hands:——I will kneel upon the ground seven times a day, to seek the best track I can with it——and having done that, I will trust myself and the issue of my journey to thee, who art the fountain of joy." Cf. also *TS,* 7.1.479, ref. to "the fountain of life."

50–51. *tastes it*] Cf. the passages quoted from the *Sermons,* pp. 283.15–284.27*n*, below, describing the "taste" of joy God affords the religious man.

53–54. *In . . . much.*] In "The Levite and his Concubine" (*Sermons,* I, 205–206 [III.iii]), Yorick observes: " 'tis a story on which the heart cannot be at a loss for what to say, or the imagination for what to suppose—the danger is, humanity may say too much."

THE LETTER.

AMIENS.

FORTUNE had not smiled upon La Fleur; for he had been un-
successful in his feats of chivalry—and not one thing had
offer'd to signalize his zeal for my service from the time he had
enter'd into it, which was almost four and twenty hours. The poor
soul burn'd with impatience; and the Count de L***'s servant's 5
coming with the letter, being the first practicable occasion which
offered, La Fleur had laid hold of it; and in order to do honour to
his master, had taken him into a back parlour in the Auberge, and
treated him with a cup or two of the best wine in Picardy; and the
Count de L***'s servant in return, and not to be behind hand in 10
politeness with La Fleur, had taken him back with him to the
Count's hôtel. La Fleur's *prevenancy* (for there was a passport in
his very looks) soon set every servant in the kitchen at ease with
him; and as a Frenchman, whatever be his talents, has no sort of
prudery in shewing them, La Fleur, in less than five minutes, had 15
pull'd out his fife, and leading off the dance himself with the first
note, set the *fille de chambre*, the *maitre d'hotel*, the cook, the
scullion, and all the houshold, dogs and cats, besides an old monkey,
a-dancing: I suppose there never was a merrier kitchen since the
flood. 20

Madame de L***, in passing from her brother's apartments to
her own, hearing so much jollity below stairs, rung up her *fille de
chambre* to ask about it; and hearing it was the English gentleman's
servant who had set the whole house merry with his pipe, she
order'd him up. 25

---

1 ∧for∧   **3** service ⟨since⟩ ∧from the time∧   **6-7** ∧wch offer'd∧   **8** ∧in
the Auberge∧   **9** of ⟨good⟩ ∧the best∧ wine ∧in Picardy∧   **12** Count's
⟨?hotel⟩~⟨?de ?Lxxx's⟩~ ∧hotel∧ [*M1*: "Count de Lxxx's hotel"]   **12-13** *prevenancy* (for . . . looks)] *prevenancy,* for . . . looks, [the only place where parentheses are substituted in *A1* for commas in *S1*]   **14** french ∧man∧
15 ∧had∧   **18-19** scullion ⟨?&c ∧and old Monkey & all the houshold∧ a dancing:—I suppose there⟩ // ⟨—dogs & cats⟩, and ⟨and⟩ all the houshold, ∧dogs &
Cats—∧ —besides . . . there   **23** about ∧it∧

As the poor fellow could not present himself empty, he had loaden'd himself in going up stairs with a thousand compliments to Madame de L***, on the part of his master—added a long apocrypha of inquiries after Madame de L***'s health—told her,

30 that Monsieur his master was *au desespoire* for her re-establishment from the fatigues of her journey—and, to close all, that Monsieur had received the letter which Madame had done him the honour ——And he has done me the honour, said Madame de L***, interrupting La Fleur, to send a billet in return.

35   Madame de L*** had said this with such a tone of reliance upon the fact, that La Fleur had not power to disappoint her expectations—he trembled for my honour—and possibly might not altogether be unconcerned for his own, as a man capable of being attach'd to a master who could be a wanting *en egards vis a vis*

40 *d'une femme*; so that when Madame de L*** asked La Fleur if he had brought a letter—*O qu'oui*, said La Fleur: so laying down his hat upon the ground, and taking hold of the flap of his right side pocket with his left hand, he began to search for the letter with his right—then contrary-wise—*Diable!*—then sought every pocket—

45 pocket by pocket, round, not forgetting his fob—*Peste!*—then La Fleur emptied them upon the floor—pulled out a dirty cravat— a handkerchief—a comb—a whip lash—a night-cap—then gave a peep into his hat—*Quelle etourderie!* He had left the letter upon the table in the Auberge—he would run for it, and be back with it

50 in three minutes.

   I had just finished my supper when La Fleur came in to give me an account of his adventure: he told the whole story simply as it

---

27 ∧in . . . stairs∧   28 to ⟨her⟩ ∧Madam ⟨?on⟩~de~ Lxxx∧ on   29 ∧told her∧   30 her ⟨recovery⟩ ∧reestablishment∧   32 ⟨?S⟩~M~adame ["⟨?S⟩": Sterne may have started to write "She"]   32–33 honour ⟨to⟩~——~ and 34–35 send ⟨?one⟩~⟨?me⟩~ a Billet in return? / —⟨O⟩ ⟨?Yes⟩~⟨qu'Oui,⟩~ ⟨replied Le Fleur.⟩ / [no par.] Madame de Lxxx ha⟨s⟩~d~ ⟨ask∧'d∧⟩ ∧said∧   35 Madame] [*S1:* no par.; see prec. *tn*]   36 that ⟨he⟩ ∧L⟨e⟩~a~ Fleur∧   39 *egards* ⟨?vis⟩ *vis*   40 ∧that∧   43 for ⟨it⟩ ∧the Letter∧   44 — ⟨he⟩ then ⟨?pulld⟩ ⟨?out⟩~sau~ght   45–46 ∧L⟨e⟩~a~ Fleur∧   48 left ⟨?it⟩~th~e Letter 49–50 & ⟨pres⟩ be back . . . minutes   52 ⟨?and⟩~He~ told ⟨?me⟩~t~he whole

was; and only added, that if Monsieur had forgot (*par hazard*) to answer Madame's letter, the arrangement gave him an opportunity to recover the *faux pas*—and if not, that things were only as 55 they were.

Now I was not altogether sure of my *etiquette*, whether I ought to have wrote or no; but if I had—a devil himself could not have been angry: 'twas but the officious zeal of a well-meaning creature for my honour; and however he might have mistook the road—or em- 60 barrassed me in so doing—his heart was in no fault—I was under no necessity to write—and what weighed more than all—he did not look as if he had done amiss.

—'Tis all very well, La Fleur, said I.—'Twas sufficient. La Fleur flew out of the room like lightening, and return'd with pen, 65 ink, and paper, in his hand; and coming up to the table, laid them close before me, with such a delight in his countenance, that I could not help taking up the pen.

I begun and begun again; and though I had nothing to say, and that nothing might have been express'd in half a dozen lines, I 70 made half a dozen different beginnings, and could no way please myself.

In short, I was in no mood to write.

La Fleur stepp'd out and brought a little water in a glass to dilute my ink—then fetch'd sand and seal-wax—It was all one: 75 I wrote, and blotted, and tore off, and burnt, and wrote again— *Le Diable l'emporte!* said I half to myself—I cannot write this self-same letter; throwing the pen down despairingly as I said it.

---

54 gave ⟨?a [illegible word deleted]⟩~him~ an⟨d⟩ [*M1:* "gave an"]　　59 angry:·
angry· *A1,* angry: *S1* [see App. D, p. 317, n. 5]　　61 ∧me∧　　61 — ⟨besides⟩
I was　　63 ∧done∧　　64 sufficient.] sufficient:　　69–70 & ⟨?no⟩~th~at
nothing　　70 lines, ⟨Yet⟩ I [*M1:* u.v.]　　73 ⟨In Short⟩ ∧In Short∧
73 write, ⟨except to Eliza—⟩ [*M1:* u.v.]　　77 myself—] myself.—　　78 pen
. . . it] ⟨pen down as I said it⟩ [This canceled reading appears upside down at the
bottom of fol. 127ᵛ of *S1;* fol. 127 begins with "pen . . . it", l. 78, above (see p.
82.74–76*tn,* above).]

As soon as I had cast down the pen, La Fleur advanced with the
80 most respectful carriage up to the table, and making a thousand
apologies for the liberty he was going to take, told me he had a
letter in his pocket wrote by a drummer in his regiment to a corporal's wife, which, he durst say, would suit the occasion.

I had a mind to let the poor fellow have his humour—Then
85 prithee, said I, let me see it.

La Fleur instantly pull'd out a little dirty pocket-book cramm'd
full of small letters and billet-doux in a sad condition, and laying
it upon the table, and then untying the string which held them all
together, run them over one by one, till he came to the letter in
90 question—*La voila!* said he, clapping his hands: so unfolding it
first, he laid it before me, and retired three steps from the table
whilst I read it.

---

79 ∧had∧   81 ∧he∧ had   90 hands; ⟨together— ?then⟩ so   91 me ⟨on
the table⟩, and

THE LETTER.

MADAME,

JE suis penetré de la douleur la plus vive, et reduit en même
temps au desespoir par ce retour imprevû du Corporal qui rend
notre entrevue de ce soir la chose du monde la plus impossible.

Mais vive la joie! et toute la mienne sera de penser a vous.   *5*

L'amour n'est *rien* sans sentiment.

Et le sentiment est encore *moins* sans amour.

On dit qu'on ne doit jamais se desesperer.

On dit aussi que Monsieur le Corporal monte la garde Mecredi:
alors ce sera mon tour.   *10*

  Chacun a son tour.

En attendant—Vive l'amour! et vive la bagatelle!

   Je suis, MADAME,
  Avec toutes les sentiments les plus respecteux
   et les plus tendres tout a vous,   *15*

     JAQUES ROQUE.

It was but changing the Corporal into the Count—and saying
nothing about mounting guard on Wednesday—and the letter

---

12 VetV 12 Bagatelle! ⟨Vive le Roi.⟩ [*M1:* u.v.] 13 MADAME] Madame
[elsewhere, small caps. in *A1* are indicated in *S1* with two underlines] 17 It]
[*S1:* no par.] 18 guard] gard⟨?e⟩

---

6. *L'amour . . . sentiment.*] This sentence appears in *Letters,* No. 148,
quoted pp. 128.17–25*n*, above.
 13. *vive la bagatelle!*] Cf. the use of this phrase in *TS,* 1.19.53.

was neither right or wrong—so to gratify the poor fellow, who
20 stood trembling for my honour, his own, and the honour of his
letter,—I took the cream gently off it, and whipping it up in my
own way—I seal'd it up and sent him with it to Madame de L***
—and the next morning we pursued our journey to Paris.

---

19 was neither ⟨was neither⟩ right   19 wrong—] wrong.—   20–21 ∧his
own . . . Letter∧   22 him ⟨?her⟩ with

PARIS.

WHEN a man can contest the point by dint of equipage, and carry all on floundering before him with half a dozen lackies and a couple of cooks—'tis very well in such a place as Paris—he may drive in at which end of a street he will.

A poor prince who is weak in cavalry, and whose whole infantry 5 does not exceed a single man, had best quit the field; and signalize himself in the cabinet, if he can get up into it—I say *up into it*—for there is no descending perpendicular amongst 'em with a *"Me voici! mes enfans"*—here I am—whatever many may think.

I own my first sensations, as soon as I was left solitary and alone 10 in my own chamber in the hotel, were far from being so flattering as I had prefigured them. I walked up gravely to the window in my

---

4 in⟨?to⟩ ∧at∧   6 man ⟨?had [illegible word deleted]⟩ ∧had best∧   9 ∧—here I am∧   10 I own [*S1:* no par.]   12 ∧pre-∧ -figured [Sterne initially wrote "figured"]

1–4. *When . . . will.*] probably an allusion to the narrowness and congestion of the Paris streets (on which many English travelers commented: see p. 175.22–27*n*, below), and to the advantage of having running footmen clear the way for one's carriage. Yorick may also be implying here that a man can make his way into society "by dint of equipage": see the next note.

5–9. *A poor prince . . . think.*] As Vrooman observes (pp. 156–157), an English traveler who wished to gain entrée to the Paris *haut monde* could, if he was wealthy, try to make his way socially by dint of a lavish display of equipage and servants (see Mead, pp. 60–61, 220; and the comments in *Spectator* No. 15 [I, 66] on the French love of "Splendid Equipages"). A "poor prince" like Yorick, who has only La Fleur for "infantry," could try to "signalize himself" in the drawing rooms and salons by virtue of his wit and charm, if he could obtain the necessary introductions. But as Yorick remarks in his critique of the Grand Tour in his sermon on the Prodigal Son, "company which is really good, is very rare——and very shy," and Englishmen were frequently disappointed in their hopes of meeting persons of cultivation and social distinction (see App. E, p. 330, note to Preface, pp. 78–85). Sterne's literary reputation and his connections gained him immediate access to the fashionable *cabinets* of Paris: see p. 261.4–7*n*, below.

dusty black coat, and looking through the glass saw all the world in
yellow, blue, and green, running at the ring of pleasure.—The old
15 with broken lances, and in helmets which had lost their vizards—
the young in armour bright which shone like gold, beplumed with
each gay feather of the east—all—all tilting at it like fascinated
knights in tournaments of yore for fame and love.—

Alas, poor Yorick! cried I, what art thou doing here? On the
20 very first onset of all this glittering clatter, thou art reduced to an

---

15–16 vizards ∧⟨—in yellow ?tau⟩∧ —the   18 love.—] love—   19 Alas]
—Alass   19 ∧cried I∧

---

14. *running at the ring of pleasure*] *running at the ring:* a chivalric exercise in which a rider attempted to pass the point of his lance through a suspended ring (*OED*). *ring of pleasure:* "ring" is a slang term for the female
pudendum; see J. S. Farmer and W. E. Henley, *Slang and Its Analogues,*
VI (1903), 32, which cites the use of the word in this sense in Rabelais, III,
xxviii (Everyman ed., I, 360), ref. to "the ring of thy wife's commodity." In
Rabelais, II, i (Everyman ed., I, 142), there is a description of men who "did
swell in length by the member, which they call the labourer of nature, in such
sort that it grew marvellous long . . . [and] if it happened the aforesaid
member to be in good case, spooming with a full sail, bunt fair before the wind,
then to have seen those strouting champions, you would have taken them for
men that had their lances settled on their rest, to run at the ring . . ."
Tristram describes the peasants with whom he dances in Languedoc as
"running at the ring of pleasure" (*TS,* 7.43.537).

14–15. *The old . . . vizards*] Cf. Sterne's assurance to William Combe
that, if Combe is having difficulties in a love affair, "I'll put off my Cassoc &
turn Knight Errant for you, & say the kindest things of you to Dulcinea that
Dulcinea ever heard—if she has a Champion—and ⟨if⟩ words will not atchieve
it—Ill enter the Lists with him and break a spear in your behalf; tho by the
by, mine is half rusty, and should be hung up in the old family hall amongst
Pistols without Cocks, and Helmets which have lost their Vizards" (*Letters,*
No. 177, [? Jan. 1767], p. 294). In referring to helmets which have lost their
vizards, Sterne may be thinking of the helmet with which Don Quixote first
sallies forth: part of a suit of rusty armor which had belonged to his great-
grandfather, it has lost its vizor and he has to contrive one out of pasteboard
(*Don Quixote,* 1.1.1.4–5). (The barber's basin Don Quixote mistakes for
Mambrino's helmet also lacks a vizor; see *Don Quixote,* 1.3.7.142–143.)

19. *Alas, poor Yorick!*] Hamlet's address to Yorick's skull (V.i.179–180);
at the behest of Eugenius (for whom see p. 164.65*n,* below), it is inscribed on

atom—seek—seek some winding alley, with a tourniquet at the end of it, where chariot never rolled or flambeau shot its rays— there thou mayest solace thy soul in converse sweet with some kind *grisset* of a barber's wife, and get into such coteries!—

—May I perish! if I do, said I, pulling out the letter which I had 25 to present to Madame de R***.—I'll wait upon this lady, the very first thing I do. So I called La Fleur to go seek me a barber directly —and come back and brush my coat.

---

24 ⟨?her⟩~such~   25 — ⟨I'll be shot⟩ ∧May I perish!∧   25–26 which ⟨Madame de Lxxx had ?adressed to me⟩ ∧⟨given me to⟩∧ ∧I had to∧ present / ⟨myself⟩ to   27 a ⟨g⟩ barbar   28 back / ⟨back⟩ and

---

Yorick's gravestone as "his epitaph and elegy" in *Tristram Shandy* (1.12.32). It is quoted also in the *Journal*, 29–30 May, p. 346.

21. *a tourniquet*] a turnstile, preventing the passage of vehicles.

THE WIG.
PARIS.

WHEN the barber came, he absolutely refused to have any thing to do with my wig: 'twas either above or below his art: I had nothing to do, but to take one ready made of his own recommendation.

5 —But I fear, friend! said I, this buckle won't stand.—You may immerge it, replied he, into the ocean, and it will stand—

---

5 You ⟨?shall⟩ ∧may∧   6 Ocean. / ∧& ∧∧it∧∧ will stand—∧ [∧∧ ∧∧ = insertion within insertion]

THE WIG. PARIS.] On entering Paris. Tristram remarks that one might suppose all the barbers in the world had congregated there in the belief that, since *"the periwig maketh the man,* and the periwig-maker maketh the periwig,"* they would outrank everyone in the city (*TS*, 7.17.499). Before leaving London on his second trip to France, Sterne wrote Robert Foley, his banker in Paris: "It is a terrible thing to be in Paris without a perriwig to a man's head! In seven days from the date of this, I should be in that case, unless you tell your neighbour Madame Requiere to get her *bon mari de me faire une peruque à bourse, au mieux—c'est à dire—une la plus extraordinaire—la plus jolie—la plus gentille—et la plus— —Mais qu'importe? j'ai l'honneur d'être grand critique—et bien difficile encore dans les affaires de peruques"* (*Letters*, No. 151, Oct. 1765, p. 260).

Smollett observed sourly that "when an Englishman comes to Paris, he cannot appear until he has undergone a total metamorphosis. At his first arrival, he finds it necessary to send for the taylor, peruquier, hatter, shoemaker . . . The good man, who used to wear the *beau drap d'Angleterre,* quite plain all the year round, with a long bob, or tye perriwig, must here provide himself with a camblet suit trimmed with silver for spring and autumn, with silk cloaths for summer, and cloth laced with gold, or velvet for winter; and he must wear his bag-wig *a la pigeon* [i.e., arranged in "wings" on each side]. . . . Since it is so much the humour of the English at present to run abroad, I wish they had antigallican spirit enough to produce themselves in their own genuine English dress, and treat the French modes with the same philosophical contempt, which was shewn by an honest gentleman, distinguished by the name of Wig-Middleton. That unshaken patriot still appears in the same kind of scratch perriwig [a small, short wig], skimming-dish hat,

158

What a great scale is every thing upon in this city! thought I—
The utmost stretch of an English periwig-maker's ideas could have
gone no further than to have "dipped it into a pail of water"—
What difference! 'tis like time to eternity.   10

I confess I do hate all cold conceptions, as I do the puny ideas
which engender them; and am generally so struck with the great
works of nature, that for my own part, if I could help it, I never
would make a comparison less than a mountain at least. All that
can be said against the French sublime in this instance of it, is this 15
—that the grandeur is *more* in the *word*; and *less* in the *thing*.
No doubt the ocean fills the mind with vast ideas; but Paris being
so far inland, it was not likely I should run post a hundred miles
out of it, to try the experiment—the Parisian barber meant nothing.—   20

The pail of water standing besides the great deep, makes certainly but a sorry figure in speech—but 'twill be said—it has one
advantage—'tis in the next room, and the truth of the buckle
may be tried in it without more ado, in a single moment.

In honest truth, and upon a more candid revision of the matter, 25
The French expression professes more than it performs.

7–10 I.— ⟨an en-⟩ / ∧the utmost Stretch of an∧ ⟨-⟩~en~glish pery-wig makerⱽ'sⱽ
∧Ideas∧ ⟨w⟩~c~ould have // ⟨only⟩ ∧⟨have⟩ gone no further than to have∧ —"⟨You⟩
dipd it, into a pail of water"— ⟨Heavens!⟩ ∧—what difference!∧ 'tis [Sterne apparently wrote initially: "an english pery-wig maker would have only dipd it, into
a pail of water"; the sequence of the other revisions is unclear.]   11 ∧do∧ hate
14–15 least. ⟨Now I am confident,⟩ ∧⟨that⟩∧ All that can ⟨possibly⟩ be   18 should
⟨go⟩ ∧run∧   19–20 nothing.—] nothing—   21–22 ∧certainly∧   25 In]—in

---

and slit sleeve, which were worn five-and-twenty years ago, and has invariably persisted in this garb, in defiance of all the revolutions of the mode"
(*Travels,* Letter No. 6, pp. 52–54). Curtis notes (*Letters,* No. 151, p. 260, n. 2)
that even Dr. Johnson procured a Paris-made wig while traveling in France.
    23. *buckle*] curl of the wig.
    25–26. *In . . . performs.*] During his first visit to Paris, Sterne wrote Gar-
rick: "I hear no news of you, or your *empire,* I would have said *kingdom*—but
here every thing is hyperbolized—and if a woman is but simply pleased —'tis
Je suis charmée—and if she is charmed 'tis nothing less, than that she is

I think I can see the precise and distinguishing marks of national characters more in these nonsensical *minutiæ*, than in the most important matters of state; where great men of all nations
30 talk and stalk so much alike, that I would not give nine-pence to chuse amongst them.

I was so long in getting from under my barber's hands, that it was too late to think of going with my letter to Madame R*** that night: but when a man is once dressed at all points for going out,
35 his reflections turn to little account, so taking down the name of the Hotel de Modene where I lodged, I walked forth without any determination where to go—I shall consider of that, said I, as I walk along.

---

29 important ⟨of⟩ matters of   30 ⟨I⟩∼t∼hat I   33 to think] of thinking *A1*,
to think *S1*

---

ravi-sh'd—and when ravi-shd, (which may happen) there is nothing left for her but to fly to the other world for a metaphor, and swear, qu'elle etoit toute *extasiée*—which mode of speaking, is . . . here creeping into use, and there is scarce a woman who understands the *bon ton,* but is seven times in a day in a downright exstasy—that is, the devil's in her—by a small mistake of one world for the other—" (*Letters,* No. 87, April 1762, pp. 161–162).

27–31. *I think . . . them.*] Cf. *Sermons,* II, 116 (V.iv): "I would sooner form a judgment of a man's temper from his behaviour on such little occurrences of life, . . . than from the more weighed and important actions, where a man is more upon his guard;—has more preparation to disguise the true disposition of his heart,—and more temptation when disguised to impose it on others.—" Cf. also the quotation from *Tristram Shandy,* p. 162.27–29*n,* below.

36. *Hotel de Modene*] in the Rue Jacob: see map facing p. 162, below. (See Poole [p. 121.8*n,* above], "Sterne at Paris and Versailles," *London Magazine and Review,* March 1825, pp. 388–392; and *Letters,* p. 261, n. 1.)

THE PULSE.
PARIS.

HAIL ye small sweet courtesies of life, for smooth do ye make
the road of it! like grace and beauty which beget inclinations
to love at first sight; 'tis ye who open this door and let the stranger
in.

—Pray, Madame, said I, have the goodness to tell me which way 5
I must turn to go to the Opera comique:—Most willingly, Monsieur, said she, laying aside her work—

I had given a cast with my eye into half a dozen shops as I came
along in search of a face not likely to be disordered by such an
interruption; till at last, this hitting my fancy, I had walked in. 10

She was working a pair of ruffles as she sat in a low chair on the
far side of the shop facing the door—

—*Tres volentieres*; most willingly, said she, laying her work down
upon a chair next her, and rising up from the low chair she was
sitting in, with so chearful a movement and so chearful a look, 15
that had I been laying out fifty louis d'ors with her, I should have
said—"This woman is grateful."

---

3 sight;] sight,　　8–9 ∧as I ⟨had⟩ c⟨o⟩~a~me along∧　　13 —*Tres*] [*S1:* no
par.]　　16 ∧had∧

---

6. *Opera comique*] On 3 Feb. 1762, soon after Sterne reached Paris on his
first trip abroad (see p. 192.7–8*n*, below), the new Comédie Italienne, popularly called the Opéra Comique, opened at the Hôtel de Bourgogne in the Rue
Mauconseil (see map facing p. 162, below). This company had been formed
through a merger of the Opéra Comique, which had presented a mixture of
comedy, song, and vaudeville, with the impoverished Comédiens Italiens,
which had presented comic operas. The merged companies performed comic
operas and were an immediate success. On 19 March 1762 Sterne wrote
Garrick: "the whole City of Paris is *bewitch'd* with the comic opera" (*Letters*,
No. 85, Paris, p. 157; see p. 158, n. 4, and *Life*, p. 389).

You must turn, Monsieur, said she, going with me to the door
of the shop, and pointing the way down the street I was to take—
20 you must turn first to your left hand—*mais prenez guarde*—there
are two turns; and be so good as to take the second—then go down
a little way and you'll see a church, and when you are past it, give
yourself the trouble to turn directly to the right, and that will lead
you to the foot of the *pont neuf*, which you must cross—and there,
25 any one will do himself the pleasure to shew you—

She repeated her instructions three times over to me with the
same good natur'd patience the third time as the first;—and if
tones and manners have a meaning, which certainly they have,
unless to hearts which shut them out—she seem'd really interested,
30 that I should not lose myself.

25-26 You— [par.] ⟨She seem'd interested that I should not lose myself—⟩ [par.]
She repeated [cf. "she . . . myself." (ll. 29-30, below)]   27 ∧the 3ᵈ time as
⟨?S⟩~t~he first∧

18-24. *You must turn . . . pont neuf*] Although Poole claims that he located the Hôtel de Modène, in the Rue Jacob, by following the "exact in-
verse" of the *grisette's* "minute directions" (*op. cit.*, p. 160.36*n*, above,
p. 389), I have been unable to determine with any certainty the route she
pointed out to Yorick, and Sterne may not have had an actual route in mind.
However, her directions can be tentatively reconstructed as follows (see the
map facing this page) : if we assume that her shop, like the Hôtel de Modène,
was in the Rue Jacob and that she pointed down the Rue Jacob toward the
Rue du Colombier, she directed Yorick to walk along the Rue Jacob, past
the first left turn, at the Rue des Petits Augustins, and into the Rue du
Colombier. He would have proceeded along the Rue du Colombier and have
taken the second left turn, into the Rue de l'Echaudé, which would have led
him into the Rue de Seine. The Rue de Seine would have taken him past the
Chapelle du Collège des Quatre Nations, possibly the church she mentions,
to the Quai des Quatre Nations. By turning directly to the right and walking
along the Seine, he would have reached the foot of the Pont Neuf via the
Quai de Conti, along which he walked in his "return home" to the Hôtel de
Modène (see p. 187.4-5, below).
   27-29. *if . . . out*] Cf. *Sermons*, II, 239-240 (VII.xvi) : "in the present
state we are in, we find such a strong sympathy and union between our souls
and bodies, that the one cannot be touched or sensibly affected, without pro-
ducing some corresponding emotion in the other.—Nature has assigned a
different look, tone of voice, and gesture, peculiar to every passion and

I will not suppose it was the woman's beauty, notwithstanding she was the handsomest grisset, I think, I ever saw, which had much to do with the sense I had of her courtesy; only I remember, when I told her how much I was obliged to her, that I looked very full in her eyes,—and that I repeated my thanks as often as she had 35 done her instructions.

I had not got ten paces from the door, before I found I had forgot every tittle of what she had said—so looking back, and seeing her still standing in the door of the shop as if to look whether I went right or not—I returned back, to ask her whether the first turn was 40 to my right or left—for that I had absolutely forgot.—Is it possible! said she, half laughing.—'Tis very possible, replied I, when a man is thinking more of a woman, than of her good advice.

As this was the real truth—she took it, as every woman takes a matter of right, with a slight courtesy. 45

—*Attendez!* said she, laying her hand upon my arm to detain me, whilst she called a lad out of the back-shop to get ready a parcel of

---

31 ∧it was∧   33–34 remember ⟨?t⟩~ w~hen   38 of ⟨em⟩ ∧what . . . said∧
38 ∧her∧   40 not] no   40 right or no—I ⟨?went [illegible word deleted]
?to ?her ?again⟩~return'd ⟨up to ?her⟩~ ∧back∧ / to ask her [*M1:* "return'd up to her"]   42 ∧half-laughing∧   43 advice.] advice—   44 ⟨Now⟩ as this
46 —*Attendez!*] —*attendez*—   46 ∧my∧   47 ready ⟨the⟩ ∧a∧ [*M1:* u.v.]

---

affection we are subject to; and, therefore, to argue against this strict correspondence which is held between our souls and bodies,—is disputing against the frame and mechanism of human nature.—We are not angels, but men cloathed with bodies, and, in some measure, governed by our imaginations, that we have need of all these external helps which nature has made the interpreters of our thoughts."

Cf. also Walter Shandy's opinion that "There is . . . a certain mien and motion of the body and all its parts, both in acting and speaking, which argues a man *well within* . . . There are a thousand unnoticed openings . . . which let a penetrating eye at once into a man's soul; and I maintain it . . . that a man of sense does not lay down his hat in coming into a room,—or take it up in going out of it, but something escapes, which discovers him" (*TS*, 6.5.414–415).

gloves. I am just going to send him, said she, with a packet into that quarter, and if you will have the complaisance to step in, it will
50 be ready in a moment, and he shall attend you to the place.—So I walk'd in with her to the far side of the shop, and taking up the ruffle in my hand which she laid upon the chair, as if I had a mind to sit, she sat down herself in her low chair, and I instantly sat myself down besides her.

55 —He will be ready, Monsieur, said she, in a moment—And in that moment, replied I, most willingly would I say something very civil to you for all these courtesies. Any one may do a casual act of good nature, but a continuation of them shews it is a part of the temperature; and certainly, added I, if it is the same blood which
60 comes from the heart, which descends to the extremes (touching her wrist) I am sure you must have one of the best pulses of any woman in the world—Feel it, said she, holding out her arm. So laying down my hat, I took hold of her fingers in one hand, and applied the two fore-fingers of my other to the artery—

65 —Would to heaven! my dear Eugenius, thou hadst passed by, and beheld me sitting in my black coat, and in my lack-a-day-sical

---

48 gloves.] gloves— 52 ∧in my hand∧ 52–53 chair ⟨besides her⟩, as if I / ⟨to sit down; She⟩ had a mind to sit, She sat down [The process of revision here is unclear. Sterne may have originally written "as if to sit down"; then changed this to "as if She had a mind to sit"; and then changed this to "as if I had a mind to sit", by canceling "She" and inserting "I" at the end of the line.] 55–56 — ⟨?in⟩~ and~ in that 56–57 ⟨ci⟩~v~ery civil to you ∧⟨on my part⟩∧ for 57 courtesies. Any] courtesies: any 58 part of the] part the 59 ∧it is∧ 61 wrist) ⟨I will be bold to say,⟩ ∧I am sure∧ You ∧must∧ have 61–62 ∧of any woman∧ 62–63 so ⟨?I⟩ lay⟨?d⟩~ing~ 66 and beheld] & ∧hadst∧ beheld

---

65. *Eugenius*] John Hall-Stevenson (1718–1785), one of Sterne's closest friends. They became acquainted in 1735–1736, as students at Jesus College, Cambridge. In the 1740's, Hall-Stevenson established himself at the family seat at Skelton Castle, Yorkshire, which he nicknamed Crazy Castle. There he entertained a group of Rabelaisian fellow-wits, including Sterne, who called themselves the Demoniacs.

Hall-Stevenson also appears as Eugenius in *Tristram Shandy,* in the role of a sympathetic friend, discreet adviser, and fellow-wit who shares the Shandean

manner, counting the throbs of it, one by one, with as much true devotion as if I had been watching the critical ebb or flow of her fever—How wouldst thou have laugh'd and moralized upon my new profession?—and thou shouldst have laugh'd and moralized 70 on—Trust me, my dear Eugenius, I should have said, "there are worse occupations in this world *than feeling a woman's pulse.*"— But a Grisset's! thou wouldst have said—and in an open shop! Yorick—

—So much the better: for when my views are direct, Eugenius, 75 I care not if all the world saw me feel it.

67–68 much ⟨attention⟩ ∧true Devotion∧   68 ∧been∧   69–70 upon ⟨?it ?⟩
⟨my ?new ?position —⟩ ∧my∧ new profession?—   71 m⟨y⟩~e~

---

view of life (see esp. the account of Yorick's death in *TS*, 1.12.27–32). Work suggests that "Sterne probably chose the name Eugenius because of its Latin signification: well-born, noble, generous" (*TS*, p. 28*n*). (For detailed information on Hall-Stevenson, see *Life* and *Letters*.)

A bawdy sequel to *A Sentimental Journey* entitled *Yorick's Sentimental Journey Continued by Eugenius* (London, 1769) has usually been attributed to Hall-Stevenson. Karl F. Thompson has argued, however, that Hall-Stevenson may not have been the author (*Notes & Queries*, CXCV [1950], 318–319).

68. *ebb or flow*] See p. 70.6*n*, above.

70. *new profession*] Yorick's "old" profession is, of course, that of clergyman.

THE HUSBAND.
PARIS.

I HAD counted twenty pulsations, and was going on fast towards the fortieth, when her husband coming unexpected from a back parlour into the shop, put me a little out in my reckoning—'Twas no body but her husband, she said—so I began a fresh score—
5 Monsieur is so good, quoth she, as he pass'd by us, as to give himself the trouble of feeling my pulse—The husband took off his hat, and making me a bow, said, I did him too much honour—and having said that, he put on his hat and walk'd out.

Good God! said I to myself, as he went out—and can this man be
10 the husband of this woman?

Let it not torment the few who know what must have been the grounds of this exclamation, if I explain it to those who do not.

In London a shopkeeper and a shopkeeper's wife seem to be one bone and one flesh: in the several endowments of mind and body,
15 sometimes the one, sometimes the other has it, so as in general to be upon a par, and to tally with each other as nearly as man and wife need to do.

In Paris, there are scarce two orders of beings more different: for the legislative and executive powers of the shop not resting in
20 the husband, he seldom comes there—in some dark and dismal room behind, he sits commerceless in his thrum night-cap, the same rough son of Nature that Nature left him.

The genius of a people where nothing but the monarchy is *salique,* having ceded this department, with sundry others, totally

---

3 ∧a little∧   3–4 ∧twas . . . said∧   5 ∧as he . . . us∧   5 to] to /
to   6 ⟨?pull⟩~to~ok   9 Good] [*S1:* no par.]   13 ∧be∧   15 ∧it∧
16 ∧to∧ tally

23–24. *is salique*] observes the Salic law, "orig., the alleged fundamental law of the French monarchy, by which females were excluded from succession

to the women—by a continual higgling with customers of all ranks 25
and sizes from morning to night, like so many rough pebbles shook
long together in a bag, by amicable collisions, they have worn down
their asperities and sharp angles, and not only become round and
smooth, but will receive, some of them, a polish like a brilliant—
Monsieur *le Mari* is little better than the stone under your foot— 30

—Surely—surely man! it is not good for thee to sit alone—thou
wast made for social intercourse and gentle greetings, and this
improvement of our natures from it, I appeal to, as my evidence.

—And how does it beat, Monsieur? said she.—With all the
benignity, said I, looking quietly in her eyes, that I expected—She 35
was going to say something civil in return—but the lad came into
the shop with the gloves—*A propos*, said I; I want a couple of pair
myself.

24–25 department, ⟨totally to⟩ with . . . totally to the Wom⟨?a⟩~e~n,—by ⟨their⟩
∧a∧   27–28 ∧by amicable collisions∧ . . . angles, ⟨by amicable ?collis⟩, and
29 them] 'em   32 and ⟨friendly⟩ // [gentle] [The upper left-hand corner of fol.
148 of *S1* has been torn off; as a result, "gentle" is missing ("gentle" is the first word
on fol. 148 of *M1*).]   35 I ⟨?fore⟩ expected   36 was ⟨?just ?going ∧begin-
ning to∧ [three or four illegible words deleted]⟩~going . . . civil~   36 ⟨?boy⟩~
Lad~   37 gloves— ⟨so I took up my hat, & thank'd her.⟩ apropos
37–38 pair ⟨of⟩ myself

---

to the crown; hence *gen.*, a law excluding females from dynastic succession.
In this sense often *Salique*" (*OED*).

    26–29. *like so . . . brilliant*] See pp. 232.34–42*n*, below.

    31. *man! . . . alone*] paraphrased from Genesis 2:18: "And the Lord
God said, It is not good that the man should be alone; I will make him an help
meet for him." See *Sermons*, I, 207–208, quoted p. 237.8–11*n*, below.

THE GLOVES.
PARIS.

THE beautiful Grisset rose up when I said this, and going behind the counter, reach'd down a parcel and untied it: I advanced to the side over-against her: they were all too large. The beautiful Grisset measured them one by one across my hand—It
5 would not alter the dimensions—She begg'd I would try a single pair, which seemed to be the least—She held it open—my hand slipp'd into it at once—It will not do, said I, shaking my head a little—No, said she, doing the same thing.

There are certain combined looks of simple subtlety—where
10 whim, and sense, and seriousness, and nonsense, are so blended, that all the languages of Babel set loose together could not express them—they are communicated and caught so instantaneously, that you can scarce say which party is the infecter. I leave it to your men of words to swell pages about it—it is enough in the present to say
15 again, the gloves would not do; so folding our hands within our arms, we both loll'd upon the counter—it was narrow, and there was just room for the parcel to lay between us.

The beautiful Grisset look'd sometimes at the gloves, then sideways to the window, then at the gloves—and then at me. I was not
20 disposed to break silence—I follow'd her example: so I look'd at the gloves, then to the window, then at the gloves, and then at her —and so on alternately.

I found I lost considerably in every attack—she had a quick black eye, and shot through two such long and silken eye-lashes

---

5 ∧I would try∧   6 ∧to be∧   7 ∧at once∧   11 ⟨?tongu⟩~la~nguages
13 which ⟨is⟩ party is   14 ∧about it∧   14–15 ∧to say again∧   16 both
⟨leand⟩∧loll'd∧   17 us.] us.—   19 ⟨?at⟩~to~∧the∧ Window   19 me.]
me: 20 I ⟨could only⟩ follow∨'d∨   23–24 a ⟨?b⟩ quick black

9–14. *There . . . about it*] Cf. the passages quoted from the *Sermons* and from *Tristram Shandy*, p. 162.27–29*n*, above.

with such penetration, that she look'd into my very heart and reins 25
—It may seem strange, but I could actually feel she did—

—It is no matter, said I, taking up a couple of the pairs next me,
and putting them into my pocket.

I was sensible the beautiful Grisset had not ask'd above a single
livre above the price—I wish'd she had ask'd a livre more, and was 30
puzzling my brains how to bring the matter about—Do you think,
my dear Sir, said she, mistaking my embarrassment, that I could
ask a *sous* too much of a stranger—and of a stranger whose politeness, more than his want of gloves, has done me the honour to lay
himself at my mercy?—*M'en croyez capable?*—Faith! not I, said I; 35
and if you were, you are welcome—So counting the money into her
hand, and with a lower bow than one generally makes to a shopkeeper's wife, I went out, and her lad with his parcel followed me.

---

25 ⟨?she⟩∼tha∼t she   27 couple of ∧the∧ pair∨s∨   30 livre ⟨to⟩ above
["⟨to⟩": Sterne may have started to write "too much"]   30 ask'd ⟨a⟩ a
32 embarrassment,] embarrassment—   33 and of ⟨one⟩ a / ∧stranger∧ whose
34-35 to ⟨?buy⟩∼lay∼ / ⟨?them ?⟩ ∧himself at my mercy—∧ m'en c∧r∧oyez capable ⟨!⟩∼?∼ [Sterne apparently wrote initially: "to buy them? m'en coyez capable!";
"∧r∧" in "c∧r∧oyez" is in pencil; *M1*: "coyez"]   36 w⟨?as⟩∼ere∼   37 hand
⟨& giving it, something betwixt a shake and a squeeze, ∧as I did it∧ —We both re-
turnd our thanks together⟩, & with   37 than ⟨ever⟩ one   38 parcel
⟨under his⟩ followed

23-26. *I found . . . did*—] Cf. Tristram's description of the Widow Wadman's eye and of its effect on Uncle Toby (*TS*, 8.24-25.576-578).

29-36. *I was . . . welcome*] French shopkeepers were encouraged by the
extravagance of many English travelers to overcharge them. Cf. Yorick's
conversation with the fair *grisette*, with Smollett's exasperation as a Simple
Traveller (see p. 80.43-53*n*, above): "I must tell you, that the most repu-
table shop-keepers and tradesmen of Paris think it no disgrace to practise the
most shameful imposition. I myself know an instance of one of the most
creditable *marchands* in this capital, who demanded six francs an ell for some
lutestring laying his hand upon his breast at the same time, and declaring
en conscience, that it had cost him within three sols of the money. Yet in, less
than three minutes, he sold it for four and a half, and when the buyer up-
braided him with his former declaration, he shrugged up his shoulders, saying, *il faut marchander*. . . . The same mean disingenuity is universal all
over France, as I have been informed by several persons of veracity" (*Travels*,
Letter No. 6, p. 54).

THE TRANSLATION.
PARIS.

THERE was no body in the box I was let into but a kindly old French officer. I love the character, not only because I honour the man whose manners are softened by a profession which makes bad men worse; but that I once knew one—for he is no more—and 5 why should I not rescue one page from violation by writing his name in it, and telling the world it was Captain Tobias Shandy, the dearest of my flock and friends, whose philanthropy I never think of at this long distance from his death—but my eyes gush out with tears. For his sake, I have a predilection for the whole corps of

---

1 box] Loge   2 not] v&v not   5 violation ∧⟨?of⟩∧ by

2–9. *I love . . . Captain Tobias Shandy . . . tears.*] Uncle Toby's innocent benevolence and amiable whimsicality were almost universally admired and praised by Sterne's contemporaries. By invoking Toby's name, Sterne could "rescue one page" of Yorick's *Journey* from "violation" by those who had attacked his writings as immoral, indecent, and impious (see Howes, pp. 25–29; and pp. 5–10, above). In a similar manner, Tristram provides a blank page on which the reader can depict the "concupiscible" Widow Wadman according to his own fancy, and exclaims: "Thrice happy book! thou wilt have one page, at least, . . . which MALICE will not blacken, and which IGNORANCE cannot misrepresent" (*TS*, 6.37–38.469–472).

In his "apologetical oration" for his profession as a soldier, Toby defends war when it is fought on philanthropic principles, and answers Parson Yorick's assertion in his funeral sermon for Le Fever, "*That so soft and gentle a creature, born to love, to mercy, and kindness, as man is, was not shaped for* [war]"; Tristram publishes this oration because it "shews so sweet a temperament of gallantry and good principles" in Toby (see *TS*, 6.31–32.459–462).

In calling Toby "the dearest of my flock and friends" (ll. 6–7, above), Yorick speaks as Parson Yorick, in whose parish Shandy Hall is located. But in referring to "this long distance" from Toby's death (l. 8, above), Yorick speaks as the Sentimental Traveller, whose *Journey* takes place in 1762; in *Tristram Shandy*, Parson Yorick dies in 1748 (see p. 192.7–8n, below). The date of Toby's death is not specified in *Tristram Shandy*, although Tristram anticipates "that future and dreaded page" on which he will have to describe the funeral of "the first—the foremost of created beings" (*TS*, 6.25.452).

veterans; and so I strode over the two back rows of benches, and *10*
placed myself beside him.

The old officer was reading attentively a small pamphlet, it
might be the book of the opera, with a large pair of spectacles. As
soon as I sat down, he took his spectacles off, and putting them
into a shagreen case, return'd them and the book into his pocket *15*
together. I half rose up, and made him a bow.

Translate this into any civilized language in the world—the
sense is this:

"Here's a poor stranger come in to the box—he seems as if he
knew no body; and is never likely, was he to be seven years in Paris, *20*
if every man he comes near keeps his spectacles upon his nose—
'tis shutting the door of conversation absolutely in his face—and
using him worse than a German."

The French officer might as well have said it all aloud; and if he
had, I should in course have put the bow I made him into French *25*
too, and told him, "I was sensible of his attention, and return'd him
a thousand thanks for it."

There is not a secret so aiding to the progress of sociality, as to
get master of this *short hand*, and be quick in rendering the several
turns of looks and limbs, with all their inflections and delineations, *30*
into plain words. For my own part, by long habitude, I do it so
mechanically, that when I walk the streets of London, I go translating all the way; and have more than once stood behind in the circle,

---

19 in to the box] into" / "loge   24 said ⟨?a⟩~i~t all aloud   25 ∧I made him∧

---

23. *using . . . German*] At the time of Yorick's *Journey*, the Seven Years
War, in which the French and the Prussians were on opposing sides, was
still in progress; see p. 192.7–8*n*, below.

28–36. *There . . . sworn to.*] For similar comments in the *Sermons* and
Tristram Shandy on the way in which looks and gestures express thoughts
and feelings, see p. 162.27–29*n*, above. When Toby offers to show the Widow
Wadman the place where he was wounded, Tristram "translates" her blushes
"for the sake of the unlearned reader" (*TS*, 9.20.623).

33. *the circle*] the group surrounding a distinguished person at Court, at a
levee, etc.

where not three words have been said, and have brought off twenty
35 different dialogues with me, which I could have fairly wrote down
and sworn to.

I was going one evening to Martini's concert at Milan, and was
just entering the door of the hall, when the Marquesina di F***
was coming out in a sort of a hurry—she was almost upon me be-
40 fore I saw her; so I gave a spring to one side to let her pass—She
had done the same, and on the same side too; so we ran our heads
together: she instantly got to the other side to get out: I was just as
unfortunate as she had been; for I had sprung to that side, and
opposed her passage again—We both flew together to the other
45 side, and then back—and so on—it was ridiculous; we both
blush'd intolerably; so I did at last the thing I should have done at
first—I stood stock still, and the Marquesina had no more difficulty. I had no power to go into the room, till I had made her so

---

34 words have // ⟨words have⟩ been   38 the ⟨Mar⟩ Marquesina   42 ∧to get
out∧   43 had ⟨run⟩ ∧sprung∧

37–70. *I . . . Italy.*] Sterne traveled in Italy in 1765–1766, on his second
trip abroad (see pp. 11–12, above); he stopped at Milan sometime between
15 Nov. and 18 Dec. 1765 (see *Letters,* No. 154, p. 263; No. 156, p. 265).
   If, by the time Sterne wrote this incident, he knew that *A Sentimental
Journey* would be published without the two additional volumes, presumably
of Yorick's journey through Italy, he had promised to his subscribers but did
not live to complete (see App. D, §3), his insertion of this incident in Yorick's
journey through France may have been intended partly as a foretaste of his
travels in Italy, just as Tristram's encounter with Maria was intended as a
kind of "advertisement" for *A Sentimental Journey* (see pp. 13–16, above,
including the anecdote Tristram tells about his experiences in Milan, in *TS,*
9.24.628–629).
   37. *Martini's concert*] probably a ref. to Giovanni Battista Martini (1706–
1784), a famous musician, composer, and musical scholar; however, according to Milic (p. 62, n. 7), Sterne is referring to a theater manager of Milan in
the 1660's and 1670's.
   38. *the Marquesina di F***]* For a discussion of her identity, and of whether
Yorick's encounter with her is based on an actual experience of Sterne's in
Milan, see App. E, pp. 343–344, note to p. 172.38.

much reparation as to wait and follow her with my eye to the end
of the passage—She look'd back twice, and walk'd along it rather 50
side-ways, as if she would make room for any one coming up stairs
to pass her—No, said I—that's a vile translation: the Marquesina
has a right to the best apology I can make her; and that opening is
left for me to do it in—so I ran and begg'd pardon for the embarrassment I had given her, saying it was my intention to have made 55
her way. She answered, she was guided by the same intention
towards me—so we reciprocally thank'd each other. She was at the
top of the stairs; and seeing no *chichesbeo* near her, I begg'd to hand
her to her coach—so we went down the stairs, stopping at every
third step to talk of the concert and the adventure—Upon my 60
word, Madame, said I when I had handed her in, I made six different efforts to let you go out—And I made six efforts, replied she,
to let you enter—I wish to heaven you would make a seventh, said
I—With all my heart, said she, making room—Life is too short to
be long about the forms of it—so I instantly stepp'd in, and she 65
carried me home with her—And what became of the concert, St.
Cecilia, who, I suppose, was at it, knows more than I.

I will only add, that the connection which arose out of that
translation, gave me more pleasure than any one I had the honour
to make in Italy. 70

---

53 apolog⟨ies⟩∼y∼　　54 I ⟨?ran followed⟩ ran　　55 her,— ⟨and added⟩ saying　　57 other. ⟨The Marquesina⟩ She　　58 *chichesbeo*] *chichesbee A1*, Chichesbeo *S1*　　59 her ⟨down⟩ to　　59 down ⟨?s⟩∼t∼he stairs stopping
61 word, Madame, said] word, said　　62 out—And] out.—and　　66 of ⟨Mar-
tini's⟩ ∧the∧ Concert

---

58. *chichesbeo*] On the Italian *cicisbei* and Sharp's and Smollett's attacks on
them, see App. E, pp. 344–345, note to p. 173.58.

66–67. *St. Cecilia*] the patron saint of music. Her festival (22 Nov.) was
annually celebrated in England ca. 1683–ca. 1703, and odes, songs, and
hymns were composed for the occasion. Both Dryden and Pope composed
odes to her.

THE DWARF.

PARIS.

I HAD never heard the remark made by any one in my life, except by one; and who that was, will probably come out in this chapter; so that being pretty much unprepossessed, there must have been grounds for what struck me the moment I cast my eyes
5 over the *parterre*—and that was, the unaccountable sport of nature in forming such numbers of dwarfs—No doubt, she sports at certain times in almost every corner of the world; but in Paris, there is no end to her amusements—The goddess seems almost as merry as she is wise.

10 As I carried my idea out of the *opera comique* with me, I measured every body I saw walking in the streets by it—Melancholy application! especially where the size was extremely little—the face extremely dark—the eyes quick—the nose long—the teeth white—the jaw prominent—to see so many miserables, by force of acci-

---

1 remark made ⟨?th⟩~b~y ["b" is superimposed on what appears to be an "h"; Sterne may have started to write "that"]   1–2 except ∧by∧
6 ⟨?a⟩~n~umber∨s∨   6 ∧no doubt∧   6–7 at certain times . . . world, ⟨at certain times⟩ but   7–8 Paris the∨re∨ ⟨?Goddess⟩~is no~ end . . . The Goddesse ⟨is⟩ ∧seems∧   12 whe⟨?n⟩~re~   13–14 white; ⟨to⟩~——~ the . . . to see

---

1–3. *I . . . chapter*] a ref. to Smollett; see p. 175.22–27*n*, below.

5–8. *the unaccountable sport of nature . . . amusements*] Yorick's observation parallels the view of some of the disputants in the debate about the stranger's nose in Slawkenbergius's Tale, that "there was a just and geometrical arrangement and proportion of the several parts of the human frame to its several destinations, offices, and functions, which could not be transgressed but within certain limits—that nature, though she sported—she sported within a certain circle;—and they could not agree about the diameter of it" (*TS*, IV, 259). See p. 175.19–21*n*, below.

12–18. *the size . . . legs*] This description is adapted from Smollett's *Travels*, Letter No. 30, quoted p. 175.22–27*n*, below: cf. the italicized portion, "*What . . . France*".

dents driven out of their own proper class into the very verge of 15
another, which it gives me pain to write down—every third man a
pigmy!—some by ricketty heads and hump backs—others by
bandy legs—a third set arrested by the hand of Nature in the sixth
and seventh years of their growth—a fourth, in their perfect and
natural state, like dwarf apple-trees; from the first rudiments and 20
stamina of their existence, never meant to grow higher.

A medical traveller might say, 'tis owing to undue bandages—a
splenetic one, to want of air—and an inquisitive traveller, to fortify
the system, may measure the height of their houses—the narrowness of their streets, and in how few feet square in the sixth and 25

14-15 ∧by . . . accidents∧   16-17 down ∧—every 3ᵈ man a Pigmy!∧ —some
by ⟨by⟩ ⟨[at least one illegible word deleted]⟩~ricketty~ / ∧heads ⟨—⟩~&~ ⟨others
by⟩ hump backs—∧ others by   19 years] year   20 apple trees; ⟨in⟩ ∧from∧
[*M1*: u.v.]   22 traveller ⟨may⟩ ∧might∧   23-24 traveller ⟨may⟩~t~o . . .
may ⟨give us⟩ ∧measure∧

19-21. *a fourth . . . higher*] Yorick's observation parallels the opinion
expressed in the controversy about the stranger's nose in Slawkenbergius's
Tale, that "if a suitable provision of veins, arteries, &c. . . . was not laid in,
for the due nourishment of such a nose, in the very first stamina and rudiments of its formation before it came into the world (bating the case of Wens)
it could not regularly grow and be sustained afterwards" (*TS*, IV, 258). It
also parallels the view expressed in the *Sermons*, I, 118 (II.x), that God seems
"evidently to have prescribed the same laws to man, as well as all living creatures, in the first rudiments of which, there are contained the specifick powers
of their growth, duration and extinction."

22-27. *A medical traveller . . . together*] As Milic points out ("Sterne and
Smollett's 'Travels' "), Sterne is citing the views of Tobias Smollett, M.D.
Remarking that "the infants at the *enfans trouvés* in Paris, [were] so swathed
with bandages, that the very sight of them made my eyes water," Smollett observes:

> *those accursed bandages* [italics added] must heat the tender infant into a
> fever; . . . [and] while the refluent blood is obstructed in the veins, which
> run on the surface of the body, the arteries, which lie deep, without the
> reach of compression, are continually pouring their contents into the head,
> where the blood meets with no resistance . . . The vessels of the brain are
> naturally lax, and the very sutures of the skull are yet unclosed. *What are
> the consequences of this cruel swaddling? the limbs are wasted; the joints grow*

seventh stories such numbers of the *Bourgoisie* eat and sleep together; but I remember, Mr. Shandy the elder, who accounted for
nothing like any body else, in speaking one evening of these matters, averred, that children, like other animals, might be increased
30 almost to any size, provided they came right into the world; but the

---

27 ∧I remember∧   29 like ⟨other⟩ other

---

*rickety; the brain is compressed, and a hydrocephalus, with a great head and
sore eyes, ensues. I take this abominable practice to be one great cause of the
bandy legs, diminutive bodies, and large heads, so frequent in the south of
France* [italics added], *and in Italy.* [*Travels,* Letter No. 30, pp. 254–255;
cited in part by Vrooman, p. 166]
Sterne may also have in mind here: (1) Smollett's assertion earlier in the
same letter (p. 253) that the inhabitants of ancient Rome "were strangely
crouded together . . . That they were crouded together appears from *the
height of their houses* [italics added; quoted by Milic, "Sterne and Smollett's
'Travels' "] . . . In order to remedy this inconvenience, Augustus Caesar
published a decree, that for the future no houses should be built above . . .
six stories [italics added]"; (2) Smollett's observation in another letter that if,
as "is said," Paris is fifteen miles in circumference, "it must be much more
populous than London; for the streets are very narrow, and the houses very
high, with a different family on every floor" (*Travels,* Letter No. 6, p. 49).
(Smollett frequently measures the dimensions of monuments and buildings;
see, e.g., p. 117.33–35*n*, above.)
The observation that the streets of Paris were narrow was a commonplace
among English travelers. Vrooman cites (p. 166) Thicknesse, who notes also
the prevalence of deformity in France: "I cannot account for it, but this kingdom abounds more with human deformity, than any part of the world I have
ever seen; and I must now remind you to be particularly careful how you walk
in the streets of Paris, the narrowness of which, the great numbers of coaches,
carts, cabriolets, and various kinds of voitures, together with the multitude of
people crowding through every street, render walking in Paris very dangerous" (*Observations,* p. 80). Tristram remarks, on entering the city, that "the
streets are so villainously narrow, that there is not room in all *Paris* to turn
a wheel-barrow . . . In the grandest city of the whole world, it would not
have been amiss, if they had been left a thought wider; nay were it only so
much in every single street, as that a man might know (was it only for satisfaction) on which side of it he was walking" (*TS,* 7.17.499). On the narrowness of the Paris streets and the loftiness of the buildings, see also Cole,
Journey to Paris, pp. 45–46.
27–37. *Mr. Shandy the elder . . . leg.*] See App. E, pp. 345–347, note to
p. 176.27–37.

misery was, the citizens of Paris were so coop'd up, that they had not actually room enough to get them—I do not call it getting any thing, said he—'tis getting nothing—Nay, continued he, rising in his argument, 'tis getting worse than nothing, when all you have got, after twenty or five and twenty years of the tenderest care and *35* most nutritious aliment bestowed upon it, shall not at last be as high as my leg. Now, Mr. Shandy being very short, there could be nothing more said upon it.

As this is not a work of reasoning, I leave the solution as I found it, and content myself with the truth only of the remark, which is *40* verified in every lane and by-lane of Paris. I was walking down that which leads from the Carousal to the Palais Royal, and observing a little boy in some distress at the side of the gutter, which ran down the middle of it, I took hold of his hand, and help'd him over. Upon turning up his face to look at him after, I perceived he was about *45* forty—Never mind, said I; some good body will do as much for me when I am ninety.

I feel some little principles within me, which incline me to be merciful towards this poor blighted part of my species, who have neither size or strength to get on in the world—I cannot bear to *50* see one of them trod upon; and had scarce got seated beside my old French officer, ere the disgust was exercised, by seeing the very thing happen under the box we sat in.

---

33 nothing ⟨?at⟩~——~ nay   36 ∧bestowed upon it∧ , shall ⟨at / at ∧the∧ last⟩ not ∧at last∧   37 Now ⟨?Now⟩ Mr̃   39–40 reasoning, ⟨I content myself⟩ I . . . content myself   43 r⟨?u⟩~a~n⟨s⟩ [Sterne apparently wrote "runs" initially]   44 over; ⟨and⟩ upon   45–46 I ⟨saw⟩ ∧perceived∧ he was abo⟨?ve⟩~ut~ fourty ∧⟨years old—⟩∧ —never   48 ∧little∧   48–49 be ⟨?generous⟩ ∧merciful∧   51–52 ⟨t⟩~m~y . . . officer, ⟨before my attention towards him was calld off⟩ ∧ere . . . exercised∧

---

37. *Mr. Shandy being very short*] as he himself observes to Mrs. Shandy; see *TS,* 6.18.437.

41–42. *that which leads from the Carousal to the Palais Royal*] the Rue St. Nicaise (Poole, *op. cit.,* p. 160.36*n,* above, p. 393); see map facing p. **162,** above. *Carousal:* Carousel.

At the end of the orchestra, and betwixt that and the first side-
55 box, there is a small esplanade left, where, when the house is full,
numbers of all ranks take sanctuary. Though you stand, as in the
parterre, you pay the same price as in the orchestra. A poor defenceless being of this order had got thrust some how or other into
this luckless place—the night was hot, and he was surrounded by
60 beings two feet and a half higher than himself. The dwarf suffered
inexpressibly on all sides; but the thing which incommoded him
most, was a tall corpulent German, near seven feet high, who stood
directly betwixt him and all possibility of his seeing either the
stage or the actors. The poor dwarf did all he could to get a peep
65 at what was going forwards, by seeking for some little opening
betwixt the German's arm and his body, trying first one side, then
the other; but the German stood square in the most unaccommo-
dating posture that can be imagined—the dwarf might as well have
been placed at the bottom of the deepest draw-well in Paris; so he
70 civilly reach'd up his hand to the German's sleeve, and told him his
distress—The German turn'd his head back, look'd down upon
him as Goliah did upon David—and unfeelingly resumed his
posture.

I was just then taking a pinch of snuff out of my monk's little
75 horn box—And how would thy meek and courteous spirit, my dear
monk! so temper'd to *bear and forbear!*—how sweetly would it have
lent an ear to this poor soul's complaint!

---

62 ∧was∧   66–67 then ⟨an⟩ ∧the∧   69 ∧so∧   70 sleeve ⟨in order to⟩
∧and∧ t⟨?ell⟩~old~ ∧him∧ [Sterne apparently wrote "in order to tell" initially]
71 back, ⟨and⟩ look⟨ing⟩~'d~   76–77 have ⟨given way⟩ lent an ear to this ⟨com-
plaint!⟩ poor soul's complaint.   77 complaint!] complaint. [see prec. *tn*]

54–55. *At . . . left*] According to Poole (*op. cit.,* p. 160.36*n,* above, p.
393), this description is accurate.

57–73. *A poor defenceless being . . . posture.*] Sterne adapted this incident
from Scarron's *Roman comique;* see App. E, pp. 347–348, note to p. 178.57–73.

76. *to bear and forbear*] Cf. *Letters,* No. 94, Paris, June 1762, p. 174: "to
bear and forbear will ever be my maxim" (this maxim has been traced to
Epictetus).

The old French officer seeing me lift up my eyes with an emotion, as I made the apostrophe, took the liberty to ask me what was the matter—I told him the story in three words; and added, how *80* inhuman it was.

By this time the dwarf was driven to extremes, and in his first transports, which are generally unreasonable, had told the German he would cut off his long queue with his knife—The German look'd back coolly, and told him he was welcome if he could reach *85* it.

An injury sharpened by an insult, be it to who it will, makes every man of sentiment a party: I could have leaped out of the box to have redressed it.—The old French officer did it with much less confusion; for leaning a little over, and nodding to a centinel, and *90* pointing at the same time with his finger to the distress—the centinel made his way up to it.—There was no occasion to tell the grievance—the thing told itself; so thrusting back the German instantly with his musket—he took the poor dwarf by the hand, and placed him before him.—This is noble! said I, clapping my *95* hands together—And yet you would not permit this, said the old officer, in England.

—In England, dear Sir, said I, *we sit all at our ease.*

The old French officer would have set me at unity with myself, in case I had been at variance,—by saying it was a *bon mot*—and as *100* a *bon mot* is always worth something at Paris, he offered me a pinch of snuff.

---

78 The ⟨fr⟩ old french   82–83 extreams, ⟨& told the Germa⟩ & in . . . had told the german   87–88 insult ⟨is insufferable⟩ ∧be . . . party∧ : I could ⟨could⟩ have   89 it.—The] it—the   91 ∧at . . . time∧   92 it.—There] it— there   96–97 said v t ∨he ∧old officer∧ [Sterne apparently wrote "he" initially] 98 —In] [*S1:* no par.]   98 England, ⟨said I,⟩ dear Sir, said I,   99 ⟨?in⟩~at~

---

85. *look'd back coolly*] Cf., in the last sentence quoted from Scarron, App. E, p. 348, note to p. 178.57–73: "returned him only a cold and indifferent Glance."

90. *a centinel*] an armed guard to quell the frequent disturbances in the theater.

THE ROSE.
PARIS.

IT was now my turn to ask the old French officer "What was the matter?" for a cry of "*Haussez les mains, Monsieur l'Abbe*," re-echoed from a dozen different parts of the parterre, was as unintelligible to me, as my apostrophe to the monk had been to him.

5   He told me, it was some poor Abbe in one of the upper loges, who he supposed had got planted perdu behind a couple of grissets in order to see the opera, and that the parterre espying him, were insisting upon his holding up both his hands during the representation.—And can it be supposed, said I, that an ecclesiastick 10 would pick the Grisset's pockets? The old French officer smiled, and whispering in my ear, open'd a door of knowledge which I had no idea of—

Good God! said I, turning pale with astonishment—is it possible, that a people so smit with sentiment should at the same time 15 be so unclean, and so unlike themselves—*Quelle grossierte!* added I.

The French officer told me, it was an illiberal sarcasm at the church, which had begun in the theatre about the time the Tartuffe was given in it, by Moliere—but, like other remains of Gothic manners, was declining—Every nation, continued he, have 20 their refinements and *grossiertes*, in which they take the lead, and lose it of one another by turns—that he had been in most countries, but never in one where he found not some delicacies, which others seemed to want. *Le* POUR, *et le* CONTRE *se trouvent en chaque nation;*

2–3 re-echoed] re- / -echoed *A1*, reechoed *S1* [cf. "re-establishment", p. 150.30, above, which is hyphenated within the line in *A1*]   13 Good] [*S1*: no par.]

19–30. *Every . . . love.*] Cf. Smollett's opinions in his *Travels*, Letter No. 5, quoted p. 182.50–55*n*, below.

23–24. *Le pour . . . every where*] Cf. *Letters*, No. 113, to Lord Fauconberg, Montpellier, Sept. 1763, p. 201: "I'm more than half tired of France, there is a balance, said he, of good and bad every where; and nothing but the knowing it is so can emancipate one half of the world 25 from the prepossessions which it holds against the other—that the advantage of travel, as it regarded the *sçavoir vivre*, was by seeing a great deal both of men and manners; it taught us mutual toleration; and mutual toleration, concluded he, making me a bow, taught us mutual love. 30

The old French officer delivered this with an air of such candour and good sense, as coincided with my first favourable impressions of his character—I thought I loved the man; but I fear I mistook the object—'twas my own way of thinking—the difference was, I could not have expressed it half so well. 35

It is alike troublesome to both the rider and his beast—if the latter goes pricking up his ears, and starting all the way at every object which he never saw before—I have as little torment of this kind as any creature alive; and yet I honestly confess, that many a thing gave me pain, and that I blush'd at many a word the first 40 month—which I found inconsequent and perfectly innocent the second.

Madame de Rambouliet, after an acquaintance of about six weeks with her, had done me the honour to take me in her coach

---

23–25 want; ⟨?and ?nothing but⟩ *"Le . . . nation;"* ⟨said he⟩ there is a ballance, ⟨?every ?where⟩~said he, of~ good & bad every where; and nothing but 37–38 every ⟨thing⟩ ∧object∧   44 to ⟨m⟩ take me

---

as fine a Country as it is—but there is the *Pour* & the *Contre* for every place,— all wᶜʰ being ballanced, I think Old England preferable to any Kingdome in the world—" (For Sterne's disenchantment with the French, see the letters quoted p. 230.20–26n, below.)

27. *sçavoir vivre*] See Sterne's comment on the *sçavoir vivre* of the Parisians in *Letters*, No. 83, quoted in App. E, p. 352, note to p. 261.4–7.

43. *Madame de Rambouliet*] Considering her indecorous behavior and the politesse of Yorick's *Journey*, it seems unlikely that Sterne is referring to an actual person whom he expected his readers to recognize. Her name and Yorick's description of her correctness and "purity of heart" (ll. 46–47, below) suggest that her actions are intended to typify the conduct many

45 about two leagues out of town—Of all women, Madame de Rambouliet is the most correct; and I never wish to see one of more
virtues and purity of heart—In our return back, Madame de
Rambouliet desired me to pull the cord—I ask'd her if she wanted
any thing—*Rien que pisser*, said Madame de Rambouliet—

50 Grieve not, gentle traveller, to let Madame de Rambouliet p--ss
on—And, ye fair mystic nymphs! go each one *pluck your rose*, and

---

48 cord] string [cf. "cord", p. 209.3, below]   49–50 any thing— ⟨nothing said
She, but to / piss. [par.] —grieve not, gentle Traveller!⟩ ∧[par.] —*"rien que ⟨d⟩ pisser,*
said Madame ⟨R⟩∼d∼e Rambouliet—∧ // ∧—Grieve not gentle Traveller∧ to [Sterne
apparently wrote initially: "any thing—nothing said She, but to piss. [par.] —grieve
not, gentle Traveller! to let . . ."]   50 Grieve] [*S1:* no par.]   50 p--s] piss

---

English travelers thought characteristic of Frenchwomen; and that Sterne
may be ironically contrasting "Madame de Rambouliet's" vulgar behavior
with the ideal of refinement in language and manners made fashionable by
the *précieuses* who frequented the salon of the Marquise de Ramboulliet (1588–
1665) and whose extravagant *préciosité* Molière satirized in *Les Précieuses
ridicules* (1659). (See Yorick's ref. to a *"physical precieuse,"* p. 69.21, above.)
    50–55. *Grieve not . . . decorum.*] Unlike Yorick, many British travelers ex-
pressed shock and disgust at what they considered the gross indecency of the
French (and Italians) with respect to bodily functions. As Vrooman points
out (p. 303), Sterne may be thinking here of Smollett's indignant protest
(*Travels,* Letter No. 5, p. 35):

> there is no cleanliness among [the French], much less . . . delicacy,
> which is the cleanliness of the mind. Indeed they are utter strangers to
> what we call common decency; and I could give you some high-flavoured
> instances, at which even a native of Edinburgh would stop his nose. There
> are certain mortifying views of human nature, which undoubtedly ought
> to be concealed as much as possible, in order to prevent giving offence:
> and nothing can be more absurd, than to plead the difference of custom
> in different countries, in defence of those usages which cannot fail giving
> disgust to the organs and senses of all mankind. Will custom exempt from
> the imputation of gross indecency a French lady, who shifts her frowsy
> smock in presence of a male visitant, and talks to him of her *lavement,* her
> *medecine,* and her *bidet!* . . . I have known a lady handed to the house of
> office by her admirer, who stood at the door, and entertained her with
> *bons mots* all the time she was within. But I should be glad to know, whether
> it is possible for a fine lady to speak and act in this manner, without ex-

scatter them in your path—for Madame de Rambouliet did no more—I handed Madame de Rambouliet out of the coach; and had I been the priest of the chaste CASTALIA, I could not have served at her fountain with a more respectful decorum. 55

END OF VOL. I.

---

53 handed ⟨her⟩ ∧Madame de Rambouliet∧ [*M1:* u.v.]   55–56 decorum. . . . VOL. I.] [*S1* ends with "decorum." and does not have "END OF VOL. I."; *M1* accords with *S1*. See p. 291.153–154*tn*, below.]

---

citing ideas to her own disadvantage in the mind of every man who has any imagination left, and enjoys the intire use of his senses, howsoever she may be authorised by the customs of her country?

The urbane and tolerant *sçavoir vivre* of Yorick's account of his experience with Madame de Rambouliet suggests that Sterne may have intended this incident as a witty response to Smollett's final, rhetorical question.

Vrooman also cites (p. 303, n. 2) as typical of the attitude of British travelers: Cole's description of the shock of his fellow-Britishers on a channel packet when a French kitchen-maid used a chamber pot "*pour faire lacher l'Eau*" in front of them, an incident which prompts him to remark on "the Difference between English & French Education & Customs! We carry to an Excess our Delicacy in these Matters, while our Neighbours exceed in the other offensive Extreme" (*Journey to Paris,* pp. 362–363); Sharp's disgusted observation that the Venetians "let down their breeches wherever, and before whomsoever they please" and that many parts of St. Mark's square and the Doge's palace are "dedicated to *Cloacina,* and you may see the votaries at their devotions every hour of the day, as much whilst the Nobles are going in and coming out, as at any other time" (*Letters from Italy,* No. 9, p. 35); Tristram's observation that in Paris, "the SCHOOL of URBANITY herself, . . . the walls are besh-t" (*TS,* 7.17.498); Smollett's description of the "shocking condition" of the "temple of Cloacina" at an inn in Nîmes (*Travels,* Letter No. 12, p. 106).

51. *pluck your rose*] a euphemism for easing oneself; cf. Swift, "Strephon and Chloe" (ll. 15–18): Chloe "Would so discreetly Things dispose, / None ever saw her pluck a Rose. / Her dearest Comrades never caught her / Squat on her Hams, to make Maid's Water" (*Poems,* ed. Harold Williams, 2d ed. [Oxford, 1958], II, 584). Eric Partridge notes that the expression probably

originated from the fact that the rural privy was often in the garden (*Diction-ary of Slang and Unconventional English,* 5th ed. [New York, 1961]).

54. *the chaste Castalia*] a nymph who, to escape Apollo, threw herself into a spring on Mt. Parnassus, near Delphi; consecrated to Apollo and the Muses, the Castalian spring was credited with powers of poetic inspiration, and pilgrims to the shrine of Apollo at Delphi purified themselves in its waters before consulting the oracle.

A

SENTIMENTAL JOURNEY

THROUGH

FRANCE AND ITALY.

BY

Mr. YORICK.

VOL. II.

LONDON:

Printed for T. BECKET and P. A. DE HONDT,
in the Strand. MDCCLXVIII.

THE
FILLE DE CHAMBRE.
PARIS.

WHAT the old French officer had deliver'd upon travelling, bringing Polonius's advice to his son upon the same subject into my head—and that bringing in Hamlet; and Hamlet, the rest of Shakespear's works, I stopp'd at the Quai de Conti in my return home, to purchase the whole set.   5

The bookseller said he had not a set in the world—*Comment!* said I; taking one up out of a set which lay upon the counter betwixt us. ——He said, they were sent him only to be got bound, and were to be sent back to Versailles in the morning to the Count de B****.

—And does the Count de B****, said I, read Shakespear? *10 C'est un Esprit fort*; replied the bookseller.—He loves English books; and what is more to his honour, Monsieur, he loves the English too. You speak this so civilly, said I, that 'tis enough to oblige an Englishman to lay out a Louis d'or or two at your shop— the bookseller made a bow, and was going to say something, when a *15* young decent girl of about twenty, who by her air and dress, seemed to be *fille de chambre* to some devout woman of fashion,

---

title. CHAMBRE.] CHAMBRE *A2, M2*   10 B****,] B**** *A2, M2*
12 loves] love *A2,* loves *M2*   16 girl of about] girl about   17 be *fille*] be a fille

---

2. *Polonius's advice*] in *Hamlet,* I.iii.55–81.
4. *Quai de Conti*] See map facing p. 162, above.
10–13. *the Count de B**** . . . too.*] Claude de Thiard (1721–1810), comte de Bissy, distinguished soldier, "beneficent friend of Louis XV, and butt of the wits, who ridiculed the literary pretensions which had won for him election to the Académie" (*Letters,* p. 153, n. 8; see also *Life,* pp. 303–304); he translated Bolingbroke's *Patriot King.* Sterne met him during his first trip to Paris; see p. 215.2–3*n*, below.

came into the shop and asked for *Les Egarments du Coeur & de
l'Esprit:* the bookseller gave her the book directly; she pulled out a
20 little green sattin purse run round with a ribband of the same
colour, and putting her finger and thumb into it, she took out the
money, and paid for it. As I had nothing more to stay me in the
shop, we both walked out at the door together.

——And what have you to do, my dear, said I, with *The Wander-*
25 *ings of the Heart,* who scarce know yet you have one? nor till love
has first told you it, or some faithless shepherd has made it ache,
can'st thou ever be sure it is so.—*Le Dieu m'en guard!* said the
girl.—With reason, said I—for if it is a good one, 'tis pity it should
be stolen: 'tis a little treasure to thee, and gives a better air to your
30 face, than if it was dress'd out with pearls.

The young girl listened with a submissive attention, holding her
sattin purse by its ribband in her hand all the time—'Tis a very
small one, said I, taking hold of the bottom of it—she held it towards me—and there is very little in it, my dear, said I; but be but
35 as good as thou art handsome, and heaven will fill it: I had a parcel
of crowns in my hand to pay for Shakespear; and as she had let go
the purse intirely, I put a single one in; and tying up the ribband
in a bow-knot, returned it to her.

---

28 if it is] if is *A2,* it is *M2*   38 it to her] it her

18–19. *Les . . . l'Esprit*] a novel (publ. 1736) by Claude-Prosper Jolyot
de Crébillon (1707–1777), wit and friend of the Baron d'Holbach, Diderot,
Voltaire, et al. After he met Crébillon in Paris in 1762, Sterne informed
Garrick: "Crebillion . . . has agreed to write me an expostulat[o]ry letter
upon the indecorums of T. Shandy—which is to be answered by recrimina-
tion upon the liberties in his own works—these are to be printed together—
Crebillion against Sterne—Sterne against Crebillion—the copy to be sold,
and the money equally divided" (*Letters,* No. 87, Paris, April 1762, p. 162;
Curtis notes that the scheme was apparently never carried out). Sterne cites
the title of *Les Egaremens* twice in his letters: No. 47, [? York], Jan. 1760,
p. 88; No. 142, York, [? May 1765], p. 245.
    31–37. *her sattin purse . . . one in*] Is there, perhaps, a sexual innuendo
here based on the meaning of "purse"? See p. 236.59–68n, below.

The young girl made me more a humble courtesy than a low one
—'twas one of those quiet, thankful sinkings where the spirit bows 40
itself down—the body does no more than tell it. I never gave a girl a
crown in my life which gave me half the pleasure.

My advice, my dear, would not have been worth a pin to you,
said I, if I had not given this along with it: but now, when you see
the crown, you'll remember it—so don't, my dear, lay it out in 45
ribbands.

Upon my word, Sir, said the girl, earnestly, I am incapable—in
saying which, as is usual in little bargains of honour, she gave me
her hand—*En verite, Monsieur, je mettrai cet argent apart*, said she.

When a virtuous convention is made betwixt man and woman, it 50
sanctifies their most private walks: so notwithstanding it was dusky,
yet as both our roads lay the same way, we made no scruple of
walking along the Quai de Conti together.

She made me a second courtesy in setting off, and before we got
twenty yards from the door, as if she had not done enough before, 55
she made a sort of a little stop to tell me again,—she thank'd me.

It was a small tribute, I told her, which I could not avoid paying
to virtue, and would not be mistaken in the person I had been
rendering it to for the world—but I see innocence, my dear, in your
face—and foul befal the man who ever lays a snare in its way! 60

The girl seem'd affected some way or other with what I said—she
gave a low sigh—I found I was not impowered to enquire at all
after it—so said nothing more till I got to the corner of the Rue de
Nevers, where we were to part.

—But is this the way, my dear, said I, to the hotel de Modene? 65

---

40 'twas one] 'twas one one *A2*, 'twas one *M2*   53 together.] together *A2*, together. *M2*   64 where] when

---

63–64. *Rue de Nevers*] enters the Quai de Conti near the Pont Neuf. For
this street and the others mentioned in this chapter, see the map facing p. 162,
above.

she told me it was—or, that I might go by the Rue de Guineygaude,
which was the next turn.—Then I'll go, my dear, by the Rue de
Guineygaude, said I, for two reasons; first I shall please myself, and
next I shall give you the protection of my company as far on your
70 way as I can. The girl was sensible I was civil—and said, she wish'd
the hotel de Modene was in the Rue de St. Pierre—You live there?
said I.—She told me she was *fille de chambre* to Madame R****—
Good God! said I, 'tis the very lady for whom I have brought a
letter from Amiens—The girl told me that Madame R****, she
75 believed expected a stranger with a letter, and was impatient to see
him—so I desired the girl to present my compliments to Madame
R****, and say I would certainly wait upon her in the morning.

We stood still at the corner of the Rue de Nevers whilst this
pass'd—We then stopp'd a moment whilst she disposed of her
80 *Egarments de Coeur,* &c. more commodiously than carrying them
in her hand—they were two volumes; so I held the second for her
whilst she put the first into her pocket; and then she held her
pocket, and I put in the other after it.

'Tis sweet to feel by what fine-spun threads our affections are
85 drawn together.

We set off a-fresh, and as she took her third step, the girl put her
hand within my arm—I was just bidding her—but she did it of
herself with that undeliberating simplicity, which shew'd it was out
of her head that she had never seen me before. For my own part, I
90 felt the conviction of consanguinity so strongly, that I could not

---

72 R****] *R**** A2*, R**** *M2*   74 R****] *R**** A2*, R**** *M2*

---

66. *Guineygaude*] i.e., "Guénégaud."

71. *Rue de St. Pierre*] As Edward W. West has pointed out (*Notes &
Queries,* 7th ser., IX [1890], 366), this is apparently an error for the Rue des
Saints Pères, which crosses the Rue Jacob, where Yorick's hotel was located
(see p. 160.36n, above).

89–93. *I felt . . . relations?*] Cf. Sterne's declaration to Mr. or Mrs.
James: "I could not wish y\u02b3 happiness and the Successe of what[e]*ver conduces*
to [i]t, more than I do, was I your Brother——but good god! are we not all

help turning half round to look in her face, and see if I could trace out any thing in it of a family likeness—Tut! said I, are we not all relations?

When we arrived at the turning up of the Rue de Guineygaude, I stopp'd to bid her adieu for good an all: the girl would thank me again for my company and kindness—She bid me adieu twice—I repeated it as often; and so cordial was the parting between us, that had it happen'd any where else, I'm not sure but I should have signed it with a kiss of charity, as warm and holy as an apostle.

But in Paris, as none kiss each other but the men—I did, what amounted to the same thing——

——I bid God bless her.

---

brothers and Sisters, who are friendly & virtuous & good?" (*Letters*, No. 226, Dec. 1767, p. 408); cf. also *Sermons*, II, 223–224 (VII.xiv), on the "natural bond of brotherhood" between men as a natural motive to "peaceable commerce" and "social intercourse"; and *Letters*, No. 170B, to Ignatius Sancho, quoted in App. E, pp. 348–349, note to p. 199.87–89.

THE PASSPORT.
PARIS.

WHEN I got home to my hotel, La Fleur told me I had been enquired after by the Lieutenant de Police—The duce take it! said I——I know the reason. It is time the reader should know it, for in the order of things in which it happened, it was omitted; 5 not that it was out of my head; but that had I told it then, it might have been forgot now—and now is the time I want it.

I had left London with so much precipitation, that it never enter'd my mind that we were at war with France; and had reach'd Dover, and look'd through my glass at the hills beyond Boulogne, 10 before the idea presented itself; and with this in its train, that there was no getting there without a passport. Go but to the end of a

---

7–8. *I . . . war with France*] a reference to the fact that when Sterne reached Paris in January 1762, on his first trip abroad, England and France were still officially engaged in the Seven Years War (the Treaty of Paris was not signed until February 1763), although hostilities between them had ceased. Curtis notes that Sterne was "among the first to take advantage of the cessation of hostilities and journey to Paris" (*Letters*, p. 146, n. 2).

This ref. and the ref. to May, p. 234.16, below, set Yorick's journey to Paris in May 1762, during the same period as Sterne's first trip to Paris. In *Tristram Shandy*, Yorick dies in 1748 (though "the country people,—and some others, believe" that his ghost "*still walks*" [*TS*, 2.17.143]). Did Sterne intend us to realize that, in terms of the chronology of *Tristram Shandy*, Yorick is dead before he sets out on his *Journey*? If he did, is this, perhaps, a wild, Shandean jest—a jest prompted partly by the fact that the newspapers had reported that Sterne had died on his first trip abroad (see p. 2, above), and partly by the fact that Yorick's name and his skull are emblems of the final "VEXATION" of traveling? Yorick is "lineally descended" from Shakespeare's jester (*TS*, 1.11.24), whose skull epitomizes mortality. And, as Professor Traugott has remarked (p. vii), "that son of a whore, Death, participated in all the excellent fopperies of the Sentimental Journey."

11. *without a passport*] When Sterne reached Paris in January 1762, he had to obtain a passport with the aid of various French officials and men of letters; see p. 226.33–35*n*, below.

192

street, I have a mortal aversion for returning back no wiser than I set out; and as this was one of the greatest efforts I had ever made for knowledge, I could less bear the thoughts of it: so hearing the Count de **** had hired the packet, I begg'd he would take me in 15 his *suite*. The Count had some little knowledge of me, so made little or no difficulty—only said, his inclination to serve me could reach no further than Calais; as he was to return by way of Brussels to Paris: however, when I had once pass'd there, I might get to Paris without interruption; but that in Paris I must make friends 20 and shift for myself.—Let me get to Paris, Monsieur le Count, said I—and I shall do very well. So I embark'd, and never thought more of the matter.

When La Fleur told me the Lieutenant de Police had been en- quiring after me—the thing instantly recurred—and by the time 25 La Fleur had well told me, the master of the hotel came into my room to tell me the same thing, with this addition to it, that my passport had been particularly ask'd after: the master of the hotel concluded with saying, He hoped I had one.—Not I, faith! said I.

The master of the hotel retired three steps from me, as from an 30 infected person, as I declared this—and poor La Fleur advanced three steps towards me, and with that sort of movement which a good soul makes to succour a distress'd one—the fellow won my heart by it; and from that single *trait*, I knew his character as per- fectly, and could rely upon it as firmly, as if he had served me with 35 fidelity for seven years.

Mon seignior! cried the master of the hotel—but recollecting himself as he made the exclamation, he instantly changed the tone of it—If Monsieur, said he, has not a passport (*apparament*) in all

---

13 set] sat *A2, M2*   24, 26, 31 La Fleur] Le Fleur *A2, M2* [see App. C, §4, (4), p. 311]

12–13. *returning . . . out*] In calculating the expenses of Bobby's Grand Tour, Walter is compelled, by Obadiah's repeated interruptions, "to return back to *Calais* (like many others) as wise as he had set out" (*TS*, 5.2.348–349).

40 likelihood he has friends in Paris who can procure him one.—Not
that I know of, quoth I, with an air of indifference.—Then *certes*,
replied he, you'll be sent to the Bastile or the Chatelet, *au moins*.
Poo! said I, the king of France is a good natured soul—he'll hurt
no body.—*Cela n'empeche pas*, said he—you will certainly be sent
45 to the Bastile to-morrow morning.—But I've taken your lodgings
for a month, answer'd I, and I'll not quit them a day before the
time for all the kings of France in the world. La Fleur whisper'd in
my ear, That no body could oppose the king of France.

Pardi! said my host, *ces Messieurs Anglois sont des gens tres*
50 *extraordinaires*—and having both said and sworn it—he went out.

THE PASSPORT.
The Hotel at Paris.

I COULD not find in my heart to torture La Fleur's with a serious look upon the subject of my embarrassment, which was the reason I had treated it so cavalierly: and to shew him how light it lay upon my mind, I dropt the subject entirely; and whilst he waited upon me at supper, talk'd to him with more than usual 5 gaiety about Paris, and of the opera comique.—La Fleur had been there himself, and had followed me through the streets as far as the bookseller's shop; but seeing me come out with the young *fille de chambre*, and that we walk'd down the Quai de Conti together, La Fleur deem'd it unnecessary to follow me a step further—so making 10 his own reflections upon it, he took a shorter cut——and got to the hotel in time to be inform'd of the affair of the Police against my arrival.

As soon as the honest creature had taken away, and gone down to sup himself, I then began to think a little seriously about my 15 situation.—

—And here, I know, Eugenius, thou wilt smile at the remembrance of a short dialogue which pass'd betwixt us the moment I was going to set out——I must tell it here.

Eugenius, knowing that I was as little subject to be overburthen'd 20 with money as thought, had drawn me aside to interrogate me how much I had taken care for; upon telling him the exact sum, Eugenius shook his head, and said it would not do; so pull'd out his purse in order to empty it into mine.—I've enough in conscience, Eugenius, said I.——Indeed, Yorick, you have not, replied Eu- 25 genius—I know France and Italy better than you.——But you don't consider, Eugenius, said I, refusing his offer, that before I have been three days in Paris, I shall take care to say or do some-

---

28–29 say or do something] say something

thing or other for which I shall get clapp'd up into the Bastile, and
30 that I shall live there a couple of months entirely at the king of
France's expence.—I beg pardon, said Eugenius, drily: really, I
had forgot that resource.

Now the event I treated gaily came seriously to my door.

Is it folly, or nonchalance, or philosophy, or pertinacity—or
35 what is it in me, that, after all, when La Fleur had gone down stairs,
and I was quite alone, that I could not bring down my mind to
think of it otherwise than I had then spoken of it to Eugenius?

—And as for the Bastile! the terror is in the word—Make the
most of it you can, said I to myself, the Bastile is but another word
40 for a tower—and a tower is but another word for a house you can't
get out of—Mercy on the gouty! for they are in it twice a year—
but with nine livres a day, and pen and ink and paper and patience,
albeit a man can't get out, he may do very well within—at least for
a month or six weeks; at the end of which, if he is a harmless fellow
45 his innocence appears, and he comes out a better and wiser man
than he went in.

I had some occasion (I forget what) to step into the court-yard,
as I settled this account; and remember I walk'd down stairs in no

---

45 and wiser] and a wiser

29–31. *the Bastile . . . expence*] Thicknesse observed that "the Bastile is
the only prison in France, which is not many degrees worse than Newgate;
but whoever is sent to that royal prison is lodged in good apartments, and has
a table provided at the king's expence, suitable to the condition of life in
which the prisoner used to live" (*Useful Hints*, p. 227). He recounts an
anecdote about an indigent Scotch gentleman, unjustly imprisoned in the
Bastille (in 1745) as an enemy to the state, who was at first "greatly alarmed
and terrified upon being so confined; but finding himself lodged in handsom
apartments, and every necessary of life provided for him at the King's expence (for he was a royal prisoner) besides an excellent dinner," became so
satisfied with his lot that he was distraught upon hearing he was to be re-
leased (*Observations*, pp. 51–52).

42–44. *pen . . . within*] Is Sterne perhaps thinking of Cervantes here?
See p. 201.10–17*n*, below.

small triumph with the conceit of my reasoning—Beshrew the *sombre* pencil! said I vauntingly—for I envy not its powers, which 50 paints the evils of life with so hard and deadly a colouring. The mind sits terrified at the objects she has magnified herself, and blackened: reduce them to their proper size and hue she overlooks them—'Tis true, said I, correcting the proposition—the Bastile is not an evil to be despised—but strip it of its towers—fill up the 55 fossè—unbarricade the doors—call it simply a confinement, and suppose 'tis some tyrant of a distemper—and not of a man which holds you in it—the evil half vanishes, and you bear the other half without complaint.

I was interrupted in the hey-day of this soliloquy, with a voice 60 which I took to be of a child, which complained "it could not get out."—I look'd up and down the passage, and seeing neither man, woman, or child, I went out without further attention.

In my return back through the passage, I heard the same words repeated twice over; and looking up, I saw it was a starling hung in 65 a little cage.—"I can't get out—I can't get out," said the starling.

I stood looking at the bird: and to every person who came through the passage it ran fluttering to the side towards which they approach'd it, with the same lamentation of its captivity—"I can't get out," said the starling—God help thee! said I, but I'll let thee 70 out, cost what it will; so I turn'd about the cage to get to the door; it was twisted and double twisted so fast with wire, there was no getting it open without pulling the cage to pieces—I took both hands to it.

---

55 fill up the] fill the   58 evil half vanishes] evil vanishes *A*2, evil half vanishes
*M*2   70 out,"] out", *A*2, *out*"— *M*2

49–59. *Beshrew . . . complaint.*] Cf. Walter's soliloquy on Death, in which he "strips" Death of its terrible aspects (*TS,* 5.3.356).
65–66. *a starling . . . cage*] The appropriateness of the caged starling as an emblem of Yorick's threatened confinement in the Bastille may depend partly on an association between "starling" and "Sterne"; see p. 205.37–40*n,* below.

75   The bird flew to the place where I was attempting his deliver-
ance, and thrusting his head through the trellis, press'd his breast
against it, as if impatient—I fear, poor creature! said I, I cannot
set thee at liberty—"No," said the starling—"I can't get out—I
can't get out," said the starling.

80   I vow, I never had my affections more tenderly awakened; or do
I remember an incident in my life, where the dissipated spirits, to
which my reason had been a bubble, were so suddenly call'd home.
Mechanical as the notes were, yet so true in tune to nature were
they chanted, that in one moment they overthrew all my systematic
85 reasonings upon the Bastile; and I heavily walk'd up stairs, unsay-
ing every word I had said in going down them.

---

78 starling—"I can't] Starling—"I cannot   83 the notes] thenotes *A*2, the notes
*M*2

80–85. *I vow . . . Bastile*] Cf. Yorick's emotions with the description of
the disinterested benevolence of the Good Samaritan in *Sermons*, I, 27–28,
32 (I.iii):
    . . . in such calamities as a man has fallen into through mere misfortune,
    . . . there is something . . . so truly interesting, that at the first sight
    we generally make them our own, not altogether from a reflection that
    they might have been or may be so, but oftener from a certain generosity
    and tenderness of nature which disposes us for compassion, abstracted
    from all considerations of self. . . . In benevolent natures the impulse to
    pity is so sudden, that like instruments of music which only obey the
    touch—the objects which are fitted to excite such impressions work so
    instantaneous an effect, that you would think the will was scarce con-
    cerned, and that the mind was altogether passive in the sympathy which
    her own goodness has excited. The truth is,—the soul is generally in such
    cases so busily taken up and wholly engrossed by the object of pity, that
    she does not attend to her own operations, or take leisure to examine the
    principles upon which she acts. So that the Samaritan, though the mo-
    ment he saw him he had compassion on him, yet sudden as the emotion is
    represented, you are not to imagine that it was mechanical, but that there
    was a settled principle of humanity and goodness which operated within
    him, and influenced not only the first impulse of kindness, but the con-
    tinuation of it throughout the rest of so engaging a behaviour.

Disguise thyself as thou wilt, still slavery! said I—still thou art
a bitter draught; and though thousands in all ages have been made
to drink of thee, thou art no less bitter on that account.—'tis thou,
thrice sweet and gracious goddess, addressing myself to LIBERTY, *90*
whom all in public or in private worship, whose taste is grateful,
and ever wilt be so, till NATURE herself shall change—no *tint* of

---

92 herself shall change] herself change

87–89. *Disguise . . . account.*] Cf. *Sermons,* I, 122 (II.x): "Consider
slavery——what it is,——how bitter a draught, and how many millions have
been made to drink of it;—which if it can poison all earthly happiness when
exercised barely upon our bodies, what must it be, when it comprehends both
the slavery of body and mind?——To conceive this, look into the history of
the Romish church and her tyrants, . . . who seem to have taken pleasure
in the pangs and convulsions of their fellow-creatures.——Examine the pris-
ons of the inquisition, hear the melancholy notes sounded in every cell . . ."
(it is characteristic of the cosmopolitan tolerance of Yorick's *Journey* that in
echoing this passage Sterne omits the refs. to the tyranny of the "Romish
church"; see p. 74.27–29*n*, above).

For Sterne's comments on slavery elsewhere in his writings and for a discussion of the possibility that Yorick's remarks on slavery may have been
prompted at least indirectly by the appeal of a former Negro slave, see App.
E, pp. 348–349, note to p. 199.87–89.

90–97. *Liberty . . . ascent*] Informed that, by royal decree, he must pay
for traveling from Lyons to Avignon by post, although he has decided to go
by water, Tristram declares: "I will go to ten thousand Bastiles first——O
England! England! thou land of liberty, and climate of good sense, thou
tenderest of mothers—and gentlest of nurses, cried I, kneeling upon one
knee, as I was beginning my apostrophe" (*TS,* 7.34.526–527). Yorick refers
to England as a "land of liberty and good sense" at the conclusion of the sermon on conscience, as reprinted in *TS,* 2.17.140.

Although Englishmen never tired of praising Liberty and congratulating
themselves on their virtues and advantages as freeborn Englishmen, some
considered their apostrophes to the goddess as mechanical as the starling's
complaint against its confinement. Vrooman quotes (p. 85, n. 3) the observation by Goldsmith's Chinese traveler that in England, "Liberty is echoed in
all their assemblies; and thousands might be found ready to offer up their
lives for the sound, though perhaps not one of all the number understands its
meaning" (*Citizen of the World,* No. 4, in *Works,* ed. Peter Cunningham
[London, 1908], IV, 25).

words can spot thy snowy mantle, or chymic power turn thy
sceptre into iron—with thee to smile upon him as he eats his crust,
95 the swain is happier than his monarch, from whose court thou art
exiled—Gracious heaven! cried I, kneeling down upon the last
step but one in my ascent—grant me but health, thou great Be-
stower of it, and give me but this fair goddess as my companion—
and shower down thy mitres, if it seems good unto thy divine
100 providence, upon those heads which are aching for them.

93–94 thy sceptre] the Scepter

99–100. *shower . . . them*] One of Sterne's many refs. to the frustration of
his ambitions in the church (see p. 105.31–32n, above), this passage is anticipated in Sterne's other writings and echoes *Don Quixote.* In a letter he
wrote to Elizabeth Montagu soon after returning to England from his first
trip abroad, Sterne referred to those "who are rackd & torn up with ambition—or whose heads are aching for Mitres" (*Letters,* No. 124, [? June 1764],
p. 216). In *Tristram Shandy,* Eugenius expresses his hopes that, in spite of
the attacks of Yorick's enemies, "there is still enough left of [him] to make a
bishop." Yorick replies that his head is "so bruised and mis-shapen'd with
the blows which ***** and *****, and some others have so unhandsomely
given me in the dark, that I might say with *Sancho Pança,* that should I recover, and 'Mitres thereupon be suffer'd to rain down from heaven as thick
as hail, not one of 'em would fit it' " (*TS,* 1.12.31). As Work notes (*TS,* p. 31,
n. 4), Yorick is paraphrasing Sancho's reply to Don Quixote's assurance that
when Sancho is a king his wife will become a queen: "I doubt of it, . . . for
I can't help believing, that though it should rain Kingdoms down upon the
Face of the Earth, not one of them would sit well upon *Mary Gutierez's* Head"
(*Don Quixote,* 1.1.7.43). Sterne echoed Sancho's words in two other allusions
to his hopes for preferment: he assured Eliza that "if a Mitre was offer'd me,
I would not have it, till I could have thee too, to make it sit easy upon my
brow" (*Journal,* 3 Aug., p. 386); and he declared that, without Lydia, "if a
mitre was offered me, it would sit uneasy upon my brow" (*Letters,* No. 224,
Dec. 1767, p. 406).

THE CAPTIVE.
PARIS.

THE bird in his cage pursued me into my room; I sat down close to my table, and leaning my head upon my hand, I begun to figure to myself the miseries of confinement. I was in a right frame for it, and so I gave full scope to my imagination.

I was going to begin with the millions of my fellow creatures 5 born to no inheritance but slavery; but finding, however affecting the picture was, that I could not bring it near me, and that the multitude of sad groups in it did but distract me.—

—I took a single captive, and having first shut him up in his dungeon, I then look'd through the twilight of his grated door to 10 take his picture.

---

8 of] of of *A2,* of *M2*   8 me—] me.— *A2,* me— *M2*

---

3. *the miseries of confinement*] Cf. Trim's reflection, partly apropos of his brother Tom's imprisonment by the Inquisition, that "Nothing . . . can be so sad as confinement for life—or so sweet . . . as liberty" (*TS,* 9.4.603).

5–6. *the millions . . . slavery*] Cf. *Sermons,* I, 124 (II.x), ref. to "Millions of our fellow-creatures, born to no inheritance but poverty and trouble"; and the ref. to "millions . . . made to drink of [slavery]" in the passage quoted from this sermon, p. 199.87–89*n,* above. See also the correspondence between Sterne and Ignatius Sancho, quoted in App. E, pp. 348–349, note to p. 199.87–89.

9–10. *—I took . . . dungeon*] Yorick's choice of an imprisoned captive to exemplify slavery may owe something to Matthew 25:36–40: "I was in prison, and ye came unto me. . . . Verily I say unto you, Inasmuch as ye have done it unto one of the least of these my brethren, ye have done it unto me." Matthew 25:35–36 is cited and paraphrased in *Sermons,* I, 35–36 (I.iii), to show that "our blessed SAVIOUR in describing the day of judgment does it in such a manner, as if the great enquiry then, was to relate principally to this one virtue of compassion."

10–17. *the twilight of his grated door . . . breathed through his lattice*] Cf. Tristram's invocation to the spirit of Cervantic humor which presides over his account of his meeting with Maria (see p. 13, above): "Gentle Spirit of

I beheld his body half wasted away with long expectation and confinement, and felt what kind of sickness of the heart it was which arises from hope deferr'd. Upon looking nearer I saw him
15 pale and feverish: in thirty years the western breeze had not once fann'd his blood—he had seen no sun, no moon in all that time— nor had the voice of friend or kinsman breathed through his lattice —his children—

—But here my heart began to bleed—and I was forced to go on
20 with another part of the portrait.

He was sitting upon the ground upon a little straw, in the fur- thest corner of his dungeon, which was alternately his chair and bed: a little calender of small sticks were laid at the head notch'd all over with the dismal days and nights he had pass'd there—he
25 had one of these little sticks in his hand, and with a rusty nail he was etching another day of misery to add to the heap. As I dark- ened the little light he had, he lifted up a hopeless eye towards the

---

27 a] his

---

sweetest humour, who erst didst sit upon the easy pen of my beloved CER-
VANTES; Thou who glided'st daily through his lattice, and turned'st the twi-
light of his prison into noon-day brightness by thy presence" (*TS*, 9.24.628).
As Work points out (*TS*, p. 628*n*), from the remark in the Preface to *Don Quixote* that "You may suppose it the Child of Disturbance, engendred in some dismal Prison, where Wretchedness keeps its Residence, and every dismal Sound its Habitation," it has been supposed that Cervantes may have conceived and even begun writing *Don Quixote* in prison. Sterne refers to this tradition in a letter to Elizabeth Montagu in which he asked to be numbered among those who had died jesting (*Letters*, No. 234, quoted p. 20, above): "tell me the reason, why Cervantes could write so fine and humourous a Satyre, in the melancholly regions of a damp prison—"
    12–13. *his body . . . confinement*] Cf. the sermon on Conscience: "Behold this helpless victim [of the Inquisition] delivered up to his tormentors. His body . . . wasted with sorrow and long confinement . . ." (*Sermons*, II, 79 [IV.xii]; cf. the version in *TS*, 2.17.138–139).
    13–14. *sickness . . . deferr'd*] an echo of Proverbs 13:12: "Hope deferred maketh the heart sick" [Milic, p. 82, n. 1].
    23–26. *a little calender . . . heap*] Cf. *Sermons*, I, 177 (II.xv): the man who lifts "his eyes towards heaven . . . feels not the weight of his chains, or counts the days of his captivity."

door, then cast it down—shook his head, and went on with his
work of affliction. I heard his chains upon his legs, as he turn'd his
body to lay his little stick upon the bundle—He gave a deep sigh— *30*
I saw the iron enter into his soul—I burst into tears—I could not
sustain the picture of confinement which my fancy had drawn—I
startled up from my chair, and calling La Fleur, I bid him bespeak
me a *remise*, and have it ready at the door of the hotel by nine in
the morning.　　*35*

—I'll go directly, said I, myself to Monsieur Le Duke de Choiseul.

La Fleur would have put me to bed; but not willing he should
see any thing upon my cheek, which would cost the honest fellow
a heart ache—I told him I would go to bed by myself—and bid *40*
him go do the same.

---

33 startled] started　　　40 bed by myself] bed by himself *A2*, bed myself *M2*

29–31. *his chains . . . soul*] Cf. Psalms 105:18: Joseph's "feet they hurt
with fetters: he was laid in iron"; and the paraphrase of this verse in the
Book of Common Prayer (cited by Milic, p. 82, n. 2): Joseph's "feet they
hurt in the stocks: the iron entered into his soul." These texts are combined
in *Sermons,* I, 143 (II.xii): Joseph "had felt [the anguish] of a prison, where
he had long lain neglected in a friendless condition; . . . the Psalmist ac-
quaints [us] that his sufferings were . . . grievous;—*That his feet were hurt
with fetters,* and the iron entered *even into his soul.*"
　　30. *He gave . . . sigh*] Cf. Yorick's sermon entitled "Vindication of
Human Nature" (*Sermons,* I, 88 [II.vii]): "Compassion has so great a share
in our nature, and the miseries of this world are so constant an exercise of it,
as to leave it in no one's power (who deserves the name of man) in this respect,
to live to himself [Romans 14:7] . . . *The sorrowful sighing of the prisoners
will come before him* " (cf. Psalms 79:11). Cf. also the ref. to the "melancholy
notes sounded in every cell" of the Inquisition, in *Sermons,* I, 122, quoted
p. 199.87–89*n*, above.
　　34. *remise*] a hired carriage.
　　36–37. *Monsieur Le Duke de Choiseul*] César-Gabriel de Choiseul (1712–
1785), Minister for Foreign Affairs 1761–1766 (*Letters,* p. 152, n. 4). For
Sterne's application to him for a passport, see p. 226.33–35*n*, below.

THE STARLING.
ROAD TO VERSAILLES.

I GOT into my *remise* the hour I proposed: La Fleur got up behind, and I bid the coachman make the best of his way to Versailles.

As there was nothing in this road, or rather nothing which I look
5 for in travelling, I cannot fill up the blank better than with a short
history of this self-same bird, which became the subject of the last
chapter.

Whilst the Honourable Mr. **** was waiting for a wind at Dover
it had been caught upon the cliffs before it could well fly, by an
10 English lad who was his groom; who not caring to destroy it, had
taken it in his breast into the packet—and by course of feeding it,
and taking it once under his protection, in a day or two grew fond
of it, and got it safe along with him to Paris.

At Paris the lad had laid out a livre in a little cage for the starling,
15 and as he had little to do better the five months his master stay'd
there, he taught it in his mother's tongue the four simple words—
(and no more)—to which I own'd myself so much it's debtor.

Upon his master's going on for Italy—the lad had given it to
the master of the hotel—But his little song for liberty, being in an
20 *unknown* language at Paris—the bird had little or no store set by
him—so La Fleur bought both him and his cage for me for a bottle
of Burgundy.

In my return from Italy I brought him with me to the country
in whose language he had learn'd his notes—and telling the story
25 of him to Lord A—Lord A begg'd the bird of me—in a week Lord
A gave him to Lord B—Lord B made a present of him to Lord
C—and Lord C's gentleman sold him to Lord D's for a shilling—

---

2 best] most   9 upon] up   14 out a] out a a *A2*, out a *M2*   17 it's] a
19 being] was   27 —and Lord] —and Lord's *A2*, —& Lord *M2*

204

Lord D gave him to Lord E—and so on—half round the alphabet —From that rank he pass'd into the lower house, and pass'd the hands of as many commoners——But as all these wanted to *get in*— 30 and my bird wanted to get out—he had almost as little store set by him in London as in Paris.

It is impossible but many of my readers must have heard of him; and if any by mere chance have ever seen him—I beg leave to inform them, that that bird was my bird—or some vile copy set up to 35 represent him.

I have nothing further to add upon him, but that from that time to this, I have borne this poor starling as the crest to my arms.— Thus:

——And let the heralds officers twist his neck about if they dare. 40

---

38 this poor] that poor

---

30. *get in*] i.e., into the House of Lords.
37–40. *I have . . . dare.*] Yorick is probably daring the heralds officers

to do away with the starling on his arms, by twisting about (i.e., wringing) its neck, because he has placed it on his arms illegally, without the authority of the heralds officers. He has placed the starling on his arms in defiance of the laws of heraldry and in deference to the laws of sentiment, presumably in part because of an association between "starling"—dialectical *starn* (fr. OE *stearn*), Latin *sturnus*—and "Sterne" (see *Life*, p. 2). This association makes "this poor starling" a fittingly emblematic crest to the arms of a senti-mental, quixotic knight-errant like "poor Yorick" (p. 156, above), Sterne's alter ego; and it also makes the caged starling a fitting emblem of Yorick's threatened confinement in the Bastille. (Yorick's use of the starling on his arms invites comparison with the burlesque devices on the shields of the imaginary knights Don Quixote encounters in 1.3.4.114–115.)

The arms pictured above appear, with the starling as crest (but without the rococo embellishments), on Sterne's seal next to his signature on a memorial of an indenture dtd. 10 Nov. 1744, in the Registry of Deeds, North Riding of Yorkshire (I am indebted to Professor Arthur Cash for this in-formation). The arms and crest used by Sterne on his seal were used by Sterne's great-grandfather Richard Sterne (1596?–1683), Archbishop of York (1664–1683), on his episcopal seal (I am indebted here to Professor Cash's description of a copy of the seal in the York Minster Library). Accord-ing to the records of the College of Arms, the branch of the Sterne family to which the Archbishop and Laurence Sterne belonged never established a legal right to these arms (a black chevron between three crosses flory, or patonce, sable, on a gold shield). Furthermore, the only authority in the records of the College for a crest to these arms is given in the 1634 Heralds Visitation of Hertfordshire: the crest is a bird rising, of an unspecified and indeterminate species; the pedigree accompanying these arms begins with Robert Sterne of Malden, co. Cambridge (I am indebted for the foregoing information on the Sterne family arms to J. P. Brooke-Little, Bluemantle Pursuivant of Arms, College of Arms).

Cross states that the "more learned of the [Sterne] family evidently as-sociated their name with the old English word *stearn,* dialectical *starn* to this day, signifying a *starling;* for as soon as they rose to rank and wealth, their arms appeared . . . 'surmounted with a starling in proper colors for a crest' " (*Life*, pp. 2–3); Cross does not indicate the source of the information he encloses in quotation marks.

THE ADDRESS.
VERSAILLES.

I SHOULD not like to have my enemy take a view of my mind, when I am going to ask protection of any man: for which reason I generally endeavour to protect myself; but this going to Monsieur Le Duc de C***** was an act of compulsion—had it been an act of choice, I should have done it, I suppose, like other people.   5

How many mean plans of dirty address, as I went along, did my servile heart form! I deserved the Bastile for every one of them.

Then nothing would serve me, when I got within sight of Versailles, but putting words and sentences together, and conceiving attitudes and tones to wreath myself into Monsieur Le Duc de 10 C*****'s good graces—This will do——said I—Just as well, retorted I again, as a coat carried up to him by an adventurous taylor, without taking his measure—Fool! continued I—see Monsieur Le Duc's face first—observe what character is written in it; take notice in what posture he stands to hear you—mark the turns and expres- 15 sions of his body and limbs—And for the tone—the first sound which comes from his lips will give it you; and from all these together you'll compound an address at once upon the spot, which cannot disgust the Duke—the ingredients are his own, and most likely to go down.   20

Well! said I, I wish it well over—Coward again! as if man to man was not equal, throughout the whole surface of the globe; and if in the field—why not face to face in the cabinet too? And trust me, Yorick, whenever it is not so, man is false to himself; and betrays his own succours ten times, where nature does it once. Go to the 25 Duc de C**** with the Bastile in thy looks—My life for it, thou wilt be sent back to Paris in half an hour, with an escort.

I believe so, said I—Then I'll go to the Duke, by heaven! with all the gaity and debonairness in the world.—

---

4. *C*****]* Choiseul; see p. 203.36–37*n*, above.

30 —And there you are wrong again, replied I—A heart at ease,
Yorick, flies into no extremes—'tis ever on its center.—Well! well!
cried I, as the coachman turn'd in at the gates—I find I shall do
very well: and by the time he had wheel'd round the court, and
brought me up to the door, I found myself so much the better for
35 my own lecture, that I neither ascended the steps like a victim to
justice, who was to part with life upon the topmost,—nor did I
mount them with a skip and a couple of strides, as I do when I fly
up, Eliza! to thee, to meet it.

As I enter'd the door of the saloon, I was met by a person who
40 possibly might be the maitre d'hotel, but had more the air of one
of the under secretaries, who told me the Duc de C**** was busy
—I am utterly ignorant, said I, of the forms of obtaining an audience, being an absolute stranger, and what is worse in the present
conjuncture of affairs, being an Englishman too.——He replied,
45 that did not increase the difficulty.—I made him a slight bow, and
told him, I had something of importance to say to Monsieur Le Duc.
The secretary look'd towards the stairs, as if he was about to leave
me to carry up this account to some one—But I must not mislead
you, said I—for what I have to say is of no manner of importance to
50 Monsieur Le Duc de C****—but of great importance to myself.—
C'est une autre affaire, replied he——Not at all, said I, to a man of
gallantry.—But pray, good sir, continued I, when can a stranger
hope to have *accesse?* In not less than two hours, said he, looking
at his watch. The number of equipages in the court-yard seem'd
55 to justify the calculation, that I could have no nearer a prospect—
and as walking backwards and forwards in the saloon, without a
soul to commune with, was for the time as bad as being in the Bastile itself, I instantly went back to my *remise*, and bid the coachman
drive me to the *cordon bleu*, which was the nearest hotel.

60 I think there is a fatality in it—I seldom go to the place I set
out for.

58–59 bid . . . to] bid ∧him drive to∧

LE PATISSER.
VERSAILLES.

BEFORE I had got half-way down the street, I changed my mind: as I am at Versailles, thought I, I might as well take a view of the town; so I pull'd the cord, and ordered the coachman to drive around some of the principal streets—I suppose the town is not very large, said I.—The coachman begg'd pardon for setting me 5 right, and told me it was very superb, and that numbers of the first dukes and marquises and counts had hotels—The Count de B****, of whom the bookseller at the Quai de Conti had spoke so handsomely the night before, came instantly into my mind.—And why should I not go, thought I, to the Count de B****, who has so 10 high an idea of English books, and Englishmen—and tell him my story? so I changed my mind a second time—In truth it was the third; for I had intended that day for Madame de R**** in the Rue St. Pierre, and had devoutly sent her word by her *fille de chambre* that I would assuredly wait upon her—but I am govern'd by cir- 15 cumstances—I cannot govern them: so seeing a man standing with a basket on the other side of the street, as if he had something to sell, I bid La Fleur go up to him and enquire for the Count's hotel.

La Fleur return'd a little pale; and told me it was a Chevalier de St. Louis selling *patès*—It is impossible, La Fleur! said I.—La 20 Fleur could no more account for the phenomenon than myself; but persisted in his story: he had seen the croix set in gold, with its red ribband, he said, tied to his button-hole—and had look'd into the basket and seen the *patès* which the Chevalier was selling; so could not be mistaken in that. 25

---

5 coachman] coachmen *A2*, coachman *M2*   19 de] of

15–16. *I am . . . them*] Cf. *Letters*, No. 106, Toulouse, April 1763, pp. 193–194: "in all things I am governed by circumstances."
19–20. *Chevalier de St. Louis*] Instituted in 1693 by Louis XIV, the Order of St. Louis was awarded to Catholic officers for distinguished military service (*Larousse du XX*ᵉ *Siècle,* Paris, 1931).

Such a reverse in man's life awakens a better principle than curiosity: I could not help looking for some time at him as I sat in the *remise*—the more I look'd at him—his croix and his basket, the stronger they wove themselves into my brain—I got out of the
30 *remise* and went towards him.

He was begirt with a clean linen apron which fell below his knees, and with a sort of a bib went half way up his breast; upon the top of this, but a little below the hem, hung his croix. His basket of little *patès* was cover'd over with a white damask napkin;
35 another of the same kind was spread at the bottom; and there was a look of *propreté* and neatness throughout; that one might have bought his *patès* of him, as much from appetite as sentiment.

He made an offer of them to neither; but stood still with them at the corner of a hotel, for those to buy who chose it, without
40 solicitation.

He was about forty-eight—of a sedate look, something approaching to gravity. I did not wonder.—I went up rather to the basket than him, and having lifted up the napkin and taken one of his *patès* into my hand—I begg'd he would explain the appearance
45 which affected me.

He told me in a few words, that the best part of his life had pass'd in the service, in which, after spending a small patrimony, he had obtain'd a company and the croix with it; but that at the conclusion of the last peace, his regiment being reformed, and the whole corps,
50 with those of some other regiments, left without any provision— he found himself in a wide world without friends, without a livre— and indeed, said he, without any thing but this—(pointing, as he said it, to his croix)—The poor chevalier won my pity, and he finish'd the scene, with winning my esteem too.

---

51 found] had found

---

49. *the last peace*] presumably the Treaty of Aix-la-Chapelle, ending, in 1748, the War of the Austrian Succession. The Treaty of Paris, ending the Seven Years War, was not signed until 1763, and Yorick's *Journey* takes place in 1762.

The king, he said, was the most generous of princes, but his generosity could neither relieve or reward every one, and it was only his misfortune to be amongst the number. He had a little wife, he said, whom he loved, who did the *patisserie*; and added, he felt no dishonour in defending her and himself from want in this way—unless Providence had offer'd him a better.

It would be wicked to with-hold a pleasure from the good, in passing over what happen'd to this poor Chevalier of St. Louis about nine months after.

It seems he usually took his stand near the iron gates which lead up to the palace, and as his croix had caught the eye of numbers, numbers had made the same enquiry which I had done—He had told them the same story, and always with so much modesty and good sense, that it had reach'd at last the king's ears—who hearing the Chevalier had been a gallant officer, and respected by the whole regiment as a man of honour and integrity—he broke up his little trade by a pension of fifteen hundred livres a year.

As I have told this to please the reader, I beg he will allow me to relate another out of its order, to please myself—the two stories reflect light upon each other,—and 'tis a pity they should be parted.

---

56 or] nor   71 by] with

55–56. *his generosity . . . every one*] According to Thicknesse, at this time the Order of St. Louis was "as common as acorns in an oak forest" (*Useful Hints*, p. 211).

THE SWORD.
RENNES.

WHEN states and empires have their periods of declension, and feel in their turns what distress and poverty is—I stop not to tell the causes which gradually brought the house d'E**** in Britany into decay. The Marquis d'E**** had fought up against
5 his condition with great firmness; wishing to preserve, and still shew to the world some little fragments of what his ancestors had been—their indiscretions had put it out of his power. There was enough left for the little exigencies of *obscurity*—But he had two boys who look'd up to him for *light*—he thought they deserved it.
10 He had tried his sword—it could not open the way—the *mounting* was too expensive—and simple œconomy was not a match for it—there was no resource but commerce.

In any other province in France, save Britany, this was smiting the root for ever of the little tree his pride and affection wish'd to
15 see reblossom—But in Britany, there being a provision for this, he avail'd himself of it; and taking an occasion when the states were assembled at Rennes, the Marquis, attended with his two boys,

---

9–10 *light* . . . He had] *light*—He had   15 this] his

---

10. *mounting*] hilt; also, a soldier's equipment (*OED*), and here, perhaps, also the expense of a commission (Milic, p. 89, n. 1).

13–22. *In . . . reclaim it.*] Milic points out (p. 90, n. 3) that until the Revolution, for a French noble to engage in most forms of commercial activity was, by ancient usage, to commit an offense called *déroger à noblesse*—to offend against and consequently to forfeit one's noble rank. Milic notes that in Brittany an ancient custom permitted a nobleman who wished to engage in a commercial activity normally forbidden his rank to suspend his nobility without notice, and allowed him or his descendants to resume their rank by desisting from the activity and declaring to a Judge-Royal that they had done so. (Milic cites [p. 148] M. A. N. Duparc Poullain, *Coutûmes générales du païs et duché de Bretagne*, Rennes, 1745.)

16–17. *the states . . . Rennes*] presumably a ref. to an assembly at Rennes (capital of Brittany) of the Provincial Estates, representing the three estates:

enter'd the court; and having pleaded the right of an ancient law of the duchy, which, though seldom claim'd, he said, was no less in force; he took his sword from his side—Here—said he—take it; 20 and be trusty guardians of it, till better times put me in condition to reclaim it.

The president accepted the Marquis's sword—he stay'd a few minutes to see it deposited in the archives of his house—and departed.   25

The Marquis and his whole family embarked the next day for Martinico, and in about nineteen or twenty years of successful application to business, with some unlook'd for bequests from distant branches of his house—return'd home to reclaim his nobility and to support it.   30

It was an incident of good fortune which will never happen to any traveller, but a sentimental one, that I should be at Rennes at the very time of this solemn requisition: I call it solemn—it was so to me.

The Marquis enter'd the court with his whole family: he sup- 35 ported his lady—his eldest son supported his sister, and his youngest was at the other extreme of the line next his mother.—he put his handkerchief to his face twice—

—There was a dead silence. When the Marquis had approach'd within six paces of the tribunal, he gave the Marchioness to his 40 youngest son, and advancing three steps before his family—he reclaim'd his sword. His sword was given him, and the moment he

---

nobility, clergy, and the Third Estate (represented by delegates of municipalities). In pre-Revolutionary France, the Provincial Estates of Brittany and Languedoc were the most powerful in the country. Sterne's reference to "the court" (l. 35, above) suggests that he may also be thinking of the aristocratic Parlement of Rennes, the supreme or "sovereign" law court, comprised solely of members of the nobility. See Georges Lefebvre, *The Coming of the French Revolution 1789,* trans. R. R. Palmer (New York, 1958), pp. 16–19; Jean Egret, "Les origines de la Révolution en Bretagne (1788–1789)," *Revue Historique,* CCXIII (1955), 189–215.

32. *I . . . Rennes*] I know of no evidence that Sterne ever visited Rennes.

got it into his hand he drew it almost out of the scabbard—'twas the shining face of a friend he had once given up—he look'd atten-
45 tively along it, beginning at the hilt, as if to see whether it was the same—when observing a little rust which it had contracted near the point, he brought it near his eye, and bending his head down over it—I think I saw a tear fall upon the place: I could not be deceived by what followed.

50   "I shall find, said he, some *other way*, to get it off."

When the Marquis had said this, he return'd his sword into its scabbard, made a bow to the guardians of it—and, with his wife and daughter and his two sons following him, walk'd out.

O how I envied him his feelings!

THE PASSPORT.
VERSAILLES.

I FOUND no difficulty in getting admittance to Monsieur Le Count de B****. The set of Shakespears was laid upon the table, and he was tumbling them over. I walk'd up close to the table, and giving first such a look at the books as to make him conceive I knew what they were—I told him I had come without any 5 one to present me, knowing I should meet with a friend in his apartment who, I trusted, would do it for me—it is my countryman the great Shakespear, said I, pointing to his works—*et ayez la bontè, mon cher ami*, apostrophizing his spirit, added I, *de me faire cet honneur la.*—— 10

The Count smil'd at the singularity of the introduction; and seeing I look'd a little pale and sickly, insisted upon my taking an arm-chair: so I sat down; and to save him conjectures upon a visit so out of all rule, I told him simply of the incident in the book-seller's shop, and how that had impell'd me rather to go to him 15 with the story of a little embarrassment I was under, than to any other man in France—And what is your embarrassment? let me hear it, said the Count. So I told him the story just as I have told it the reader—

2–3. *The set of Shakespears . . . over.*] Cf. *Letters*, No. 83, to Garrick, Paris, Jan. 1762, p. 151: " 'Twas an odd incident when I was introduced to the Count de Bissie, which I was at his desire—I found him reading Tristram—" Although Sterne told Garrick that *Tristram Shandy* was "almost as much known" in Paris as in London, the book was less well known than he liked to suppose; see App. E, p. 352, note to p. 261.4–7.

12. *I look'd . . . sickly*] Cf. *Letters*, No. 84, Paris, March 1762, p. 155: "I have got a colour into my face now, though I came with no more than there is in a dishclout"; just before he sailed for France in January 1762, Sterne wrote from Dover: "I hope I shall not go so speedily into [the next world] as my Phiz seems to prophesy" (Cash, "Sterne Letters"). Cf. also Tristram's description of himself in_*TS*, 7.34.527, quoted p. 272.2*n*, below.

20   —And the master of my hotel, said I, as I concluded it, will
needs have it, Monsieur le Count, that I shall be sent to the Bastile
—but I have no apprehensions, continued I—for in falling into
the hands of the most polish'd people in the world, and being conscious I was a true man, and not come to spy the nakedness of the
25 land, I scarce thought I laid at their mercy.—It does not suit the
gallantry of the French, Monsieur le Count, said I, to shew it
against invalids.

An animated blush came into the Count de B****'s cheeks,
as I spoke this—*Ne craignez rien*—Don't fear, said he—Indeed I
30 don't, replied I again—besides, continued I a little sportingly—
I have come laughing all the way from London to Paris, and I do
not think Monsieur le Duc de Choiseul is such an enemy to mirth,
as to send me back crying for my pains.

——My application to you, Monsieur le Compte de B**** (mak-
35 ing him a low bow) is to desire he will not.

The Count heard me with great good nature, or I had not said
half as much—and once or twice said—*C'est bien dit.* So I rested
my cause there—and determined to say no more about it.

The Count led the discourse: we talk'd of indifferent things;
40 —of books and politicks, and men—and then of women—God
bless them all! said I, after much discourse about them—there is
not a man upon earth who loves them so much as I do: after all the
foibles I have seen, and all the satires I have read against them,
still I love them; being firmly persuaded that a man who has not a
45 sort of an affection for the whole sex, is incapable of ever loving a
single one as he ought.

29 *rien*] pas   35 a low bow] a bow   37 *bien dit*] *bon*   45 of an affection]
of affection

24–25. *I was . . . land*] Cf. Genesis 42:9: "Ye are spies; to see the nakedness of the land ye are come." In November 1763, Sterne commented that he
"traversed the South of France so often that I ran a risk of being taken up for
a Spy" (*Letters*, No. 116, Montpellier, p. 205).

Hèh bien! Monsieur *l'Anglois,* said the Count, gaily—You are not come to spy the nakedness of the land—I believe you—*ni encore,* I dare say, *that* of our women—But permit me to conjecture—if, *par hazard,* they fell in your way—that the prospect would 50 not affect you.

I have something within me which cannot bear the shock of the least indecent insinuation: in the sportability of chit-chat I have often endeavoured to conquer it, and with infinite pain have hazarded a thousand things to a dozen of the sex together—the least 55 of which I could not venture to a single one, to gain heaven.

Excuse me, Monsieur Le Count, said I—as for the nakedness of your land, if I saw it, I should cast my eyes over it with tears in them—and for that of your women (blushing at the idea he had excited in me) I am so evangelical in this, and have such a fellow- 60 feeling for what ever is *weak* about them, that I would cover it with a garment, if I knew how to throw it on—But I could wish, continued I, to spy the *nakedness* of their hearts, and through the

---

50 way—that the] way the   56 could] would

61–62. *I would . . . on*] Perhaps we are intended to recall here Genesis 9:23: "And Shem and Japheth took a garment, and laid it upon both their shoulders, and went backward, and covered the nakedness of their father; and their faces were backward, and they saw not their father's nakedness" (see Genesis 9:20–22, quoted p. 83.92–96*n,* above). Cf. also *Sermons,* II, 24–25, ref. to covering "the naked with a garment," quoted in App. E, p. 339, n. 6; and Matthew 25:36: "Naked, and ye clothed me."

62–63. *But . . . hearts*] Cf. Tristram's description of the advantages a biographer would enjoy if a "*Momus's* glass" could have been placed in the human breast: "nothing more would have been wanting, in order to have taken a man's character, but to have . . . look'd in,—view'd the soul stark naked;—observ'd all her motions,—her machinations . . ." (*TS,* 1.23.74). Cf. also *Sermons,* I, 23 (I.ii): "could we see [the heart] naked as it is—stripped of all its passions, unspotted by the world . . ."

63–65. *through . . . by*] Cf. "difference . . . habits," p. 78.13, above; "by tasting . . . our own," in the sermon on the Prodigal Son, App. E, pp. 327–328, note to Preface, pp. 78–85; and the passages from Locke and from the *Spectator,* quoted in App. E, p. 328, n. 5.

different disguises of customs, climates, and religion, find out what
65 is good in them, to fashion my own by—and therefore am I come.

It is for this reason, Monsieur le Compte, continued I, that I
have not seen the Palais royal—nor the Luxembourg—nor the
Façade of the Louvre—nor have attempted to swell the catalogues
we have of pictures, statues, and churches—I conceive every fair
70 being as a temple, and would rather enter in, and see the original

---

64 of] &   70 enter in, and] enter and

---

65. *therefore . . . come*] Cf. Genesis 42:9, quoted p. 216.24–25*n*, above.
66–69. *It is . . . churches*] In declaring that he has seen none of the
standard *videnda* in Paris, Yorick goes one step beyond a forerunner like
Smollett. Smollett assured his readers that he would not repeat the "trite
observations" on the standard sights of the Grand Tour already "circum-
stantially described by twenty different authors of travels" (*Travels,* Letter
No. 27, p. 227; see also Letter No. 6, p. 44, "I shall not . . . perused"); and
he declared: "I don't talk of the busts, the statues, and pictures which
abound at Versailles, and other places, in and about Paris, particularly the
great collection of capital pieces in the Palais-royal" (Letter No. 6, p. 49).
But he "could not leave Paris, without . . . [seeing] the most remarkable
places in and about this capital, such as the Luxemburg, the Palais-Royal, the
Thuilleries, the Louvre" (Letter No. 6, p. 46; cited by Milic, "Sterne and
Smollett's 'Travels' "). Sharp commences his travels with the assurance that
"I do not mean to trouble you . . . with descriptions of churches, statues,
and pictures . . . [which] every account of *Italy,* every guide for travellers,
furnishes in a most tedious abundance" (*Letters from Italy,* Letter No. 1, p. 1).
66–67. *I have not seen the Palais royal*] Cf. Yorick's statement, as the Sentimental Traveller, with Sterne's remark to Garrick that "the Count de Bissie
. . . does me great honours, and gives me leave to go a private way through
his apartments into the palais royal, to view the Duke of Orleans' collections,
every day I have time" (*Letters,* No. 83, Paris, Jan. 1762, p. 151); the comte
de Bissy's apartments were in the Palais Royal (*Life,* p. 304). The duc d'Or-
léans commissioned, for his collection, the sketch of Sterne by Carmontelle
following p. 292, below.
67–68. *Palais royal . . . Louvre*] *Palais royal, Façade of the Louvre:* see map
facing p. 162, above; *the Luxembourg:* the Palais du Luxembourg, in the Quartier du Luxembourg.
69–70. *I conceive . . . temple*] In the *Sermons,* I, 200 (III.ii), Yorick remarks that it is "a pleasing allusion the scripture makes use of in calling us
sometimes a house, and sometimes a temple, according to the more or less

drawings and loose sketches hung up in it, than the transfiguration of Raphael itself.

The thirst of this, continued I, as impatient as that which inflames the breast of the connoisseur, has led me from my own home into France—and from France will lead me through Italy—'tis a 75 quiet journey of the heart in pursuit of NATURE, and those affections which rise out of her, which make us love each other—and the world, better than we do.

The Count said a great many civil things to me upon the occasion; and added very politely how much he stood obliged to Shake- 80

---

exalted qualities of the spiritual guest which is lodged within us" (see esp. John 2:21; I Corinthians 3:16, 6:19; II Corinthians 6:16). Sterne refers to the "temple" erected by Pity in the bosom of Elizabeth Lumley (*Letters,* No. 4, p. 18); and describes the "romantic Apartments" he imagines for himself and Eliza in Shandy Hall as a "Temple" of which she will be the goddess (*Journal,* 29 June, pp. 366–367; 7 June, p. 352). See also his remark that he has been admitted to the "shrines" of the "best Goddesses" in Paris, in *Letters,* No. 85, quoted p. 265.66–71*n,* below; and his ref. to "your Shrine" in the letter he redirected from the "Countess ******" to Eliza (*Letters,* No. 201, Coxwold, [? June 1767], p. 361).

70–71. *would . . . it*] Having observed that Frenchwomen paint their faces so heavily that their true appearance is completely concealed (see p. 93.30–31*n,* above), Smollett comments: "In what manner the insides of their heads are furnished, I would not presume to judge from the conversation of a very few to whom I have had access: but from the nature of their education, which I have heard described, and the natural vivacity of their tempers, I should expect neither sense, sentiment, nor discretion" (*Travels,* Letter No. 7, pp. 57–58).

71. *loose sketches*] Cf. Sterne's hope that in his letters to Eliza, she "will perceive loose touches of an honest heart, in every one of them; which speak more than the most studied periods; and will give thee more ground of trust and reliance upon Yorick, than all that laboured eloquence could supply" (*Letters,* No. 191, March 1767, p. 316).

71–72. *the transfiguration of Raphael*] Cf. Smollett: "You need not doubt but that I went . . . to view the celebrated transfiguration, by Raphael, which, if it was mine, I would cut in two parts" (*Travels,* Letter No. 33, p. 288; cited by Milic, "Sterne and Smollett's 'Travels' ").

75–78. *'tis . . . do*] paraphrased from Sterne's letter to Mrs. William James (*Letters,* No. 218), quoted p. 19, above. Cf. Sterne's other statements about his "design" in *A Sentimental Journey,* cited pp. 19–20, above.

spear for making me known to him—but, *a-propos*, said he—
Shakespear is full of great things—He forgot a small punctillio of
announcing your name—it puts you under a necessity of doing it
yourself.

THE PASSPORT.
VERSAILLES.

THERE is not a more perplexing affair in life to me, than to set about telling any one who I am—for there is scarce any body I cannot give a better account of than of myself; and I have often wish'd I could do it in a single word—and have an end of it. It was the only time and occasion in my life, I could accomplish this 5 to any purpose—for Shakespear lying upon the table, and recollecting I was in his books, I took up Hamlet, and turning immediately to the grave-diggers scene in the fifth act, I lay'd my finger upon YORICK, and advancing the book to the Count, with my finger all the way over the name—*Me, Voici!* said I. 10

Now whether the idea of poor Yorick's skull was put out of the Count's mind, by the reality of my own, or by what magic he could

---

3 than of myself] than myself   10 —*Me, Voici!*] —Me, *Voici! A2,* —Voici! *M2* [cf. *"Me voici!"* (p. 155.8-9, above), which is not underlined in *S1* to indicate italics]

1–6. *There . . . purpose*] Cf. Tristram's conversation with the commissary of the French post: "——My good friend, quoth I——as sure as I am I—and you are you—— ——And who are you? said he.—— ——Don't puzzle me; said I" (*TS,* 7.33.525). For Sterne, a "heteroclite . . . creature in all his declensions" (*TS,* 1.11.25), the problem of identity is a puzzling and fascinating one which is central to *Tristram Shandy* and *A Sentimental Journey.*
11–12. *Now . . . own*] Yorick's reference to his skull (see p. 192.7-8n, above) recalls the explanation he gives in *Tristram Shandy* for riding "a lean, sorry, jack-ass of a horse" that "was full brother to *Rosinante*": "as he never carried one single ounce of flesh upon his own bones, being altogether as spare a figure as his beast, . . . they were, centaur-like,—both of a piece. . . . he found himself going off fast in a consumption; and, with great gravity, would pretend, he could not bear the sight of a fat horse without a dejection of heart, . . . [and] had made choice of the lean one he rode upon, not only to keep himself in countenance, but in spirits. . . . on such a one he could sit mechanically, and meditate as delightfully *de vanitate mundi et fugâ sæculi,* as with the advantage of a death's head before him; . . . he could unite and reconcile every thing,—he could compose his sermon,—he could compose his cough . . ." (*TS,* 1.10.18–20).

drop a period of seven or eight hundred years, makes nothing in
this account—'tis certain the French conceive better than they
15 combine—I wonder at nothing in this world, and the less at this;
inasmuch as one of the first of our own church, for whose candour
and paternal sentiments I have the highest veneration, fell into the
same mistake in the very same case.—"He could not bear, he said,
to look into sermons wrote by the king of Denmark's jester."—

16–19. *one . . . jester.*"] a ref. to the furor caused by Sterne's publication
of Vols. I and II of the *Sermons* under the pseudonym of Yorick; see pp. 5–6,
above. If Sterne is alluding to a specific person, the most obvious candi-
date is Bishop William Warburton, whose initial patronage of Sterne (partly
to avoid being satirized in *Tristram Shandy*) and later disapproval of his indecencies and indiscretions were well known: see *Letters,* esp. No. 48, pp.
92–96; No. 52, pp. 102–103; Nos. 60–65, pp. 110–119; *Life,* pp. 210–211; *TS,*
4.20.298, 9.8.610. For an excellent summary of the relationship between Warburton and Sterne, see Howes, p. 28, n. 5.

As Thomas Gray shrewdly remarked of Vols. I and II of the *Sermons,* in
A Sentimental Journey Yorick is frequently "tottering on the verge of laughter,
& ready to throw his perriwig in the face of his audience" (*Correspondence,*
ed. P. Toynbee and L. Whibley [Oxford, 1935], II, 681). But unlike Tristram,
Yorick discreetly keeps his wig on, at least most of the time. Sterne hoped
that *A Sentimental Journey* would "take in all Kinds of Readers" and be read
by women in the parlor (see pp. 19–21, above). However, the jester's bells are,
I think, muted for another reason. As Shaftesbury observes, nothing requires
more "legerdemain in argument" and "tenderness of hand" than the "art or
science" of exciting a man's laughter and then turning it "against him by his
own consent and with his own concurrence" (see *Characteristics,* ed. Robert-
son, I, 104–105). The critical reception of *Tristram Shandy* proved the hobby-
horsical fondness of "men of feeling" for pathos and refined sentiment, and
"a man's Hobby-Horse is as tender a part as he has about him" (*TS,*
2.12.115). As Tristram remarks, "there is no disputing against Hobby-
Horses"—"the wisest of men in all ages . . . [have] had their Hobby-
Horses"—provided "a man rides his Hobby-Horse peaceably and quietly
along the King's highway, and neither compels you or me to get up behind
him" (*TS,* 1.7–8.13). Some of the grave and "sentimental" readers of Tristram's *Life and Opinions* and of Yorick's *Sermons* who had insisted that Sterne
get up behind them must have found the subtly equivocal oscillations of the
"*Vehicle*" of Yorick's *Journey* disconcertingly irregular and disobliging,
especially the simple travelers (see p. 85, above): "For, to speak the truth,
Yorick had an invincible dislike and opposition in his nature to gravity . . .

Good, my lord! said I—but there are two Yoricks. The Yorick 20
your lordship thinks of, has been dead and buried eight hundred
years ago; he flourish'd in Horwendillus's court—the other Yorick
is myself, who have flourish'd my lord in no court—He shook his
head—Good God! said I, you might as well confound Alexander
the Great, with Alexander the Copper-smith, my lord——'Twas 25
all one, he replied—

—If Alexander king of Macedon could have translated your
lordship, said I—I'm sure your Lordship would not have said so.

The poor Count de B**** fell but into the same *error*—

——*Et, Monsieur, est il Yorick?* cried the Count.—*Je le suis*, said 30
I.—*Vous?*—*Moi—moi qui ai l'honneur de vous parler, Monsieur le
Compte*—*Mon Dieu!* said he, embracing me——*Vous etes Yorick.*

The Count instantly put the Shakespear into his pocket—and
left me alone in his room.

---

20 Good,] good   20 Yoricks] Yorick's *A2, Yoricks M2*

---

as it appeared a cloak for ignorance, or for folly; and then, whenever it fell
in his way, however sheltered and protected, he seldom gave it much quarter.
. . . In the naked temper which a merry heart discovered, he would say
. . . it was no better, but often worse, than . . . *A mysterious carriage of
the body to cover the defects of the mind*" (*TS*, 1.11.26; the italicized maxim is
from La Rochefoucauld).

20–23. *The Yorick . . . court*] In *Tristram Shandy*, Yorick is said to be
"lineally descended" from "*Hamlet*'s *Yorick*," who was "chief Jester" in the
court of "*Horwendillus*, King of *Denmark*" (*TS*, 1.11.24); in Saxo Gram-
maticus' *Historia Danica*, Horwendillus is father of Amlethus, prototype of
Shakespeare's Hamlet. Tristram observes that "*Yorick . . .* as *Shakespear*
said of his ancestor—'*was a man of jest*' " (*TS*, 4.27.324).

24–26. *Good God! . . . replied*—] Is Sterne thinking of the question
Hamlet asks as he holds up Yorick's skull—"Dost thou think Alexander
looked o' this fashion i' th' earth?"—and of his reflections on Alexander's
mortality (*Hamlet*, V.i.185–199)? Perhaps the Count is right in replying
" 'Twas all one."

THE PASSPORT.
VERSAILLES.

I COULD not conceive why the Count de B**** had gone so
abruptly out of the room, any more than I could conceive why
he had put the Shakespear into his pocket—*Mysteries which must
explain themselves, are not worth the loss of time, which a conjecture*
5 *about them takes up*: 'twas better to read Shakespear; so taking up,
"*Much Ado about Nothing*," I transported myself instantly from
the chair I sat in to Messina in Sicily, and got so busy with Don
Pedro and Benedick and Beatrice, that I thought not of Versailles,
the Count, or the Passport.

10   Sweet pliability of man's spirit, that can at once surrender itself
to illusions, which cheat expectation and sorrow of their weary

---

10–13. *Sweet . . . ground*] Cf. the following passages in the *Letters*:
(1) No. 136, Nov. 1764, p. 234: "we must bring three parts in four of the
treat along with us—In short we must be happy within—and then few things
without us make much difference—This is my Shandean philosophy";
(2) No. 77, to John Hall-Stevenson, June 1761, p. 139: "if God, for my consolation under [my miseries], had not poured forth the spirit of Shandeism
into me, which will not suffer me to think two moments upon any grave subject, I would else, just now lay down and die—die——and yet, in half an
hour's time, I'll lay a guinea, I shall be as merry as a monkey—and as mis-
chievous too, and forget it all"; (3) No. 169, July 1766, p. 284, written soon
after returning from his second trip abroad: "with a disposition to be happy,
'tis neither this place, nor t'other that renders us the reverse.—In short each
man's happiness depends upon himself—he is a fool if he does not enjoy it."
Cf. also *TS*, 7.1.479: "Now as for my spirits, little have I to lay to their
charge . . . (unless the mounting me upon a long stick, and playing the
fool with me . . . be accusations) . . . on the contrary, I have much—much
to thank 'em for: cheerily have ye made me tread the path of life with all the
burdens of it (except its cares) upon my back; in no one moment of my existence, that I remember, have ye once deserted me, or tinged the objects which
came in my way, either with sable, or with a sickly green; in dangers ye gilded
my horizon with hope, and when DEATH himself knocked at my door—ye bad
him come again; and in so gay a tone of careless indifference, did ye do it,
that he doubted of his commission"; and cf. Tristram's definition of a hobby-
horse as "*any thing*, which a man makes a shift to get a stride on, to canter it
away from the cares and solicitudes of life" (*TS*, 8.31.584).

moments!—long—long since had ye number'd out my days, had I
not trod so great a part of them upon this enchanted ground:
when my way is too rough for my feet, or too steep for my strength,
I get off it, to some smooth velvet path which fancy has scattered 15
over with rose-buds of delights; and having taken a few turns in it,
come back strengthen'd and refresh'd—When evils press sore
upon me, and there is no retreat from them in this world, then I
take a new course—I leave it—and as I have a clearer idea of the
elysian fields than I have of heaven, I force myself, like Eneas, into 20
them—I see him meet the pensive shade of his forsaken Dido—and
wish to recognize it—I see the injured spirit wave her head, and
turn off silent from the author of her miseries and dishonours—I
lose the feelings for myself in hers—and in those affections which
were wont to make me mourn for her when I was at school. 25

---

12. *number'd out my days*] Cf. Psalms 90:12: "teach us to number our days"
(paraphrased in *Sermons*, II, 12 [IV.vii]).

15–16. *some . . . delights*] Cf. *Letters*, No. 129, Aug. 1764, p. 224, to
Sarah Tuting, who was about to leave England for Naples, in hopes of recovering her health: "The gentle Sally T—— is made up of too fine a texture
for the rough wearing of the world—some gentle Brother . . . [should] pick
carefully out the smoothest tracks for her—scatter roses on them—& when
the lax'd and weary fibre tells him she is weary—take her up in his arms";
and No. 95, June 1762, p. 176, in which he regrets he could not "strew roses
on [his wife's] way" from York to Paris. Cf. also *Sermons*, I, 178 (II.xv): "I
own there are instances of some, who seem to pass through the world, as if all
their paths had been strewed with rose buds of delight;—but a little experience will convince us, 'tis a fatal expectation to go upon"; II, 20 (IV.viii):
"paths strewed with rose-buds of delight" (for a parallel passage in Leightenhouse, see Hammond, p. 134). J.-B. Tollot wrote John Hall-Stevenson in
April 1762 that he envied "les heureuses dispositions de notre ami M^r.
Sterne; tous les objets sont couleur de rose pour cet heureux mortel, et ce
qui se presente aux yeux des autres sous un aspect triste et lugubre, prende
aux siens une face gaye et riante" (quoted from *Letters*, p. 159, n. 10).

20. *elysian fields*] In the *Journal*, Sterne refers to "the Elysium we have so
often and rapturously talk'd of . . . The Bramin of the Vally, shall follow the
track wherever it leads him, to get to his Eliza, & invite her to his Cottage,"
which he elsewhere describes as being "as secluded as the elysian fields"
(16 April, p. 323; 5 July, p. 374; for other refs. to his "Cottage," see p.
273.21–23n, below).

20–21. *Eneas . . . Dido*] *Aeneid*, VI, 450–476.

25. *mourn . . . school*] Toby mourned as a schoolboy for the misfortunes
suffered by the Greeks and Trojans during the siege of Troy (*TS*, 6.32.461).

Surely this is not walking in a vain shadow—nor does man disquiet himself in vain, *by it*—he oftener does so in trusting the issue of his commotions to reason only.—I can safely say for myself, I was never able to conquer any one single bad sensation in my heart so decisively, as by beating up as fast as I could for some kindly and gentle sensation, to fight it upon its own ground.

When I had got to the end of the third act, the Count de B**** entered with my Passport in his hand. Mons. le Duc de C****, said the Count, is as good a prophet, I dare say, as he is a statesman —*Un homme qui rit,* said the duke, *ne sera jamais dangereuz.*—

---

30 kindly] kind   33 entered with my] enter'd my   35 *jamais*] *pas*

26–27. *Surely . . . himself in vain*] paraphrased from Psalms 39:6: "Surely every man walketh in a vain shew: surely they are disquieted in vain . . ." Cf. *Sermons,* II, 14 (IV.vii): "Poor unfortunate creature that [man] is! as if the causes of anguish in the heart were not enow——but he must fill up the measure, with those of caprice; and not only walk in a vain shadow,——but disquiet himself in vain too."

28–31. *I can . . . ground.*] Cf. *Letters,* No. 38A, Summer 1759, p. 76: "One Passion is only ["is best"—*Letters,* No. 38B, p. 79] to be combated by Another."

33–35. *Mons. le Duc de C**** . . . dangereuz.*] C****: Choiseul; see p. 203.36–37n, above. See *Letters,* No. 83, Paris, Jan. 1762, p. 151, to Garrick: "My application to the Count de Choisuiel goes on swimmingly, for not only Mr. Pelletiere . . . has undertaken my affair, but the Count de Limbourgh— the Baron d'Holbach, has offered any security for the inoffensiveness of my behaviour in France—'tis more, you rogue! than you will do—This Baron is one of the most learned noblemen here, the great protector of wits, and the Scavans who are no wits"; and No. 88, Paris, May 1762, p. 164: "The D. of Choiseul has treated me with great Indulgence as to my Stay in France, & has this moment sent me Passports for my family to join me."

See also *Letters,* No. 85, Paris, March 1762, p. 157: to Garrick: "I Shandy it away fifty times more than I was ever wont, talk more nonsense than ever you heard me talk in your days—and to all sorts of people. *Qui le diable est ce homme là*—said Choiseul, t'other day—ce Chevalier Shandy—"; and No. 87, Paris, April 1762, p. 163, to Garrick: "I laugh 'till I cry, and in the same tender moments *cry 'till I laugh.* I Shandy it more than ever, and verily do believe, that by mere Shandeism sublimated by a laughter-loving

Had it been for any one but the king's jester, added the Count, I could not have got it these two hours.—*Pardonnez moi*, Mons. Le Compte, said I—I am not the king's jester.—But you are Yorick?—Yes.—*Et vous plaisantez?*—I answered, Indeed I did jest—but was not paid for it—'twas entirely at my own expence.   *40*

We have no jester at court, Mons. Le Compte, said I, the last we had was in the licentious reign of Charles the IId—since which time our manners have been so gradually refining, that our court at present is so full of patriots, who wish for *nothing* but the honours and wealth of their country—and our ladies are all so chaste, *45* so spotless, so good, so devout—there is nothing for a jester to make a jest of—

Voila un persiflage! cried the Count.

---

people, I fence as much against infirmities, as I do by the benefit of air and climate." (For Sterne's explanation of how he became known in Paris as the "Chevalier Shandy," on his first visit, see Cash, "Sterne Letters," letter dtd. 8 March 1762.) On Sterne's social success in Paris during this period, see p. 261.4–7n, below.

39–40. *Indeed . . . expence.*] in part, an allusion to the decline of Sterne's literary fortunes, which he hoped *A Sentimental Journey* would restore; see pp. 10–11, above.

41–42. *the last . . . Charles the IId*] probably a ref. to Thomas Killigrew (1612–1683), a favorite companion of Charles II, who was appointed master of the revels in 1673. Killigrew was known as Charles II's jester, although he apparently held no official appointment. See Enid Welsford, *The Fool: His Social and Literary History* (New York, n.d.), pp. 187–188; and *DNB*.

44–45. *patriots . . . country*] an ironic thrust at those professing a disinterested zeal for England's welfare in order to further their own ambitions. After the "patriots" led by Pulteney, Carteret, the elder Pitt, et al. came to power in 1742, after Walpole's resignation, their conduct brought professions of "patriotism" into disrepute, and "patriot" was widely used as an ironic term for "a factious disturber of the government" (Johnson, *Dictionary*, 4th ed. [London, 1773]; see also his *Patriot* [London, 1774]).

THE PASSPORT.
VERSAILLES.

A S the Passport was directed to all lieutenant governors, governors, and commandants of cities, generals of armies, justiciaries, and all officers of justice, to let Mr. Yorick, the king's jester, and his baggage, travel quietly along—I own the triumph
5 of obtaining the Passport was not a little tarnish'd by the figure I cut in it—But there is nothing unmixt in this world; and some of the gravest of our divines have carried it so far as to affirm, that enjoyment itself was attended even with a sigh—and that the greatest *they knew of*, terminated *in a general way*, in little better
10 than a convulsion.

I remember the grave and learned Bevoriskius, in his commentary upon the generations from Adam, very naturally breaks off in the middle of a note to give an account to the world of a couple of sparrows upon the out-edge of his window, which had incommoded
15 him all the time he wrote, and at last had entirely taken him off from his genealogy.

—'Tis strange! writes Bevoriskius; but the facts are certain, for I have had the curiosity to mark them down one by one with my pen—but the cock-sparrow during the little time that I could have
20 finished the other half this note, has actually interrupted me with the reiteration of his caresses three and twenty times and a half.

3–4 Yorick . . . and his] Yorick and his   4–5 own . . . the Passport] own the Passport   8 with] in   20 half this] half of this

---

11–22. *I remember the grave and learned Bevoriskius . . . creatures!*] See App. E, pp. 349–351, note to 228.11–22.

228

How merciful, adds Bevoriskius, is heaven to his creatures!

Ill fated Yorick! that the gravest of thy brethren should be able to write that to the world, which stains thy face with crimson, to copy in even thy study. 25

But this is nothing to my travels—So I twice—twice beg pardon for it.

24–25 crimson . . . in] crimson in

CHARACTER.
VERSAILLES.

AND how do you find the French? said the Count de B****, after he had given me the Passport.

The reader may suppose that after so obliging a proof of courtesy, I could not be at a loss to say something handsome to the 5 enquiry.

—*Mais passe, pour cela*—Speak frankly, said he; do you find all the urbanity in the French which the world give us the honour of? —I had found every thing, I said, which confirmed it—*Vraiment*, said the count.—*Les François sont polis.*—To an excess, replied I.

10 The count took notice of the word *excesse*; and would have it I meant more than I said. I defended myself a long time as well as I could against it—he insisted I had a reserve, and that I would speak my opinion frankly.

I believe, Mons. Le Compte, said I, that man has a certain com- 15 pass, as well as an instrument; and that the social and other calls have occasion by turns for every key in him; so that if you begin a note too high or too low, there must be a want either in the upper or under part, to fill up the system of harmony.—The Count de B**** did not understand music, so desired me to explain it some 20 other way. A polish'd nation, my dear Count, said I, makes every

---

13 frankly] *sans menagement*   18 part] parts

20–26. *A polish'd nation . . . the French*] In July 1762, during his first stay in Paris, Sterne observed that "the French have a great deal of urbanity in their composition, and to stay a little time amongst them will be agreeable" (*Letters,* No. 96, p. 178). However, in October 1762 he wrote John Hall-Stevenson from Toulouse that he had become bored with "the eternal platitude of the French characters—little variety, no originality in it at all . . . they are very civil—but civility itself, in that uniform, wearies and bodders one to death" (*Letters,* No. 100, p. 186). And in February 1764, toward the

one its debtor; and besides urbanity itself, like the fair sex, has so
many charms; it goes against the heart to say it can do ill; and
yet, I believe, there is but a certain line of perfection, that man,
take him altogether, is empower'd to arrive at—if he gets beyond,
he rather exchanges qualities, than gets them. I must not presume 25
to say, how far this has affected the French in the subject we are
speaking of—but should it ever be the case of the English, in the
progress of their refinements, to arrive at the same polish which
distinguishes the French, if we did not lose the *politesse de cœur,*

---

22 the heart] the the heart *A2,* the heart *M2*   28 refinements] resentments *A2,*
refinements *M2*

---

end of his first trip abroad, he was determined "to leave France, for I am
heartily tired of it—That insipidity there is in French characters has disgusted your friend Yorick" (*Letters,* No. 120, Montpellier, p. 209). See also
Letters, No. 98, to John Hall-Stevenson, Toulouse, Aug. 1762, p. 181: "The
humour is over for France, and Frenchmen"; and Sterne's criticism of the
lack of "separation" in the characters of Diderot's *Fils naturel,* in *Letters,*
No. 87, quoted p. 257.6–8n, below.

27–33. *but should . . . besides.*] The contrast Yorick draws between the
English character and the French character was a commonplace. Englishmen
prided themselves on the variety and the originality of the English character,
which were considered products of the variety of humors generated by the
English climate and fostered by English liberty (see Hooker, passim; Tave,
pp. 91–105), and were regarded as "the true and natural cause that . . .
[English] Comedies are so much better than those of *France*" (*TS,* 1.21.63).
Like Toby, Yorick is one of the "first-rate productions" of English humor
(see *TS,* 1.21.63–65; 3.20.197). As Sterne's alter ego, Yorick is as "heteroclite" as any English humorist and a singularly original and striking illustration of the view he expresses to the Count de B****. (On Smollett's portrayal
of himself as an English humorist in his *Travels,* see p. 37, above.)

29. *politesse de cœur*] After his second trip to France, Sterne promised Lydia
that when she visited him in England, "I will shew you more real politesses
than any you have met with in France, as mine will come warm from the heart"
(*Letters,* No. 210, Coxwold, Aug. 1767, p. 391).

Smollett observed sourly: "If I was obliged to define politeness, I should
call it, the art of making one's self agreeable. I think it an art that necessarily
implies a sense of decorum, and a delicacy of sentiment. These are qualities,
of which (as far as I have been able to observe) a Frenchman has no idea;

30 which inclines men more to human actions, than courteous ones—
we should at least lose that distinct variety and originality of character, which distinguishes them, not only from each other, but
from all the world besides.

I had a few king William's shillings as smooth as glass in my
35 pocket; and foreseeing they would be of use in the illustration of
my hypothesis, I had got them into my hand, when I had proceeded so far—

See, Mons. Le Compte, said I, rising up, and laying them before
him upon the table—by jingling and rubbing one against another
40 for seventy years together in one body's pocket or another's,
they are become so much alike, you can scarce distinguish one
shilling from another.

The English, like antient medals, kept more apart, and passing
but few peoples hands, preserve the first sharpnesses which the
45 fine hand of nature has given them—they are not so pleasant to
feel—but in return, the legend is so visible, that at the first look

---

34 few king] few of King   39 rubbing] ribbing *A2*, rubbing *M2*   46 but in
return] *mais en revenche*

---

therefore he never can be deemed polite, except by those persons among whom
they are as little understood" (*Travels,* Letter No. 7, p. 61). See also Smollett's comments on the lack of delicacy among the French, quoted p. 182.50–
55*n*, above.

30. *human*] i.e., humane.

34–42. *I had . . . another.*] Curtis notes (*Letters,* p. 188, n. 10) that this
comparison had previously been attributed to Sterne, in the *London Chronicle,*
16–18 April 1765, p. 373: " 'They tell us a pleasant anecdote relating to Mr.
Sterne when he was at Paris: A French Gentleman asked him, If he had found
in France no original characters that he could make use of in his history? *No,*
replied he, *The French resemble old pieces of coin, whose impression is worn
out by rubbing.*' " (Cf. Sterne's use in *Tristram Shandy,* Vol. IX, of an anecdote about his shirts which had previously been reported in the papers [see
p. 13, n. 45, above].)

king William's shillings] issued during the reign of William III (1689–
1702) and bearing his likeness.

you see whose image and superscription they bear.—But the French, Mons. Le Compte, added I, wishing to soften what I had said, have so many excellencies, they can the better spare this— they are a loyal, a gallant, a generous, an ingenious, and good temper'd people as is under heaven—if they have a fault—they are too *serious*.

Mon Dieu! cried the Count, rising out of his chair.

Mais vous plaisantez, said he, correcting his exclamation.—I laid my hand upon my breast, and with earnest gravity assured him, it was my most settled opinion.

The Count said he was mortified, he could not stay to hear my reasons, being engaged to go that moment to dine with the Duc de C****.

But if it is not too far to come to Versailles to eat your soup with me, I beg, before you leave France, I may have the pleasure of knowing you retract your opinion—or, in what manner you support it.—But if you do support it, Mons. Anglois, said he, you must do it with all your powers, because you have the whole world against you.—I promised the Count I would do myself the honour of dining with him before I set out for Italy—so took my leave.

60–67 But . . . leave.] [par.] —but if it is too far to Versailles to ⟨come⟩ eat your soup with me, I beg you will write me a Letter before you leave Paris, that I may have the pleasure of knowing you retract your opinion—or in what manner you support it, Monsᵗ anglois, said he, you must do it with all your powers, because you have the whole world against you— [par.] I promis'd the Count I would do myself either the honour of dining with him, or writing to him before I set out for Italy—so took my leave.

47–65. *the French . . . are too serious . . . against you.*] The opinion Yorick expresses here runs counter to the popular view that, in comparison with the philosophic seriousness of the English (see p. 96.13–14n, above), the French were a gay people (see p. 248.67–70n, below). Cf. Sterne's ref. to the French as a "laughter-loving people" in *Letters*, No. 87, quoted p. 226.33–35n, above. Tristram remarks, at one point in his journey through France, that "The *French* have a *gay* way of treating every thing that is Great" (*TS*, 7.18.501), and, at another, that the French are so serious they cannot understand irony (*TS*, 7.34.526).

THE TEMPTATION.
PARIS.

WHEN I alighted at the hotel, the porter told me a young woman with a band-box had been that moment enquiring for me. — I do not know, said the porter, whether she is gone away or no. I took the key of my chamber of him, and went up stairs; and
5 when I had got within ten steps of the top of the landing before my door, I met her coming easily down.

It was the fair *fille de chambre* I had walked along the Quai de Conti with: Madame de R**** had sent her upon some commissions to a *merchande de modes* within a step or two of the hotel de
10 Modene; and as I had fail'd in waiting upon her, had bid her enquire if I had left Paris; and if so, whether I had not left a letter address'd to her.

As the fair *fille de chambre* was so near my door she turned back, and went into the room with me for a moment or two whilst I
15 wrote a card.

It was a fine still evening in the latter end of the month of May—the crimson window curtains (which were of the same colour of those of the bed) were drawn close—the sun was setting and reflected through them so warm a tint into the fair *fille de chambre*'s
20 face—I thought she blush'd—the idea of it made me blush myself—we were quite alone; and that super-induced a second blush before the first could get off.

There is a sort of a pleasing half guilty blush, where the blood is more in fault than the man—'tis sent impetuous from the heart,
25 and virtue flies after it—not to call it back, but to make the sensation of it more delicious to the nerves—'tis associated.—

---

1 When] Whey *A2,* When *M2*   1 the hotel] my hotel   2 had been that
moment] had that moment been   17 colour of] colour with   21 were quite
alone] were alone

But I'll not describe it.—I felt something at first within me which was not in strict unison with the lesson of virtue I had given her the night before—I sought five minutes for a card—I knew I had not one.—I took up a pen—I laid it down again—my hand 30 trembled—the devil was in me.

I know as well as any one, he is an adversary, whom if we resist, he will fly from us—but I seldom resist him at all; from a terror, that though I may conquer, I may still get a hurt in the combat—so I give up the triumph, for security; and instead of thinking to make 35 him fly, I generally fly myself.

The fair *fille de chambre* came close up to the bureau where I was looking for a card—took up first the pen I cast down, then offered to hold me the ink: she offer'd it so sweetly, I was going to accept it—but I durst not—I have nothing, my dear, said I, to 40 write upon.—Write it, said she, simply, upon any thing.—

I was just going to cry out, Then I will write it, fair girl! upon thy lips.—

If I do, said I, I shall perish—so I took her by the hand, and led her to the door, and begg'd she would not forget the lesson I had 45 given her—She said, Indeed she would not—and as she utter'd it with some earnestness, she turned about, and gave me both her hands, closed together, into mine—it was impossible not to compress them in that situation—I wish'd to let them go; and all the time I held them, I kept arguing within myself against it—and still 50 I held them on.—In two minutes I found I had all the battle to fight over again—and I felt my legs and every limb about me tremble at the idea.

The foot of the bed was within a yard and a half of the place where we were standing—I had still hold of her hands—and how 55 it happened I can give no account, but I neither ask'd her—nor drew her—nor did I think of the bed—but so it did happen, we both sat down.

---

34 conquer . . . in] conquer that I may scratch in

I'll just shew you, said the fair *fille de chambre*, the little purse I
60 have been making to-day to hold your crown. So she put her hand
into her right pocket, which was next me, and felt for it for some
time—then into the left—"She had lost it."—I never bore expectation more quietly—it was in her right pocket at last—she pulled it
out; it was of green taffeta, lined with a little bit of white quilted
65 sattin, and just big enough to hold the crown—she put it into my
hand—it was pretty; and I held it ten minutes with the back of my
hand resting upon her lap—looking sometimes at the purse, sometimes on one side of it.

A stitch or two had broke out in the gathers of my stock—
70 the fair *fille de chambre*, without saying a word, took out her little
hussive, threaded a small needle, and sew'd it up—I foresaw it
would hazard the glory of the day; and as she passed her hand in
silence across and across my neck in the manœuvre, I felt the
laurels shake which fancy had wreath'd about my head.

75 A strap had given way in her walk, and the buckle of her shoe
was just falling off—See, said the *fille de chambre*, holding up her
foot—I could not for my soul but fasten the buckle in return, and
putting in the strap—and lifting up the other foot with it, when I
had done, to see both were right—in doing it too suddenly—it un-
80 avoidably threw the fair *fille de chambre* off her center—and then—

---

62 then into] then into into *A2,* then into *M2*   73 across and across] across
76–77 *chambre . . . I*] chambre—I   77 but fasten] avoid fastening
79–80 see . . . then—] see if both were right—in doing it— / in doing it too suddenly, it unavoidably forced the fair fille de chambre back—& then—

59–68. *I'll . . . one side of it.*] There may be a sexual innuendo here based
on the (common) slang use of "purse" as a term for the female pudendum
(see Eric Partridge, *Dictionary of Slang and Unconventional English,* 5th ed.
[New York, 1961]). J. S. Farmer and W. E. Henley (*Slang and Its Analogues,*
V [1902], 329) cite an instance of this use of the word ca. 1720 in "The
Turnep Ground," a broadside song (J. S. Farmer, ed., *Merry Songs and Bal-
lads* [1897], I, 224): "[When] gently down I L'ayd her, She Op't a Purse as
black as Coal, To hold my Coin."

71. *hussive*] or "housewife": "A pocket-case for needles, pins, thread,
scissors, etc." (*OED*).

THE CONQUEST.

YES——and then—Ye whose clay-cold heads and luke-warm
hearts can argue down or mask your passions—tell me, what
trespass is it that man should have them? or how his spirit stands
answerable, to the father of spirits, but for his conduct under them?

If nature has so wove her web of kindness, that some threads of 5
love and desire are entangled with the piece—must the whole web
be rent in drawing them out?—Whip me such stoics, great governor of nature! said I to myself—Wherever thy providence shall
place me for the trials of my virtue—whatever is my danger—
whatever is my situation—let me feel the movements which rise 10

---

1 Yes——and then] ——and then   4 answerable . . . but] answerable, but

---

5–7. *If . . . out?*] Cf. *Sermons*, I, 214–215 (III.iii), "The Levite and his
Concubine": "What then, ye rash censurers of the world! . . . [if] the *Virtues* in their excesses have approached too near the confines of VICE, Are they
therefore to be cast down the precipice?" Cf. also Tristram's reference to the
extremes of delicacy and the beginnings of concupiscence, quoted p. 40,
above.

5. *wove her web*] Cf. the sermon on "The Abuses of Conscience" (*Sermons,*
II, 67 [IV.xii]; *TS*, 1.17.126): "the mind . . . is conscious of the web she
has wove"; *Letters*, No. 4, p. 18, ref. to Pity's "web of tenderness." Cf. also
"wove into the frame," in the sermon on the Prodigal Son, quoted in App. E,
p. 327, note to Preface, pp. 78–85.

7. *Whip me such stoics*] Cf. *Sermons*, I, 175 (II.xv), the assertion that Job's
serenity did not arise from "stoical stupidity"; I, 233, ref. to the "cold
Stoick," quoted pp. 283.15–27n, below; Tristram's comments on the stoics
catalogued in *TS*, 3.4.160–61. On the antistoicism of Sterne's sermons, see
pp. 28–31, above.

Whip me such] possibly an echo of "Whip me such honest knaves!" in
Othello, I.i.49; for paraphrases and echoes of *Othello* elsewhere in Sterne's
writings, see p. 118.41–43n, above.

8–11. *Wherever . . . man*] Cf. *Sermons*, I, 207–208 (III.iii; parallel noted
by Hammond, pp. 61–62), "The Levite and his Concubine": " '*it is not good*

out of it, and which belong to me as a man—and if I govern them as a good one—I will trust the issues to thy justice, for thou hast made us—and not we ourselves.

As I finish'd my address, I raised the fair *fille de chambre* up by
15 the hand, and led her out of the room—she stood by me till I lock'd the door and put the key in my pocket—*and then*—the victory being quite decisive—and not till then, I press'd my lips to her cheek, and, taking her by the hand again, led her safe to the gate of the hotel.

---

12 issues] Issue

---

for man to be alone' [Genesis 2:18, quoted p. 167.31*n*, above]: . . . Nature will have her yearnings for society and friendship;——a good heart wants some object to be kind to——and the best parts of our blood [cf. p. 115.16, above], and the purest of our spirits suffer most under the destitution. Let the torpid Monk seek heaven comfortless and alone——GOD speed him! For my own part, I fear, I should never so find the way: let me be wise and religious ——but let me be MAN: wherever thy Providence places me, or whatever be the road I take to get to thee——give me some companion in my journey . . . to whom I may say, How fresh is the face of nature! How sweet the flowers of the field! How delicious are these fruits!''

    12–13. *thou . . . ourselves*] paraphrased from Psalms 100:3: ''Know ye that the Lord he is God: it is he that hath made us, and not we ourselves . . .'

THE MYSTERY.

PARIS.

IF a man knows the heart, he will know it was impossible to go back instantly to my chamber—it was touching a cold key with a flat third to it, upon the close of a piece of musick, which had call'd forth my affections—therefore, when I let go the hand of the *fille de chambre*, I remain'd at the gate of the hotel for some time, 5 looking at every one who pass'd by, and forming conjectures upon them, till my attention got fix'd upon a single object which confounded all kind of reasoning upon him.

It was a tall figure of a philosophic serious, adust look, which pass'd and repass'd sedately along the street, making a turn of 10 about sixty paces on each side of the gate of the hotel—the man was about fifty-two—had a small cane under his arm—was dress'd in a dark drab-colour'd coat, waistcoat, and breeches, which seem'd to have seen some years service—they were still clean, and there was a little air of frugal *proprete* throughout him. By his pull- 15 ing off his hat, and his attitude of accosting a good many in his way, I saw he was asking charity; so I got a sous or two out of my pocket ready to give him, as he took me in his turn—he pass'd by me without asking any thing—and yet did not go five steps further before he ask'd charity of a little woman—I was much more likely 20 to have given of the two—He had scarce done with the woman, when he pull'd off his hat to another who was coming the same way.—An ancient gentleman came slowly—and, after him, a young smart one—He let them both pass, and ask'd nothing: I stood observing him half an hour, in which time he had made a dozen turns 25 backwards and forwards, and found that he invariably pursued the same plan.

There were two things very singular in this, which set my brain to work, and to no purpose—the first was, why the man should

---

4 I let] I had let   9 It] He

30 only tell his story to the sex—and secondly—what kind of story it was, and what species of eloquence it could be, which soften'd the hearts of the women, which he knew 'twas to no purpose to practise upon the men.

There were two other circumstances which entangled this mys-
35 tery—the one was, he told every woman what he had to say in her ear, and in a way which had much more the air of a secret than a petition—the other was, it was always successful—he never stopp'd a woman, but she pull'd out her purse, and immediately gave him something.

40   I could form no system to explain the phenomenon.

I had got a riddle to amuse me for the rest of the evening, so I walk'd up stairs to my chamber.

THE CASE OF CONSCIENCE.
PARIS.

I WAS immediately followed up by the master of the hotel, who came into my room to tell me I must provide lodgings else where.—How so, friend? said I.—He answer'd, I had had a young woman lock'd up with me two hours that evening in my bed-chamber, and 'twas against the rules of his house.—Very well, said 5 I, we'll all part friends then—for the girl is no worse—and I am no worse—and you will be just as I found you.——It was enough, he said, to overthrow the credit of his hotel.—*Voyez vous, Monsieur,* said he, pointing to the foot of the bed we had been sitting upon.— I own it had something of the appearance of an evidence; but my 10 pride not suffering me to enter into any detail of the case, I ex-horted him to let his soul sleep in peace, as I resolved to let mine do that night, and that I would discharge what I owed him at breakfast.

I should not have minded, *Monsieur,* said he, if you had had 15 twenty girls—'Tis a score more, replied I, interrupting him, than I ever reckon'd upon—Provided, added he, it had been but in a morning.—And does the difference of the time of the day at Paris make a difference in the sin?—It made a difference, he said, in the scandal.—I like a good distinction in my heart; and cannot say I 20 was intolerably out of temper with the man.—I own it is necessary, re-assumed the master of the hotel, that a stranger at Paris should have the opportunities presented to him of buying lace and silk stockings and ruffles, *et tout cela*—and 'tis nothing if a woman comes with a band box.——O' my conscience, said I, she had one; but I 25

4–5 bed-chamber] chamber   17 been but in] been in   20 and cannot] and I cannot   22 re-assumed] resumed

---

4. *two hours*] Cf. the *apparent* duration of Yorick's colloquy with the *fille de chambre* as recounted pp. 234–238, above. See p. 114.6–12n, above.

never look'd into it.—Then, *Monsieur*, said he, has bought nothing.—Not one earthly thing, replied I.—Because, said he, I could
recommend one to you who would use you *en conscience.*—But I
must see her this night, said I.—He made me a low bow and walk'd
30 down.

Now shall I triumph over this *maitre d'hotel*, cried I—and what
then?—Then I shall let him see I know he is a dirty fellow.—
And what then?—What then!—I was too near myself to say it was
for the sake of others.—I had no good answer left—there was more
35 of spleen than principle in my project, and I was sick of it before the
execution.

In a few minutes the Grisset came in with her box of lace—I'll
buy nothing however, said I, within myself.

The Grisset would shew me every thing—I was hard to please:
40 she would not seem to see it; she open'd her little magazine, laid
all her laces one after another before me—unfolded and folded
them up again one by one with the most patient sweetness—I
might buy—or not—she would let me have every thing at my own
price—the poor creature seem'd anxious to get a penny; and laid
45 herself out to win me, and not so much in a manner which seem'd
artful, as in one I felt simple and caressing.

If there is not a fund of honest cullibility in man, so much the
worse—my heart relented, and I gave up my second resolution as
quietly as the first—Why should I chastise one for the trespass
50 of another? if thou art tributary to this tyrant of an host, thought
I, looking up in her face, so much harder is thy bread.

If I had not had more than four *Louis d'ors* in my purse, there
was no such thing as rising up and shewing her the door, till I
had first laid three of them out in a pair of ruffles.

_____

42 with the most] with most

—The master of the hotel will share the profit with her—no 55
matter—then I have only paid as many a poor soul has *paid* before
me for an act he *could* not do, or think of.

---

57. *an act he could not do*] In *Tristram Shandy,* as Professor Work has remarked, "with a curiously perverse and possibly self-revelatory sense of the
incongruous [Sterne] grins again and again over sexual impotence, the
suspicion of which hovers like a dubious halo over the head of every Shandy
male, including the bull" (*TS*, p. lx).

In a facetious letter to a "Mrs. F——," Sterne described himself as "totally
spiritualized out of all form for conubial purposes— . . . I have not an ounce
& a half of carnality about me—" (*Letters,* No. 140, [? April 1765], pp. 240–
241). In the *Journal,* 24 April (p. 329), he told Eliza he was being treated for
venereal disease, although he had protested to his doctors that "I have had no
commerce whatever with the Sex—not even with my wife . . . these 15
Years—"; and he repeated this statement in recounting the story to the Earl
of Shelburne (*Letters,* No. 196, London, May 1767, p. 343).

THE RIDDLE.
PARIS.

WHEN La Fleur came up to wait upon me at supper, he told me how sorry the master of the hotel was for his affront to me in bidding me change my lodgings.

A man who values a good night's rest will not lay down with 5 enmity in his heart if he can help it—So I bid La Fleur tell the master of the hotel, that I was sorry on my side for the occasion I had given him—and you may tell him, if you will, La Fleur, added I, that if the young woman should call again, I shall not see her.

10 This was a sacrifice not to him, but myself, having resolved, after so narrow an escape, to run no more risks, but to leave Paris, if it was possible, with all the virtue I enter'd in.

C'est deroger à noblesse, Monsieur, said La Fleur, making me a bow down to the ground as he said it—*Et encore Monsieur,* said he, 15 may change his sentiments—and if (*par hazard*) he should like to amuse himself—I find no amusement in it, said I, interrupting him—

Mon Dieu! said La Fleur—and took away.

In an hour's time he came to put me to bed, and was more than 20 commonly officious—something hung upon his lips to say to me, or ask me, which he could not get off: I could not conceive what it was; and indeed gave myself little trouble to find it out, as I had another riddle so much more interesting upon my mind, which was that of the man's asking charity before the door of the hotel—I 25 would have given any thing to have got to the bottom of it; and that, not out of curiosity—'tis so low a principle of enquiry, in

---

26 so low a] a low

---

13. *deroger à noblesse*] See p. 212.13–22*n,* above.

244

general, I would not purchase the gratification of it with a two-sous piece—but a secret, I thought, which so soon and so certainly soften'd the heart of every woman you came near, was a secret at least equal to the philosopher's stone: had I had both the Indies, *30* I would have given up one to have been master of it.

I toss'd and turn'd it almost all night long in my brains to no manner of purpose; and when I awoke in the morning, I found my spirit as much troubled with my *dreams*, as ever the king of Babylon had been with his; and I will not hesitate to affirm, it *35* would have puzzled all the wise men of Paris, as much as those of Chaldea, to have given its interpretation.

---

36 puzzled all the] puzzled the

---

30. *both the Indies*] the West Indies, and the East Indies and India (traditionally associated with fabulous wealth). During the Seven Years War, England had seized several French possessions in the West Indies and broken France's power in India by 1761, the year before Yorick's *Journey*.

33–37. *I found . . . interpretation.*] See Daniel 2:1–11. Nebuchadnezzar's dream is cited in *Sermons*, I, 119 (II.x).

LE DIMANCHE.
PARIS.

IT was Sunday; and when La Fleur came in, in the morning, with my coffee and role and butter, he had got himself so gallantly array'd, I scarce knew him.

I had covenanted at Montriul to give him a new hat with a silver
5 button and loop, and four Louis d'ors *pour s'adoniser*, when we got to Paris; and the poor fellow, to do him justice, had done wonders with it.

He had bought a bright, clean, good scarlet coat and a pair of breeches of the same—They were not a crown worse, he said, for
10 the wearing—I wish'd him hang'd for telling me—they look'd so fresh, that tho' I knew the thing could not be done, yet I would rather have imposed upon my fancy with thinking I had bought them new for the fellow, than that they had come out of the *Rue de friperie.*

15 This is a nicety which makes not the heart sore at Paris.

He had purchased moreover a handsome blue sattin waistcoat, fancifully enough embroidered—this was indeed something the

---

4 Montriul] Montreal *A2* Montrieul *M2* [cf. ch. titles, pp. 121, 124, 126, 128, 132, above] 5 *s'adoniser*] [see p. 125.21–22*tn*, above]

13–14. *Rue de friperie*] See the map facing p. 162, above, which shows a Rue de la Friperie and a Rue de la petite Friperie. These streets are called the Rue de la Grande Friperie and the Rue de la Petite Friperie, respectively, in Deharme's map (see p. xi, above, description of map), and are called the Grande Rue de la Friperie and the Petite Rue de la Friperie in the map of the Quartier des Halles in Piganiol de la Force, *Description historique de la ville de Paris,* new ed., rev., corr., and augmented, III (Paris, 1765), facing p. 281. (On Sterne's use of Piganiol's *Nouveau voyage de France* in *Tristram Shandy,* see p. 335, n. 9, below.) Cross (*Life,* p. 389), Milic (p. 111, n. 5), and Poole (*op. cit.,* p. 160.36*n*, above, p. 392) identify the street Yorick refers to as the Rue de la Vieille Friperie; this name is not given to either of the Rues de la Friperie in the contemporary guides to and maps of Paris I have examined.

worse for the services it had done, but 'twas clean scour'd—the gold had been touch'd up, and upon the whole was rather showy than otherwise—and as the blue was not violent, it suited with the 20 coat and breeches very well: he had squeez'd out of the money, moreover, a new bag and a solitaire; and had insisted with the *fripier*, upon a gold pair of garters to his breeches knees—He had purchased muslin ruffles, *bien brodées*, with four livres of his own money—and a pair of white silk stockings for five more—and, to 25 top all, nature had given him a handsome figure, without costing him a sous.

He enter'd the room thus set off, with his hair dress'd in the first stile, and with a handsome *bouquet* in his breast—in a word, there was that look of festivity in every thing about him, which at 30 once put me in mind it was Sunday—and by combining both together, it instantly struck me, that the favour he wish'd to ask of me the night before, was to spend the day, as every body in Paris spent it, besides. I had scarce made the conjecture, when La Fleur, with infinite humility, but with a look of trust, as if I should 35 not refuse him, begg'd I would grant him the day, *pour faire le galant vis à vis de sa maitresse.*

Now it was the very thing I intended to do myself *vis à vis* Madame de R****—I had retain'd the *remise* on purpose for it, and it would not have mortified my vanity to have had a servant 40 so well dress'd as La Fleur was to have got up behind it: I never could have worse spared him.

But we must *feel*, not argue in these embarrassments—the sons and daughters of service part with liberty, but not with Nature in their contracts; they are flesh and blood, and have their little 45 vanities and wishes in the midst of the house of bondage, as well

---

23 to] for   36–37 *pour . . . maitresse*] [see p. 125.21–22*tn,* above]

---

22. *bag . . . solitaire*] *bag:* "A silken pouch to hold the back-hair of a wig"; *solitaire:* "A loose neck-tie of black silk or broad ribbon" (*OED*).
46. *the house of bondage*] a common Biblical phrase; see Exodus 13:3, 14; 20:2; Deuteronomy 5:6, 6:12.

as their task-masters—no doubt, they have set their self-denials at a price—and their expectations are so unreasonable, that I would often disappoint them, but that their condition puts it so much in 50 my power to do it.

Behold!—Behold, I am thy servant—disarms me at once of the powers of a master—

—Thou shalt go, La Fleur! said I.

—And what mistress, La Fleur, said I, canst thou have pick'd 55 up in so little a time at Paris? La Fleur laid his hand upon his breast, and said 'twas a *petite demoiselle* at Monsieur Le Compte de B****'s.—La Fleur had a heart made for society; and, to speak the truth of him let as few occasions slip him as his master—so that some how or other; but how—heaven knows—he had connected 60 himself with the *demoiselle* upon the landing of the stair-case, during the time I was taken up with my Passport; and as there was time enough for me to win the Count to my interest, La Fleur had contrived to make it do to win the maid to his—the family, it seems, was to be at Paris that day, and he had made a party with 65 her, and two or three more of the Count's houshold, upon the *boulevards.*

Happy people! that once a week at least are sure to lay down all your cares together; and dance and sing and sport away the weights of grievance, which bow down the spirit of other nations to the 70 earth.

---

47 have set their] have their   52 powers] power   62 interest] inte- / terest
A2, intrest *M2*

---

51. *Behold! . . . servant*] Cf. Isaiah 42:1: "Behold my servant"; Psalms 116:16: "O Lord, truly I am thy servant."

67–70. *Happy people! . . . earth.*] a commonplace observation among English travelers (see Maxwell, p. 41), in contrast to Yorick's comment that the French are too serious, which the Count de B**** finds so extraordinary (see

p. 233.47–65*n,* above). (The *Spectator* describes the French as a gay, airy people characterized by vivacity and levity, in Nos. 29 [I, 122], 104 [I, 435], 198 [II, 278], 435 [IV, 29].)

Some English travelers were critical of the gaiety of the French. Smollett considered them to be in some respects a "volatile, giddy, unthinking people," and observed that the "pomp and ceremonies of [the Catholic religion], together with the great number of holidays they observe, howsoever they may keep up the spirits of the commonalty, and help to diminish the sense of their own misery, must certainly, at the same time, produce a frivolous taste for frippery and shew, and encourage a habit of idleness, to which I, in great measure, ascribe the extreme poverty of the lower people" (*Travels,* Letter No. 4, pp. 30–31; see also No. 6, p. 47, and No. 20, pp. 174–175, in which he describes the discomforts of attending the religious festivals at Nice as a "foretaste of purgatory").

THE FRAGMENT.
PARIS.

LA Fleur had left me something to amuse myself with for the day
more than I had bargain'd for, or could have enter'd either
into his head or mine.

He had brought the little print of butter upon a currant leaf;
5 and as the morning was warm, and he had a good step to bring it,
he had begg'd a sheet of waste paper to put betwixt the currant
leaf and his hand—As that was plate sufficient, I bad him lay it
upon the table as it was, and as I resolved to stay within all day I
ordered him to call upon the *traiteur* to bespeak my dinner, and
10 leave me to breakfast by myself.

When I had finish'd the butter, I threw the currant leaf out of
the window, and was going to do the same by the waste paper—
but stopping to read a line first, and that drawing me on to a second and third—I thought it better worth; so I shut the window,
15 and drawing a chair up to it, I sat down to read it.

It was in the old French of Rabelais's time, and for ought I
know might have been wrote by him—it was moreover in a Gothic
letter, and that so faded and gone off by damps and length of time,
it cost me infinite trouble to make any thing of it—I threw it down;
20 and then wrote a letter to Eugenius—then I took it up again, and

---

4 little print] Patte   6 of waste paper] of Paper   11 had . . . butter]
had eat the Pattè of butter   17 know] knew   19 of it—I] of. I

---

9. *traiteur*] "A keeper of an eating-house . . . who supplies or sends out
meals to order" (*OED*).

16–17. *and . . . him*] This casual suggestion is probably not seriously intended, and no source for this anecdote has been found in Rabelais. Sterne is,
of course, extensively indebted to Rabelais in *Tristram Shandy*.

embroiled my patience with it afresh—and then to cure that, I wrote a letter to Eliza.—Still it kept hold of me; and the difficulty of understanding it increased but the desire.

I got my dinner; and after I had enlightened my mind with a bottle of Burgundy, I at it again—and after two or three hours 25 poring upon it, with almost as deep attention as ever Gruter or Jacob Spon did upon a nonsensical inscription, I thought I made sense of it; but to make sure of it, the best way, I imagined, was to turn it into English, and see how it would look then—so I went on leisurely, as a trifling man does, sometimes writing a sentence— 30 then taking a turn or two—and then looking how the world went, out of the window; so that it was nine o'clock at night before I had done it—I then begun and read it as follows.

26. *Gruter*] Jan Gruytère (1560–1627), historian and author of *Inscriptiones antiquae totius orbis Romanorum* (1603).

27. *Jacob Spon*] French antiquarian and historian (1647–1685); Tristram refers to him in *TS*, 7.31.521.

THE FRAGMENT.
PARIS.

——Now as the notary's wife disputed the point with the notary
with too much heat—I wish, said the notary, throwing down the
parchment, that there was another notary here only to set down
and attest all this——

5 —And what would you do then, Monsieur? said she, rising
hastily up—the notary's wife was a little fume of a woman, and the
notary thought it well to avoid a hurricane by a mild reply—I
would go, answer'd he, to bed.——You may go to the devil,
answer'd the notary's wife.

10 Now there happening to be but one bed in the house, the other
two rooms being unfurnish'd, as is the custom at Paris, and the
notary not caring to lie in the same bed with a woman who had
but that moment sent him pell-mell to the devil, went forth with his
hat and cane and short cloak, the night being very windy, and
15 walk'd out ill at ease towards the *pont neuf.*

Of all the bridges which ever were built, the whole world who
have pass'd over the *pont neuf,* must own, that it is the noblest—
the finest—the grandest—the lightest—the longest—the broadest
that ever conjoin'd land and land together upon the face of the
20 terraqueous globe——

16–22. *Of . . . Frenchman.*] Vrooman points out (pp. 327–328) that
Sterne is making fun of French pride in the Pont Neuf (see map facing p.
162, above), which had become a standing joke among Englishmen. He cites
Fielding's mock "letter from a French gentleman [in London] to his friend in
Paris; in imitation of Horace, Addison, and all other writers of travelling
letters," in which the Frenchman refers to "the New Bridge, which must be
greatly admired by all who have not seen the Pontneuf" (*Familiar Letters*
[London, 1747], Letter No. xli, in *Works,* ed. W. E. Henley, [London, 1903],
XVI, 32); Vrooman cites also Cole's observation that "to hear the [French]
Descriptions of the Pont-Neuf, & the Pont-Royal, one would suppose that
there were not two such Bridges to be met with any where" (*Journey to Paris,*
p. 48).

By this, it seems, as if the author of the fragment had not been a Frenchman.

The worst fault which divines and the doctors of the Sorbonne can allege against it, is, that if there is but a cap-full of wind in or about Paris, 'tis more blasphemously *sacre Dieu*'d there than in any 25 other aperture of the whole city—and with reason, good and cogent Messieurs; for it comes against you without crying *garde d'eau*, and with such unpremeditable puffs, that of the few who cross it with their hats on, not one in fifty but hazards two livres and a half, which is its full worth. 30

The poor notary, just as he was passing by the sentry, instinctively clapp'd his cane to the side of it, but in raising it up, the point of his cane catching hold of the loop of the sentinel's hat hoisted it over the spikes of the ballustrade clear into the Seine—

—*'Tis an ill wind*, said a boatsman, who catch'd it, *which blows* 35 *no body any good.*

The sentry being a gascon incontinently twirl'd up his whiskers, and levell'd his harquebuss.

Harquebusses in those days went off with matches; and an old woman's paper lanthorn at the end of the bridge happening to be 40 blown out, she had borrow'd the sentry's match to light it—it gave a moment's time for the gascon's blood to run cool, and turn the accident better to his advantage—*'Tis an ill wind*, said he, catching off the notary's castor, and legitimating the capture with the boatman's adage. 45

---

32 up, the] up the *A2*, up, the *M2*

23–26. *The worst . . . with reason*] When his hat is blown off as he is entering Avignon, Tristram observes: "I think it wrong . . . that [a man] should therefore say, '*Avignion* is more subject to high winds than any town in all *France*' " (*TS*, 7.41.533).

27. *garde d'eau*] an abbreviated form of "[Prenez] garde à l'eau," a warning given before emptying slops or other refuse from a window into the streets below, as was then customary (Milic, p. 114, n. 5).

The poor notary cross'd the bridge, and passing along the rue de Dauphine into the fauxbourgs of St. Germain, lamented himself as he walk'd along in this manner:

Luckless man! that I am, said the notary, to be the sport of
50 hurricanes all my days——to be born to have the storm of ill language levell'd against me and my profession wherever I go— to be forced into marriage by the thunder of the church to a tempest of a woman—to be driven forth out of my house by domestic winds, and despoil'd of my castor by pontific ones—to be here,
55 bare-headed, in a windy night at the mercy of the ebbs and flows of accidents—where am I to lay my head?—miserable man! what wind in the two-and-thirty points of the whole compass can blow unto thee, as it does to the rest of thy fellow creatures, good!

As the notary was passing on by a dark passage, complaining in
60 this sort, a voice call'd out to a girl, to bid her run for the next notary—now the notary being the next, and availing himself of his situation, walk'd up the passage to the door, and passing through an old sort of a saloon, was usher'd into a large chamber dismantled of every thing but a long military pike—a breast plate—a rusty
65 old sword, and bandoleer, hung up equi-distant in four different places against the wall.

An old personage, who had heretofore been a gentleman, and unless decay of fortune taints the blood along with it was a gentle-man at that time, lay supporting his head upon his hand in his bed;
70 a little table with a taper burning was set close beside it, and close by the table was placed a chair—the notary sat him down in it; and pulling out his ink-horn and a sheet or two of paper which he had in his pocket, he placed them before him, and dipping his pen in his ink, and leaning his breast over the table, he disposed every
75 thing to make the gentleman's last will and testament.

---

48 in] after   51 against me and my] against my   55 at] to   56 am I]
I am *A*2, am ∧I∧ *M*2   57 the whole compass] the compass

46–47. *rue de Dauphine*] The Rue Dauphine runs into the Pont Neuf; see map facing p. 162, above.
55. *ebbs and flows*] See p. 70.6*n*, above.

Alas! Monsieur le Notaire, said the gentleman, raising himself up a little, I have nothing to bequeath which will pay the expence of bequeathing, except the history of myself, which, I could not die in peace unless I left it as a legacy to the world; the profits arising out of it, I bequeath to you for the pains of taking it from me—it is a story so uncommon, it must be read by all mankind—it will make the fortunes of your house—the notary dipp'd his pen into his ink-horn—Almighty director of every event in my life! said the old gentleman, looking up earnestly and raising his hands towards heaven—thou whose hand has led me on through such a labyrinth of strange passages down into this scene of desolation, assist the decaying memory of an old, infirm, and broken-hearted man— direct my tongue, by the spirit of thy eternal truth, that this stranger may set down naught but what is written in that Book, from whose records, said he, clasping his hands together, I am to be condemn'd or acquitted!——the notary held up the point of his pen betwixt the taper and his eye—

—It is a story, Monsieur le Notaire, said the gentleman, which will rouse up every affection in nature—it will kill the humane, and touch the heart of cruelty herself with pity—

—The notary was inflamed with a desire to begin, and put his pen a third time into his ink-horn—and the old gentleman turning a little more towards the notary, began to dictate his story in these words—

—And where is the rest of it, La Fleur? said I, as he just then enter'd the room.

80

85

90

95

100

---

81 be] me *A2*, be *M2*

---

89. *that Book*] presumably the "book of life" in Revelation 20:12 (from which Uncle Toby's oath is blotted by the tear of the Recording Angel?—*TS*, 6.8.425).

100. *where . . . La Fleur?*] Cf. Cervantes' use of this device in *Don Quixote*, 1.1.8.50–1.2.1.53. Several stories in *Tristram Shandy* are promised but not told, or are left uncompleted: see, e.g., 4.1.272–273, 8.19.559 ff., 8.22.575, 9.6.606 ff.

THE FRAGMENT
AND the *BOUQUET.
PARIS.

WHEN La Fleur came up close to the table, and was made to comprehend what I wanted, he told me there were only two other sheets of it which he had wrapt round the stalks of a *bouquet* to keep it together, which he had presented to the *demoiselle* upon
5 the *boulevards*—Then, prithee, La Fleur, said I, step back to her to the Count de B****'s hotel, and *see if you canst get*—There is no doubt of it, said La Fleur—and away he flew.

In a very little time the poor fellow came back quite out of breath, with deeper marks of disappointment in his looks than
10 could arise from the simple irreparability of the fragment—*Juste ciel!* in less than two minutes that the poor fellow had taken his last tender farewel of her—his faithless mistress had given his *gage d'amour* to one of the Count's footmen—the footman to a young sempstress—and the sempstress to a fiddler, with my frag-
15 ment at the end of it—Our misfortunes were involved together— I gave a sigh—and La Fleur echo'd it back again to my ear—

—How perfidious! cried La Fleur—How unlucky! said I.—

—I should not have been mortified, Monsieur, quoth La Fleur, if she had lost it—Nor I, La Fleur, said I, had I found it.

20 Whether I did or no, will be seen hereafter.

* Nosegay.

---

6 *canst*] can't   21 *Nosegay.] [In *A*2 this note and the notes on pp. 257.18 and 261.18, below, are separated from the text by a line running the width of the text.]

THE ACT OF CHARITY.
PARIS.

THE man who either disdains or fears to walk up a dark entry may be an excellent good man, and fit for a hundred things; but he will not do to make a good sentimental traveller. I count little of the many things I see pass at broad noon day, in large and open streets.—Nature is shy, and hates to act before spectators; 5 but in such an unobserved corner, you sometimes see a single short scene of her's worth all the sentiments of a dozen French plays compounded together—and yet they are *absolutely* fine;—and whenever I have a more brilliant affair upon my hands than common, as they suit a preacher just as well as a hero, I generally make 10 my sermon out of 'em—and for the text—"Capadosia, Pontus and Asia, Phrygia and Pamphilia"—is as good as any one in the Bible.

There is a long dark passage issuing out from the opera comique into a narrow street; 'tis trod by a few who humbly wait for a *fiacre**, or wish to get off quietly o'foot when the opera is done. 15 At the end of it, towards the theatre, 'tis lighted by a small candle, the light of which is almost lost before you get half-way down,

* Hackney-coach.

6–8. *a single short scene . . . together*] Cf. Sterne's comment to Garrick on a translation of Diderot's *Fils naturel:* "It has too much sentiment in it, (at least for me) the speeches too long, and savour too much of *preaching*—this may be a second reason, it is not to my taste—'Tis all love, love, love, throughout, without much separation in the character; so I fear it would not do for your stage, and perhaps for the very reason which recommend[s] it to a French one" (*Letters,* No. 87, Paris, April 1762, p. 162; Curtis notes that the play was a failure).

11–12. *the text . . . Pamphilia"*] See Acts 2:1–11, esp. 9–10. (Work notes that Tristram is probably echoing Acts 2:9 in *TS,* 6.30.457, "Capadocius . . . Asius.")

13. *a long dark passage*] Poole (op. cit., p. 160.36n, above, pp. 392–393) found such a passage.

but near the door—'tis more for ornament than use: you see it as a
20 fix'd star of the least magnitude; it burns—but does little good to
the world, that we know of.

In returning along this passage, I discern'd, as I approach'd
within five or six paces of the door, two ladies standing arm in
arm, with their backs against the wall, waiting, as I imagined, for a
25 *fiacre*—as they were next the door, I thought they had a prior
right; so edged myself up within a yard or little more of them,
and quietly took my stand—I was in black, and scarce seen.

The lady next me was a tall lean figure of a woman of about
thirty-six; the other of the same size and make, of about forty;
30 there was no mark of wife or widow in any one part of either of
them—they seem'd to be two upright vestal sisters, unsapp'd by
caresses, unbroke in upon by tender salutations: I could have
wish'd to have made them happy—their happiness was destin'd,
that night, to come from another quarter.

35 A low voice, with a good turn of expression, and sweet cadence
at the end of it, begg'd for a twelve-sous piece betwixt them, for the
love of heaven. I thought it singular, that a beggar should fix the
quota of an alms—and that the sum should be twelve times as
much as what is usually given in the dark. They both seemed
40 astonish'd at it as much as myself.—Twelve sous! said one—a
twelve-sous piece! said the other—and made no reply.

The poor man said, He knew not how to ask less of ladies of
their rank; and bow'd down his head to the ground.

Poo! said they—we have no money.

45 The beggar remained silent for a moment or two, and renew'd
his supplication.

---

19 near . . . 'tis] near—tis   28 woman of about] woman about   29 other
of] other much of   45 silent for a] silent a

Do not, my fair young ladies, said he, stop your good ears against me—Upon my word, honest man! said the younger, we have no change—Then God bless you, said the poor man, and multiply those joys which you can give to others without change!— *50* I observed the elder sister put her hand into her pocket—I'll see, said she, if I have a sous.—A sous! give twelve, said the supplicant; Nature has been bountiful to you, be bountiful to a poor man.

I would, friend, with all my heart, said the younger, if I had it.

My fair charitable! said he, addressing himself to the elder— *55* What is it but your goodness and humanity which makes your bright eyes so sweet, that they outshine the morning even in this dark passage? and what was it which made the Marquis de Santerre and his brother say so much of you both as they just pass'd by?

The two ladies seemed much affected; and impulsively at the *60* same time they both put their hands into their pocket, and each took out a twelve-sous piece.

The contest betwixt them and the poor supplicant was no more —it was continued betwixt themselves, which of the two should give the twelve-sous piece in charity—and to end the dispute, they *65* both gave it together, and the man went away.

---

47 your good ears] your ears   52 give twelve] give me twelve   55 My fair
charitable!] dear Venus!   57 the] the the *A2,* the *M2*   61 pocket] pockets

---

58. *Santerre*] i.e., "sans terres"? (Milic, p. 121, n. 4).

THE RIDDLE EXPLAINED.
PARIS.

I Stepp'd hastily after him: it was the very man whose success in
asking charity of the women before the door of the hotel had so
puzzled me—and I found at once his secret, or at least the basis of
it—'twas flattery.

5   Delicious essence! how refreshing art thou to nature! how
strongly are all its powers and all its weaknesses on thy side! how
sweetly dost thou mix with the blood, and help it through the most
difficult and tortuous passages to the heart!

The poor man, as he was not straighten'd for time, had given it
10 here in a larger dose: 'tis certain he had a way of bringing it into
less form, for the many sudden cases he had to do with in the
streets; but how he contrived to correct, sweeten, concentre, and
qualify it—I vex not my spirit with the inquiry—it is enough, the
beggar gain'd two twelve-sous pieces—and they can best tell the
15 rest, who have gain'd much greater matters by it.

---

15 have gain'd much] have much

PARIS.

WE get forwards in the world not so much by doing services, as receiving them: you take a withering twig, and put it in the ground; and then you water it, because you have planted it.

Mons. Le Compte de B****, merely because he had done me one kindness in the affair of my passport, would go on and do me 5 another, the few days he was at Paris, in making me known to a few people of rank; and they were to present me to others, and so on.

I had got master of my *secret*, just in time to turn these honours to some little account; otherwise, as is commonly the case, I should have din'd or supp'd a single time or two round, and then by *trans-* 10 *lating* French looks and attitudes into plain English, I should presently have seen, that I had got hold of the *couvert** of some more entertaining guest; and in course, should have resigned all my places one after another, merely upon the principle that I could not keep them.—As it was, things did not go much amiss. 15

I had the honour of being introduced to the old Marquis de B****: in days of yore he had signaliz'd himself by some small

* Plate, napkin, knife, fork, and spoon.

2–3. *you take . . . planted it*] This image may be indebted to the parable of the twig in Ezekiel 17:1–10, which is planted and watered, and then withers.

4–7. *Mons. Le Compte de B**** . . . and so on.*] On Sterne's reception in the salons of Paris during his first stay there (he remained in Paris from January through mid-July 1762), see *Life,* pp. 292 ff.; *Letters,* pp. 151–180; and App. E, pp. 352–353, note to p. 261.4–7. The urbanely ironic politesse of Yorick's account of the Parisian salons may have been prompted partly by Sterne's awareness that he might visit Paris again after *A Sentimental Journey* was published: as he remarked to Robert Foley (his banker in Paris) of Vol. VII of *Tristram Shandy,* "I am quite civil to the parisiens—et *per Cosa,*—You know—tis likely I may see 'em again—& possibly this Spring" (*Letters,* No. 134, York, Nov. 1764, p. 231). (He considered making a third trip to Paris in December 1766; see *Letters,* No. 172, Sept. 1766, p. 288.)

16–17. *the old Marquis de B****] identified by Cross (*Life,* p. 306) as the

feats of chivalry in the *Cour d'amour*, and had dress'd himself out
20 to the idea of tilts and tournaments ever since—the Marquis de
B**** wish'd to have it thought the affair was somewhere else than
in his brain. "He could like to take a trip to England," and ask'd
much of the English ladies. Stay where you are, I beseech you,
Mons. le Marquise, said I—Les Messrs. Angloise can scarce get a
25 kind look from them as it is.—The Marquis invited me to supper.

Mons. P**** the farmer general was just as inquisitive about our
taxes.—They were very considerable, he heard—If we knew but
how to collect them, said I, making him a low bow.

I could never have been invited to Mons. P****'s concerts upon
30 any other terms.

---

duc de Biron, maréchal de France (presumably Louis-Antoine de Gontaut
[1700–1788], duc de Biron, who was made maréchal de France in 1757).
   26–30. *Mons. P**** the farmer general . . . terms.*] a ref. to Alexandre-
Jean-Joseph Le Riche de la Popelinière (1692–1762). See *Letters*, No. 84,
Paris, March 1762, p. 155: "There is Monsieur Popelinière, who lives here
like a sovereign prince; keeps a company of musicians always in his house,
and a full set of players; and gives concerts and plays alternately to the
grandees of this metropolis; he is the richest of all the farmer[s general]; he
did me the honour last night to send me an invitation to his house, while I
stayed here—that is, to his music and table." Although some of the farmers-
general were cultured patrons of the arts, many of them expended their
money on vulgar displays of wealth, and they were frequently satirized in
eighteenth-century French literature.
   The farmers-general collected the indirect taxes, e.g., the tax on salt
(*gabelle*), and excise and customs duties, at the provincial level. The difference between the amount due the Treasury and what they were able to collect
made them extremely wealthy. Their exactions were part of the crushing burden of taxes borne by the French peasantry, and they were systematically executed during the Terror. Many English travelers attacked the farmers-general
and the oppressiveness of French taxes: see, e.g., Smollett, *Travels*, Letters
No. 5, p. 39; No. 36, pp. 308 ff.; Thicknesse, *Useful Hints*, p. 43. See also
Tristram's comment on the *gabelle* and his protest to the commissary of the
post that had he treated him (Tristram) like a Frenchman, he would have
"first taken my pocket, as you do with your own people—and then left me
bare a—'d after" (*TS*, 7.34–35.526–527).

I had been misrepresented to Madame de Q*** as an *esprit*—
Madam de Q*** was an *esprit* herself; she burnt with impatience to
see me, and hear me talk. I had not taken my seat, before I saw she
did not care a sous whether I had any wit or no—I was let in, to be
convinced she had.—I call heaven to witness I never once open'd 35
the door of my lips.

Madame de Q*** vow'd to every creature she met, "She had
never had a more improving conversation with a man in her life."

There are three epochas in the empire of a French-woman—
She is coquette—then deist—then *devôte:* the empire during these 40
is never lost—she only changes her subjects: when thirty-five

---

33 hear] to hear   35 never once open'd] never open'd

---

32. *an esprit*] probably partly in the sense of "a *Bel Esprit,* or Free-
Thinker," as the Rev. William Cole called Mme Geoffrin (*Journey to Paris,*
p. 82), and partly in the sense of "what the *French* call a *Bel Esprit,* by which
they would express a Genius refined by Conversation, Reflection, and the
Reading of the most polite Authors" (*Spectator* No. 160 [II, 127]).

40. *coquette . . . deist . . . devôte] coquette:* see the descriptions in *Spectator* No. 247 (II, 459); No. 281 (II, 594–597).

deist: here, probably a general term covering the various forms of freethinking, including materialism and atheism, then fashionable in the Parisian
salons frequented by those hostile to the doctrines and institutions of ortho-
dox Christianity, particularly Roman Catholicism. (See the comment in *Spectator* No. 186 [II, 232] that in England the "Atheist . . . [is] retired into
Deism, and a Disbelief of revealed Religion.") Like many other English travelers, the Rev. William Cole remarked on "the modish French Taste, in philoso-
phizing Revelation out of Doors . . . [which] is the *Ton des François* now almost universally among Men of Fashion, & not uncommon among the Ladies"
(*Journey to Paris,* pp. 63–64; see also pp. 68, 95).

devôte: a woman ostentatiously devoted to the forms and observances of in-
stitutional religion; see the description of the character of a "*Devôtée*" in *Spectator* No. 354 (III, 320–321). Smollett observed that the "character of a
devotee, which is hardly known in England, is very common here. . . . The
rich *devotee* has her favorite confessor, whom she consults and regales in private, at her own house; and this spiritual director generally governs the whole

years and more have unpeopled her dominions of the slaves of love, she re-peoples it with slaves of infidelity—and then with the slaves of the Church.

45 Madame de V*** was vibrating betwixt the first of these epochas: the colour of the rose was shading fast away—she ought to have been a deist five years before the time I had the honour to pay my first visit.

She placed me upon the same sopha with her, for the sake of
50 disputing the point of religion more closely.—In short, Madame de V*** told me she believed nothing.

I told Madame de V*** it might be her principle; but I was sure it could not be her interest to level the outworks, without which I could not conceive how such a citadel as hers could be defended—
55 that there was not a more dangerous thing in the world, than for a beauty to be a deist—that it was a debt I owed my creed, not to conceal it from her—that I had not been five minutes sat upon the sopha besides her, but I had begun to form designs—and what is it, but the sentiments of religion, and the persuasion they had
60 existed in her breast, which could have check'd them as they rose up.

43-44 then with the slaves] then with Slaves   59-60 they had existed] they existed   60 breast, which could have] breast, had

---

family. For my own part, I never knew a fanatic that was not an hypocrite at bottom" (*Travels,* Letter No. 5, p. 41). Thicknesse commented that in France, "women of fashion are libertines in their youth, and of course devotees in old age. So soon as they find themselves neglected by the men, their passions take another turn; and, like the enthusiastic Methodist, they fansy themselves in love with Jesus Christ"; he observed that "Paris abounds with a great number of married women, from thirty-five to forty-five years of age, who are as *notorious* for their devotion, as for their incontinence" (*Useful Hints,* pp. 59, 169–170; cited by Vrooman, p. 335). In his journey through France, Tristram comments that Janatone "has a little of the *devote:* but that, sir, is a terce to a nine in your favour" (*TS,* 7.9.491; for Janatone, see p. 121.16n, above).

45. *Madame de V***] identified by Cross (*Life,* p. 307) as "Madame de Vence, said to have been a descendant of Madame de Sévigné."

We are not adamant, said I, taking hold of her hand—and there is need of all restraints, till age in her own time steals in and lays them on us—but, my dear lady, said I, kissing her hand—'tis too—too soon— 65

I declare I had the credit all over Paris of unperverting Madame de V***.—She affirmed to Mons. D*** and the Abbe M***, that in one half hour I had said more for revealed religion, than all their Encyclopedia had said against it—I was lifted directly into Madame de V***'s *Coterie*—and she put off the epocha of deism for two 70 years.

71–82 years. . . . For three weeks] years. [par.] Monsieur Le Marquis de M**** who was of the Coterie, was a Connoisseur in pictures—he had got possession of an apocryphal Piece of Poussin's, & had purchased some twenty bad ones more in Italy to accompany it—You have some good pictures in England Mons.ʳ—said the Marquis —you should come Mons.ʳ Le Marquis, & teach us to know their Value— [par.] For three weeks

66–71. *I declare . . . years.*] In March 1762 Sterne wrote Garrick from Paris: "I have been introduced to one half of their best Goddesses, and in a month more shall be admitted to the shrines of the other half—but I neither worship—or fall (much) upon my knees before them; but on the contrary, have converted many unto Shandeism—for be it known I Shandy it away fifty times more than I was ever wont . . ." (*Letters*, No. 85, p. 157).

67. *Mons. D****] Denis Diderot (1713–1784), freethinker, philosopher, novelist, satirist, and dramatist; and editor of and contributor to the *Encyclopédie*. Sterne met him during his first trip to Paris, and refers to him frequently in his letters. Of *Tristram Shandy,* which strongly influenced his novel *Jacques le fataliste* (1796), Diderot remarked: "Ce livre si fou, si sage et si gai est le Rabelais des Anglois. . . . Il est impossible de vous en donner une autre idée que celle d'une satyre universelle" (quoted from *Letters*, p. 168, n. 2).

67. *Abbe M****] André Morellet (1727–1819), who contributed articles on theology and metaphysics to the *Encyclopédie* (see next note) and frequented the salon of the Baron d'Holbach (see Sterne's letter of 8 March 1762, quoted in App. E, pp. 352–353, note to p. 261.4–7).

69. *Encyclopedia*] *L'Encyclopédie, ou dictionnaire raisonné des sciences, des arts et des métiers* (35 vols., 1751–1780). Published under the direction of Diderot and of D'Alembert, it developed from a proposal to translate Ephraim Chambers' *Cyclopedia: Or, An Universal Dictionary of Arts and Sciences* (from which

I remember it was in this *Coterie*, in the middle of a discourse, in which I was shewing the necessity of a *first cause*, that the young Count de Faineant took me by the hand to the furthest corner of
75 the room, to tell me my *solitaire* was pinn'd too strait about my neck—It should be *plus badinant*, said the Count, looking down upon his own—but a word, Mons. Yorick, to *the wise*—

—And from the wise, Mons. Le Compte, replied I, making him a bow—*is enough.*

80 The Count de Faineant embraced me with more ardour than ever I was embraced by mortal man.

For three weeks together, I was of every man's opinion I met. —*Pardi! ce Mons. Yorick a autant d'esprit que nous autres.——Il raisonne bien*, said another.—*C'est un bon enfant*, said a third.—
85 And at this price I could have eaten and drank and been merry all the days of my life at Paris; but 'twas a dishonest *reckoning*—I grew ashamed of it—it was the gain of a slave—every sentiment of honour revolted against it—the higher I got, the more was I forced upon my *beggarly system*—the better the *Coterie*—the more children
90 of Art—I languish'd for those of Nature: and one night, after a most vile prostitution of myself to half a dozen different people, I grew sick—went to bed—order'd La Fleur to get me horses in the morning to set out for Italy.

84–85 third.—And at] third—"*il entend la* peinture"— and at [see p. 265.71–82*tn*, above]   85 been] ∧have∧ been   88 was I] I was   92 bed—order'd] bed, & order

---

Sterne borrowed in *Tristram Shandy;* see App. E, p. 353, note to p. 278.15– 16). The skeptical rationalism of the *Encyclopédie* and its attacks on clerical and juridical abuses incurred the hostility of the ecclesiastical and civil authorities, and its publication was twice interrupted by official order.

75. *solitaire*] See p. 247.22*n*, above.

89–90. *children . . . Nature*] Cf. *Letters*, No. 96, Paris, July 1762, p. 179: "My wife and daughter are arrived [from England]—the latter does nothing but . . . complain of the torment of being frizzled.—I wish she may ever remain a child of nature—I hate children of art"; cf. also Sterne's description of Eliza as "the artless being nature designed you for" (*Letters,* No. 189, quoted p. 93.30–34*n,* above).

93. *to set out for Italy*] On his second trip abroad, Sterne left Paris to travel to Italy in late October or early November 1765; see *Letters,* Nos. 152, 153, pp. 260–262.

MARIA.
MOULINES.

I NEVER felt what the distress of plenty was in any one shape till now—to travel it through the Bourbonnois, the sweetest part of France—in the hey-day of the vintage, when Nature is pouring her abundance into every one's lap, and every eye is lifted up—
5 a journey through each step of which music beats time to *Labour*, and all her children are rejoicing as they carry in their clusters—to pass through this with my affections flying out, and kindling at every group before me—and every one of 'em was pregnant with adventures.

---

title. MARIA.] The Maria. *title.* MOULINES.] MOULINES *A2*, Moulines. *M2*
6 their] her   8 'em] them

1–10. *I . . . twenty volumes*] a characteristic expression of one aspect of Sterne's theory of travel. Tristram observes, in his journey through Languedoc during the vintage (*TS*, 7.42–43.534–38) : "There is nothing more pleasing to a traveller——or more terrible to travel-writers, than a large rich plain; especially if it is without great rivers or bridges; and presents nothing to the eye, but one unvaried picture of plenty: for after they have once told you that 'tis delicious! or delightful! (as the case happens) . . . that *nature pours out all her abundance* [italics added; cf. "Nature . . . abundance," l. 3, above], *&c.* . . . [Sterne's ellipsis] they have then a large plain upon their hands, which they know not what to do with—and which is of little or no use to them but to carry them to some town; and that town . . . but a new place to start from to the next plain——and so on. —This is most terrible work; judge if I don't manage my plains better." Of his adventures in "the rich plains of *Languedoc*," Tristram remarks that, unlike other travelers and travel-writers, who would have found this a "barren . . . track," the "traces" of his journey, "which are now all set o' vibrating together this moment, tell me 'tis the most fruitful and busy period of my life"; and he asserts that, "by seizing every handle, of what size or shape soever, *which chance held out to me in this journey* [italics added; cf. "—What . . . on.—", p. 114.8–12, above]—I turned my

Just heaven!—it would fill up twenty volumes—and alas! I have *10*
but a few small pages left of this to croud it into—and half of these
must be taken up with the poor Maria my friend, Mr. Shandy, met
with near Moulines.

The story he had told of that disorder'd maid affect'd me not a
little in the reading; but when I got within the neighbourhood *15*
where she lived, it returned so strong into my mind, that I could
not resist an impulse which prompted me to go half a league out of
the road to the village where her parents dwelt to enquire after her.

---

11 these] those   14 affect'd me not] affected not   15 neighbourhood]
neighbouthood *A2*, neighbourhood *M2*

---

plain into a *city* . . . I am confident . . . [I] could have passed through
Pall-Mall or St. *James*'s-Street for a month together, with fewer adventures—
and seen less of human nature." Tristram promises his readers a collection
of the "PLAIN STORIES" which "arose out of the journey across this plain,"
and, as a foretaste of them, describes some of his experiences, including his
dance in the Languedoc vineyard with Nannette, "a sun-burnt daughter of
Labour." His account, in Vol. IX, of his meeting with Maria of Moulines may,
in a sense, be considered a partial fulfillment of this promise.

Before his second trip abroad, Sterne wrote Garrick that he intended to
reach the Continent in time for the "vintage, when all nature is joyous"
(*Letters*, No. 137, quoted p. 11, above). Smollett likewise anticipated "the
pleasure of seeing the vintage" in southern France, "which is always a season
of festivity among all ranks of people" (*Travels*, Letter No. 3, p. 15). But in
passing through Champagne and Burgundy, although the "*vandage* was but
just begun, and the people were employed in gathering the grapes . . . I saw
no signs of festivity among them. Perhaps their joy was a little damped by the
bad prospect of their harvest; . . . My personal adventures on the road were
such as will not bear a recital. They consisted of petty disputes with land-
ladies, post-masters, and postilions" (*Travels*, Letter No. 8, p. 72; cited by
Milic, "Sterne and Smollett's 'Travels' ").

12–15. *the poor Maria . . . reading*] See pp. 13–16, above.

13. *Moulines*] Moulins, a town in the province of Bourbonnais, on the river
Loire.

'Tis going, I own, like the Knight of the Woeful Countenance, in
20 quest of melancholy adventures—but I know not how it is, but I
am never so perfectly conscious of the existence of a soul within
me, as when I am entangled in them.

The old mother came to the door, her looks told me the story
before she open'd her mouth—She had lost her husband; he had
25 died, she said, of anguish, for the loss of Maria's senses about a
month before.—She had feared at first, she added, that it would
have plunder'd her poor girl of what little understanding was left
—but, on the contrary, it had brought her more to herself—still
she could not rest—her poor daughter, she said, crying, was
30 wandering somewhere about the road—

—Why does my pulse beat languid as I write this? and what
made La Fleur, whose heart seem'd only to be tuned to joy, to pass
the back of his hand twice across his eyes, as the woman stood and
told it? I beckon'd to the postilion to turn back into the road.

35   When we had got within half a league of Moulines, at a little
opening in the road leading to a thicket, I discovered poor Maria
sitting under a poplar—she was sitting with her elbow in her lap,
and her head leaning on one side within her hand—a small brook
ran at the foot of the tree.

---

20 of melancholy adventures] of adventures   22 in] with

---

19. *the Knight of the Woeful Countenance*] After his encounter with the funeral cortege, Don Quixote is dubbed by Sancho "*The Knight of the woeful
Figure*" and resolves at "the first Opportunity [to] have a most woeful Face
painted on my Shield" (*Don Quixote*, 1.3.5.126–127).
     See Tristram's description of Yorick as a quixotic figure (*TS*, 1.10.18–20)
and Sterne's complaint to Bishop Warburton that the attacks on him for the
alleged immorality and indecency of *Tristram Shandy* (Vols. I and II) "are
beginning to make me sick of this foolish humour of mine of sallying forth into
this wide & wicked world to redress wrongs, &c. of wᶜʰ I shall repent as
sorely as ever Sancha Panca did of his in following his evil genius of a Don
Quixote thro thick & thin—but as the poor fellow apologised for it,—so must
I. '*it was my vile* fortune & my *Errantry & that's all that can be said* on't"
(*Letters*, No. 63, June 1760, p. 116; this paraphrase of Sancho's words in *Don
Quixote*, 2.3.33.665, is repeated almost verbatim in *Letters*, No. 135, p. 233).

I bid the postilion go on with the chaise to Moulines—and La 40
Fleur to bespeak my supper—and that I would walk after him.

She was dress'd in white, and much as my friend described her,
except that her hair hung loose, which before was twisted within a
silk net.—She had, superadded likewise to her jacket, a pale green
ribband which fell across her shoulder to the waist; at the end of 45
which hung her pipe.—Her goat had been as faithless as her lover;
and she had got a little dog in lieu of him, which she had kept tied
by a string to her girdle; as I look'd at her dog, she drew him towards her with the string.—"Thou shalt not leave me, Sylvio,"
said she. I look'd in Maria's eyes, and saw she was thinking more 50
of her father than of her lover or her little goat; for as she utter'd
them the tears trickled down her cheeks.

I sat down close by her; and Maria let me wipe them away as they
fell with my handkerchief.—I then steep'd it in my own—and then
in hers—and then in mine—and then I wip'd hers again—and as I 55
did it, I felt such undescribable emotions within me, as I am sure
could not be accounted for from any combinations of matter and
motion.

I am positive I have a soul; nor can all the books with which
materialists have pester'd the world ever convince me of the con- 60
trary.

59–61. *I am . . . contrary.*] See pp. 68–69 and notes, above.

MARIA.

WHEN Maria had come a little to herself, I ask'd her if she remember'd a pale thin person of a man who had sat down betwixt her and her goat about two years before? She said, she was unsettled much at that time, but remember'd it upon two accounts
5 —that ill as she was she saw the person pitied her; and next, that her goat had stolen his handkerchief, and she had beat him for the theft—she had wash'd it, she said, in the brook, and kept it ever since in her pocket to restore it to him in case she should ever see him again, which, she added, he had half promised her. As she told
10 me this, she took the handkerchief out of her pocket to let me see it; she had folded it up neatly in a couple of vine leaves, tied round with a tendril—on opening it, I saw an S mark'd in one of the corners.

She had since that, she told me, stray'd as far as Rome, and
15 walk'd round St. Peter's once—and return'd back—that she found her way alone across the Apennines—had travell'd over all Lombardy without money—and through the flinty roads of Savoy without shoes—how she had borne it, and how she had got supported, she could not tell—but *God tempers the wind*, said Maria, to the
20 shorn lamb.

---

8 restore it to him] restore him   15 walk'd] having walk'd   15 St.] St *A2*, S! *M2*

---

2. *a pale . . . man*] Cf. Tristram's description of himself, on his journey through France, as "a person in black, with a face as pale as ashes, . . . looking still paler by the contrast and distress of his drapery" (*TS*, 7.34.527), and his reference to his "spider legs" (*TS*, 7.1.480).

19–20. *God . . . lamb.*] Cross notes (*Life*, pp. 475–476) that this is a rendering of the French proverb "A brebis tondue Dieu mesure le vent" (which George Herbert had translated, "To a close shorne sheep God gives wind by Measure," *Outlandish Proverbs* [London, 1640], No. 861). In ch. 2 of Sterne's *Fragment* in the manner of Rabelais, it is said that Homenas' tears "did . . . temper the Wind" rising upon his discourse (cited in *Life*, p. 476n). Ger-

Shorn indeed! and to the quick, said I; and wast thou in my own land, where I have a cottage, I would take thee to it and shelter thee: thou shouldst eat of my own bread, and drink of my own cup —I would be kind to thy Sylvio—in all thy weaknesses and wanderings I would seek after thee and bring thee back—when the sun 25 went down I would say my prayers, and when I had done thou shouldst play thy evening song upon thy pipe, nor would the incense of my sacrifice be worse accepted for entering heaven along with that of a broken heart.

Nature melted within me, as I utter'd this; and Maria observing, 30 as I took out my handkerchief, that it was steep'd too much already to be of use, would needs go wash it in the stream.—And where will you dry it, Maria? said I—I'll dry it in my bosom, said she— 'twill do me good.

And is your heart still so warm, Maria? said I. 35

I touch'd upon the string on which hung all her sorrows—she look'd with wistful disorder for some time in my face; and then,

31 too much] to much *A2,* too much *M2*

ald P. Mander has noted that in 1750 the French proverb was sufficiently well known to be used in a card game for English children (*Times Literary Supplement,* 17 July 1937, p. 528).

21–23. *wast thou . . . shelter thee*] In the *Journal,* Sterne promises Eliza that he will "invite her to his Cottage" (Shandy Hall, which he often describes as being redecorated as a retreat for them), and assures her that "in the loneliest Cottage that Love & Humility ever dwelt in" he could "taste truer joys" with her than "in the most (sensual) glittering Court" (pp. 323, 333); for other refs. to his "cottage" in the *Journal,* see pp. 335, 346, 348 ("my thatch'd Palace"), 354, 380 (these refs. should be compared with his description of his "princely" manner of living and his statement that "care never enters this cottage" in *Letters,* No. 200, Coxwold, June 1767, p. 353). In the letter Sterne redirected from the "Countess ******" to Eliza, he imagines that he has been "led home by you to your retired Cottage" (*Letters,* No. 201, [? June 1767], p. 361). And in a letter which may have been written to his wife during their courtship, Sterne pictures "a little sungilt cottage" to which they will retire (*Letters,* No. 2, p. 16).

23. *eat . . . cup*] See p. 275.9–11*n,* below.

274 *Maria.*

without saying any thing, took her pipe, and play'd her service to
the Virgin—The string I had touch'd ceased to vibrate—in a
40 moment or two Maria returned to herself—let her pipe fall—and
rose up.

And where art you going, Maria? said I.—She said to Moulines.
—Let us go, said I, together.—Maria put her arm within mine, and
lengthening the string, to let the dog follow—in that order we
45 entered Moulines.

---

42 art] are

---

39. *The string . . . vibrate*] a favorite image of Sterne's: cf., in *Tristram
Shandy:* "a vibration in the strings, about the region of the heart" (4.1.273);
"one vibration . . . sensation" (2.12.114); "vibrating . . . passions" (7.21.-
506); "traces . . . o' vibrating" (7.43.536, quoted p. 268.1–10n, above); and
esp. Tristram's description of the kindly harmony he felt "vibrating" within
him when he encountered Maria (9.24.629, quoted p. 15, above). Cf. also, in
Letters: description of Mrs. Vesey as a "System of harmonic Vibrations" (No.
76, p. 138; this letter is also quoted p. 91.8–15n, above); "every Fibre ab^t
[Garrick's] heart will vibrate afresh" (No. 138, p. 236); "vibrations within"
(No. 229, p. 411, quoted p. 25, above); "vibrate sweet comfort" (No. 188,
to Eliza, p. 310); "Name of Eliza . . . to vibrate upon Yoricks ear" (*Journal,*
26 April, p. 332); "one Vibration" (*Journal,* 25 June, p. 365, quoted p.
100.15n, above). See p. 278.16–18, below, where the image of vibrations is
extended to the "great SENSORIUM" of the world.

MARIA.
MOULINES.

THO' I hate salutations and greetings in the market-place, yet
when we got into the middle of this, I stopp'd to take my last
look and last farewel of Maria.

Maria, tho' not tall, was nevertheless of the first order of fine
forms—affliction had touch'd her looks with something that was 5
scarce earthly—still she was feminine—and so much was there
about her of all that the heart wishes, or the eye looks for in woman,
that could the traces be ever worn out of her brain, and those of
Eliza's out of mine, she should *not only eat of my bread and drink of
my own cup,* but Maria should lay in my bosom, and be unto me as 10
a daughter.

---

9 *not only eat*] "*eat* / "*not only*

---

1. *I hate . . . market-place*] unlike the scribes and Pharisees, who "love
salutations in the marketplaces" (Mark 12:38; see also Matthew 23:7; Luke,
11:43, 20:46).

8–9. *could . . . mine*] In the *Journal,* Sterne asks Eliza whether "time
[has] worn out any Impression" of him in her mind, and assures her that the
pleasures he has experienced in contemplating her picture while driving in his
chaise "have left *Impressions* upon my Mind, which will last my Life" (4 June,
p. 351; 22 June, p. 364). The image of wearing out impressions or traces is
used also in *Sermons,* II, 211 (VII.xiii), "traces . . . wear out"; I, 104 (II.ix);
I, 240–241 (III.vi), "worn . . . impressions."

9–11. *she . . . daughter*] paraphrased from II Samuel 12:3: "But the poor
man had nothing, save one little ewe lamb, which he had bought and nour-
ished up: and it grew up together with him, and with his children; it did eat
of his own meat, and drank of his own cup, and lay in his bosom, and was unto
him as a daughter" (this verse is paraphrased also pp. 139.35–36, 273.23,
above). On Sterne's interest in Nathan's use of this parable, see p. 43, n. 50,
above.

10. *Maria . . . bosom*] Cf. *Journal,* 12 May, p. 338: "O Eliza! . . . that I
had [your head], reclining upon my bosome."

10–11. *be . . . daughter*] Sterne frequently describes his relationship with

Adieu, poor luckless maiden!—imbibe the oil and wine which
the compassion of a stranger, as he journieth on his way, now
pours into thy wounds—the being who has twice bruised thee can
15 only bind them up for ever.

Eliza as that of father and daughter: having admitted that "I am ninety-five in
constitution, and you but twenty-five—rather too great a disparity this!" he
promises Eliza that he will make her more famous than Swift's Stella, Scarron's
Maintenon, or Waller's Sacharissa, and urges her: "Tell me . . . that you
would (like the Spectator's mistress) have more joy in putting on an old man's
slipper, than associating with the gay, the voluptuous, and the young" (*Letters*, No. 192, March 1767, p. 319). In *Spectator* No. 449 (IV, 78–80), Steele
describes "the amiable *Fidelia*," who prefers attending her father and "helping
on an old Man's Slipper" to the attentions of suitors, and comments: "there
is no Kind of Affection so pure and angelick as that of a Father to a Daughter.
He beholds her both with, and without Regard to her Sex. In Love to our
Wives there is Desire, to our Sons there is Ambition; but in that to our Daughters, there is something which there are no Words to express" (cited in *Letters*, p. 319, n. 9). In an undated draft of a letter to Eliza's husband, Daniel
Draper, Sterne assured him that his (Sterne's) love for Eliza is "so like that I
bear my own daughter . . . that I ⟨can⟩ scarse distinguish a difference betwixt it" (*Letters*, No. 199, p. 349). In another letter he addresses Lydia and
Eliza as "the dear children of my heart" (*Letters*, No. 191, March 1767, pp.
316–317; cf. his blessing on Lydia as "thou child of my heart," *Letters*, No.
193, [March 1767], p. 320). See also the many refs. in the *Journal* to the shade
of Cordelia, whom he imagines as haunting the ruins of Byland Abbey near
Coxwold, esp. the entry for 27 July, in which he pictures Eliza catching him in
her arms over Cordelia's grave (p. 382; see pp. 323, 348); and his long colloquy with Cordelia's shade, in the letter he redirected from the "Countess******" to Eliza (*Letters*, No. 201, June [? 1767], pp. 360–361).

12–15. *the oil . . . for ever.*] paraphrased from Luke 10:33–34: "But a certain Samaritan, as he journeyed, came where he was: and when he saw him, he
had compassion on him, And went to him, and bound up his wounds, pouring
in oil and wine" (these verses are paraphrased also p. 97.20–21, above). Cf.
Journal, 11 July, p. 378, "pour . . . hearts"; 22 April, p. 326, "tye . . .
wounds" (Sterne's afflictions here are explained in *Journal*, pp. 329–330);
Sermons, I, 30–31 (I.iii), where Yorick presents the thoughts and feelings of
the Good Samaritan in a dramatic soliloquy.

THE BOURBONNOIS.

THERE was nothing from which I had painted out for myself so joyous a riot of the affections, as in this journey in the vintage, through this part of France; but pressing through this gate of sorrow to it, my sufferings had totally unfitted me: in every scene of festivity I saw Maria in the back-ground of the piece, sitting pensive 5 under her poplar; and I had got almost to Lyons before I was able to cast a shade across her—

—Dear sensibility! source inexhausted of all that's precious in our joys, or costly in our sorrows! thou chainest thy martyr down upon his bed of straw—and 'tis thou who lifts him up to HEAVEN 10 —eternal fountain of our feelings!—'tis here I trace thee—and this is thy divinity which stirs within me——not, that in some sad and

---

4 had] has *A2*, have *M2*   9–10 down upon] on   10 'tis] it is   10 lifts]
lift'st   11 'tis] it is

THE BOURBONNOIS.] the Bourbonnais, a province on the southwest border of Burgundy.

1–3. *so joyous . . . France*] Cf. the passages from *Letters,* No. 137, and from Smollett's *Travels* quoted p. 268.1–10*n*, above.

8–9. *Dear sensibility! . . . sorrows!*] Cf. *Letters,* No. 214, Sept. 1767, pp. 395–396: "my Sentimental Journey will, I dare say, convince you that my feelings are from the heart, and that that heart is not of the worst of molds— praised be God for my sensibility! Though it has often made me wretched, yet I would not exchange it for all the pleasures the grossest sensualist ever felt" (cf. *Journal,* 24 April, p. 330, where Sterne describes the way, "with all his sensibilities," he is "suffering the Chastisement of the grossest Sensualist"). Cf. also Sterne's apostrophe to "dear Enthusiasm!—thou bringst things forwards in a moment, wch Time keeps for Ages back" (*Journal,* 12 June, p. 356).

10–11. *Heaven . . . feelings!*] Cf. the ref. to God as "the fountain of joy" in *Sermons,* II, 8–9, quoted p. 148.49–52*n*, above.

12–14. *thy divinity . . . destruction"*] In his edition of *A Sentimental Journey* (London, 1929), p. 230, n. 46, Sir Herbert Read notes that this passage is

277

sickening moments, *"my soul shrinks back upon herself, and startles at destruction"*—mere pomp of words!—but that I feel some gener-
15 ous joys and generous cares beyond myself—all comes from thee, great—great SENSORIUM of the world! which vibrates, if a hair of our heads but falls upon the ground, in the remotest desert of thy creation.—Touch'd with thee, Eugenius draws my curtain when I languish—hears my tale of symptoms, and blames the weather for
20 the disorder of his nerves. Thou giv'st a portion of it sometimes to

---

13 *herself*] itself   17 falls] fall

---

paraphrased from Addison's *Cato* (1713), V.i.2–9 (italics added):

> . . . whence this pleasing hope, this fond desire,
> This longing after immortality?
> Or whence this secret dread, and inward horror,
> Of falling into nought? *why shrinks the soul*
> *Back on her self, and startles at destruction?*
> *'Tis the divinity that stirs within us;*
> 'Tis Heav'n it self, that points out an Hereafter,
> And intimates eternity to man.

14. *mere pomp of words!*] Cf. Dr. Johnson's judgment of *Cato:* "its hopes and fears communicate no vibration to the heart" (*Preface to Shakespeare,* in *Rasselas, Poems and Selected Prose,* ed. B. H. Bronson [New York, 1958], p. 261). (Addison's pedantic *Remarks on Several Parts of Italy* is ridiculed in *Tristram Shandy;* see p. 84.112–113*n*, above.)

15–16. *thee, great—great Sensorium of the world!*] See App. E, pp. 353–354, note to p. 278.15–16.

16. *vibrates*] See pp. 274.39*n*, above.

16–17. *a hair . . . ground*] adapted from Matthew 10:29–31: "Are not two sparrows sold for a farthing? and one of them shall not fall on the ground without your Father. But the very hairs of your head are all numbered. Fear ye not therefore, ye are of more value than many sparrows"; and Luke 12:7. Cf. also I Samuel 14:45: "As the Lord liveth, there shall not one hair of his [Jonathan's] head fall to the ground"; II Samuel 14:11; I Kings 1:52; and *Sermons,* II, 149 (VI.vii): "without [God's] knowledge and permission we know that not a hair of our heads can fall to the ground."

18–20. *Eugenius . . . nerves*] In *Tristram Shandy,* Eugenius (John Hall-Stevenson, for whom see p. 164.65*n*, above) visits Yorick just before he "breath'd his last," and, "Upon his drawing *Yorick's* curtain" (i.e., bed-the roughest peasant who traverses the bleakest mountains—he finds the lacerated lamb of another's flock—This moment I beheld him leaning with his head against his crook, with piteous inclination looking down upon it—Oh! had I come one moment sooner! —it bleeds to death—his gentle heart bleeds with it—   25

Peace to thee, generous swain!—I see thou walkest off with anguish—but thy joys shall balance it—for happy is thy cottage— and happy is the sharer of it—and happy are the lambs which sport about you.

---

29 you] thee

---

curtain), he hears Yorick's description of the attacks by his enemies which have brought him to death's door (*TS,* 1.12.30–31, quoted p. 200.99–100*n,* above).

A hypochondriac, Hall-Stevenson dreaded cold weather and particularly feared what Sterne humorously described, in a letter to him, as "a thin death-doing pestiferous north-east wind" (*Letters,* No. 77, June 1761, p. 139). Sterne is supposed on one occasion to have had the weather vane on Crazy Castle tied down in a westerly direction, and Hall-Stevenson, having retreated to his bed in the face of an east wind, "rose to enjoy what he believed to be the beneficial west wind" (*Letters,* p. 141, n. 2). In one version of the story, the cord eventually broke, and, when the weather vane swung round to the northeast, Hall-Stevenson immediately took to his bed (*Life,* pp. 129–130).

THE SUPPER.

A SHOE coming loose from the fore-foot of the thill-horse, at the beginning of the ascent of mount Taurira, the postilion dismounted, twisted the shoe off, and put it in his pocket; as the ascent was of five or six miles, and that horse our main dependence, 5 I made a point of having the shoe fasten'd on again, as well as we could; but the postilion had thrown away the nails, and the hammer in the chaise-box, being of no great use without them, I submitted to go on.

He had not mounted half a mile higher, when coming to a flinty 10 piece of road, the poor devil lost a second shoe, and from off his other fore-foot; I then got out of the chaise in good earnest; and seeing a house about a quarter of a mile to the left-hand, with a great deal to do, I prevailed upon the postilion to turn up to it. The look of the house, and of every thing about it, as we drew nearer,

---

| 3 in] into | 7 no great use] no use | 13 great] good | 14 and of every] |
| and every | 14 nearer] near | | |

---

1. *the thill-horse*] the wheel horse, in a tandem arrangement.
2. *mount Taurira*] Mont Tarare, about 30 miles northeast of Lyons.
13–29. *The look . . . love.*] Unlike Yorick, the Sentimental Traveller, many Englishmen described, with righteous indignation, the squalor in which peasants lived in pre-Revolutionary France, particularly the *métayers*, who rented land rather than owning it. Smollett describes the "poverty, misery, and dirt" to which many of the peasants had been reduced, both by the oppressive taxes levied on them by the farmers-general (see p. 262.26–30*n*, above) and by the exactions of local landlords and of the church (see *Travels*, Letters No. 36, p. 309; No. 8, p. 71; No. 9, p. 80; No. 20, pp. 174–175; No. 21, p. 179). English travelers tended, however, to give an exaggerated and distorted picture of rural poverty in France, partly to extol the sturdy virtues and prosperity which they felt the English peasantry had achieved in a land of liberty (see Smollett, *Travels*, Letter No. 36, pp. 308–312; Thicknesse, *Useful Hints*, pp. 43–44).

soon reconciled me to the disaster.—It was a little farm-house sur- 15
rounded with about twenty acres of vineyard, about as much corn
—and close to the house, on one side, was a *potagerie* of an acre and
a half, full of every thing which could make plenty in a French
peasant's house—and on the other side was a little wood which
furnished wherewithal to dress it. It was about eight in the evening 20
when I got to the house—so I left the postilion to manage his point
as he could—and for mine, I walk'd directly into the house.

The family consisted of an old grey-headed man and his wife,
with five or six sons and sons-in-law and their several wives, and a
joyous genealogy out of 'em. 25

They were all sitting down together to their lentil-soup; a large
wheaten loaf was in the middle of the table; and a flaggon of wine at
each end of it promised joy thro' the stages of the repast—'twas a
feast of love.

The old man rose up to meet me, and with a respectful cordiality 30
would have me sit down at the table; my heart was sat down the
moment I enter'd the room; so I sat down at once like a son of the
family; and to invest myself in the character as speedily as I could,
I instantly borrowed the old man's knife, and taking up the loaf cut
myself a hearty luncheon; and as I did it I saw a testimony in every 35
eye, not only of an honest welcome, but of a welcome mix'd with
thanks that I had not seem'd to doubt it.

---

25 'em] them   31 was sat] was set   33 to invest] invested

There are a few conventional remarks on the "pleasures of the honest
peasant" in *Sermons,* I, 158–159 [II.xiii]; see esp.: "Look into his house . . .
has he not the same domestic endearments . . . as you could conceive in the
highest station?" See also Tristram's comments on the rewards of the simple
life, in which he claims to outdo *"Rousseau,* a bar length" (*TS,* 9.17.620;
Work notes that when Sterne wrote this passage Rousseau "was himself living
simply in exile, though hardly with philosophic content, in a house procured
for him in Derbyshire by his and Sterne's friend David Hume").

35. *luncheon*] "a thick piece" (*OED*).

Was it this; or tell me, Nature, what else it was which made this morsel so sweet—and to what magick I owe it, that the draught I
40 took of their flaggon was so delicious with it, that they remain upon my palate to this hour?

If the supper was to my taste—the grace which follow'd it was much more so.

---

38 which] that

38–41. *Was it . . . hour?*] See the passages on the "taste" of joy God affords the religious man, quoted from the *Sermons,* p. 283.15–27n, below.

THE GRACE.

WHEN supper was over, the old man gave a knock upon the table with the haft of his knife—to bid them prepare for the dance: the moment the signal was given, the women and girls ran all together into a back apartment to tye up their hair—and the young men to the door to wash their faces, and change their sabots; 5 and in three minutes every soul was ready upon a little esplanade before the house to begin—The old man and his wife came out last, and, placing me betwixt them, sat down upon a sopha of turf by the door.

The old man had some fifty years ago been no mean performer 10 upon the vielle—and at the age he was then of, touch'd it well enough for the purpose. His wife sung now-and-then a little to the tune—then intermitted—and joined her old man again as their children and grand-children danced before them.

It was not till the middle of the second dance, when, from some 15 pauses in the movement wherein they all seemed to look up, I

---

11 upon] on

---

11. *vielle*] "A musical instrument with four strings played by means of a small wheel; a hurdy-gurdy" (*OED*). See Plate 12, following p. 292, below.
15–27. *It was . . . said I.*] Cf. Yorick's comments on the festivities cele-brating the return of the Prodigal Son, in the *Sermons,* I, 233 (III.v):
> When the affections so kindly break loose, Joy, is another name for Religion.
> *We look up as we taste it* [italics added; cf. "some pauses . . . look up" (ll. 15–16, above)]: the cold Stoick without, when he hears the dancing and the musick, may ask sullenly, (with the elder brother) What it means; and refuse to enter: but the humane and compassionate all fly impetuously to the banquet . . . Gentle spirits, light up the pavillion with a sacred fire; and parental love, and filial piety lead in the mask with riot and wild festivity!——Was it not for this that GOD gave man musick to strike upon

283

fancied I could distinguish an elevation of spirit different from that
which is the cause or the effect of simple jollity.—In a word, I
thought I beheld *Religion* mixing in the dance—but as I had never
20 seen her so engaged, I should have look'd upon it now, as one of
the illusions of an imagination which is eternally misleading me,
had not the old man, as soon as the dance ended, said, that this was
their constant way; and that all his life long he had made it a rule,
after supper was over, to call out his family to dance and rejoice;
25 believing, he said, that a chearful and contented mind was the best
sort of thanks to heaven that an illiterate peasant could pay—

　　——Or a learned prelate either, said I.

---

21 an] the

---

the kindly passions; that nature taught the feet to dance to its movements,
and as chief governess of the feast, poured forth wine into the goblet, to
crown it with gladness?
Cf. also *Sermons,* II, 85 (V.i): "a religious man's happiness . . . [is] felt
and tasted every hour"; II, 25 (IV.viii): "bid [a voluptuary] *taste and see how
good God is*" (paraphrased from Psalms 34:8: "O taste and see that the Lord is
good"); II, 175 (VI.x): condemnation of the view (exemplified by the teach-
ings of Methodists and Catholics) that we are not to "taste any of the pleasures, or any of the enjoyments of this life." The tendency in the *Sermons* to
identify the joys and pleasures of this world with those of the next is discussed
pp. 28–31, above, and in App. E, pp. 338–342, note to p. 120.54–64.
　　Cf. Yorick's comments on the dance of the peasant family with Tristram's
dance among the peasants of Languedoc during the vintage, to the tune of
a Gascoigne roundelay ("Viva la joia! Fidon la tristessa!"), and with his
exclamation, "Just disposer of our joys and sorrows, cried I, why could not a
man sit down in the lap of content here—and dance, and sing, and say his
prayers, and go to heaven with this nut brown maid?" (*TS,* 7.43.537–538).

THE CASE OF DELICACY.

WHEN you have gained the top of mount Taurira, you run presently down to Lyons—adieu then to all rapid movements! 'Tis a journey of caution; and it fares better with sentiments, not to be in a hurry with them; so I contracted with a Voiturin to take his time with a couple of mules, and convey me in 5 my own chaise safe to Turin through Savoy.

Poor, patient, quiet, honest people! fear not; your poverty, the treasury of your simple virtues, will not be envied you by the world, nor will your vallies be invaded by it.—Nature! in the midst of thy disorders, thou art still friendly to the scantiness thou hast 10 created—with all thy great works about thee, little hast thou left to give, either to the scithe or to the sickle—but to that little, thou grantest safety and protection; and sweet are the dwellings which stand so shelter'd.

Let the way-worn traveller vent his complaints upon the sudden 15 turns and dangers of your roads—your rocks—your precipices—the difficulties of getting up—the horrors of getting down—mountains impracticable—and cataracts, which roll down great stones from their summits, and block his road up.—The peasants had been all day at work in removing a fragment of this kind between 20 St. Michael and Madane; and by the time my Voiturin got to the place, it wanted full two hours of compleating before a passage could any how be gain'd: there was nothing but to wait with

---

3 'Tis] it is   15 vent his complaints] vent complaints   16 dangers] danger
19 block his road up] block his up road *A2*, block his road up *M2*

---

5. *Voiturin*] carriage or coach driver (*OED*).
9–11. *Nature! . . . with . . . thee*] Cf. *TS*, 7.29.517: "Nature . . . with all her great works about her——"
21. *St. Michael and Madane*] St. Michel and Modane, two towns (9–10 miles apart) on the river Arc, near the French-Italian border, southwest of Turin.

patience—'twas a wet and tempestuous night; so that by the delay,
25 and that together, the Voiturin found himself obliged to take up
five miles short of his stage at a little decent kind of an inn by the
road side.

   I forthwith took possession of my bed-chamber—got a good fire
—order'd supper; and was thanking heaven it was no worse—
30 when a voiture arrived with a lady in it and her servant-maid.

   As there was no other bed-chamber in the house, the hostess,
without much nicety, led them into mine, telling them, as she
usher'd them in, that there was no body in it but an English gentleman—that there were two good beds in it, and a closet within the
35 room which held another—the accent in which she spoke of this
third bed did not say much for it—however, she said, there were
three beds, and but three people—and she durst say, the gentleman would do any thing to accommodate matters.—I left not the
lady a moment to make a conjecture about it—so instantly made a
40 declaration I would do any thing in my power.

   As this did not amount to an absolute surrender of my bed-
chamber, I still felt myself so much the proprietor, as to have a
right to do the honours of it—so I desired the lady to sit down—
pressed her into the warmest seat—call'd for more wood—desired
45 the hostess to enlarge the plan of the supper, and to favour us with
the very best wine.

   The lady had scarce warm'd herself five minutes at the fire, before she began to turn her head back, and give a look at the beds;

---

24 'twas] it was   34 beds in it,] beds, in it *A2*, beds in it, *M2*   40 declaration I] declaration that I   48 a look] alook *A2*, a look *M2*

---

   24. *the delay*] In traveling from Lyons to Turin in November 1765, Sterne
was delayed in the mountains of Savoy by a flood at Pont de Beauvoisin, on the
border between France and Savoy; see *Letters,* No. 153, p. 262.
   28–34. *I . . . an English gentleman*] On the source of this incident, see
App. E, p. 355, note to p. 286.28–34.

and the oftener she cast her eyes that way, the more they return'd perplex'd—I felt for her—and for myself; for in a few minutes, *50* what by her looks, and the case itself, I found myself as much embarrassed as it was possible the lady could be herself.

That the beds we were to lay in were in one and the same room, was enough simply by itself to have excited all this—but the position of them, for they stood parallel, and so very close to each *55* other as only to allow space for a small wicker chair betwixt them, render'd the affair still more oppressive to us—they were fixed up moreover near the fire, and the projection of the chimney on one side, and a large beam which cross'd the room on the other, form'd a kind of recess for them that was no way favourable to the nicety of *60* our sensations—if any thing could have added to it, it was, that the two beds were both of 'em so very small, as to cut us off from every idea of the lady and 'the maid lying together; which in either of them, could it have been feasible, my lying besides them, tho' a thing not to be wish'd, yet there was nothing in it so terrible which *65* the imagination might not have pass'd over without torment.

As for the little room within, it offer'd little or no consolation to us; 'twas a damp cold closet, with a half dismantled window shutter, and with a window which had neither glass or oil paper in it to keep out the tempest of the night. I did not endeavour to stifle my cough *70* when the lady gave a peep into it; so it reduced the case in course to this alternative—that the lady should sacrifice her health to her feelings, and take up with the closet herself, and abandon the bed next mine to her maid—or that the girl should take the closet, &c. &c. *75*

The lady was a Piedmontese of about thirty, with a glow of health in her cheeks.—The maid was a Lyonoise of twenty, and as brisk and lively a French girl as ever moved.—There were difficulties

---

53 lay] lie 62 were . . . small] were so small 68 'twas] it was

---

70. *I . . . cough*] a ref. to Sterne's chronic consumption; see pp. 2, 12, above.

every way—and the obstacle of the stone in the road, which
80 brought us into the distress, great as it appeared whilst the peasants
were removing it, was but a pebble to what lay in our ways now—I
have only to add, that it did not lessen the weight which hung upon
our spirits, that we were both too delicate to communicate what we
felt to each other upon the occasion.

85   We sat down to supper; and had we not had more generous wine
to it than a little inn in Savoy could have furnish'd, our tongues had
been tied up, till necessity herself had set them at liberty—but the
lady having a few bottles of Burgundy in her voiture sent down her
Fille de Chambre for a couple of them; so that by the time supper
90 was over, and we were left alone, we felt ourselves inspired with a
strength of mind sufficient to talk, at least, without reserve upon
our situation. We turn'd it every way, and debated and considered
it in all kind of lights in the course of a two hours negociation; at
the end of which the articles were settled finally betwixt us, and
95 stipulated for in form and manner of a treaty of peace—and I
believe with as much religion and good faith on both sides, as in
any treaty which as yet had the honour of being handed down to
posterity.

They were as follows:

100   First. As the right of the bed-chamber is in Monsieur—and he
thinking the bed next to the fire to be the warmest, he insists upon
the concession on the lady's side of taking up with it.

Granted, on the part of Madame; with a proviso, That as the
curtains of that bed are of a flimsy transparent cotton, and appear
105 likewise too scanty to draw close, that the Fille de Chambre, shall
fasten up the opening, either by corking pins, or needle and thread,

---

80 the distress] this distress   80 whilst] while   81 ways] way
91 mind sufficient to] mind to   93 kind] kinds   97 which as] which has as
99 follows] follow   100 First] 1st   101 fire] fireplace   102 on the
lady's] on the part of the lady's

---

106. *corking pins*] pins of the largest size (*OED*).

in such manner as shall be deemed a sufficient barrier on the side of Monsieur.

2dly. It is required on the part of Madame, that Monsieur shall lay the whole night through in his robe de chambre.   *110*

Rejected: inasmuch Monsieur is not worth a robe de chambre; he having nothing in his portmanteau but six shirts and a black silk pair of breeches.

The mentioning the silk pair of breeches made an entire change of the article—for the breeches were accepted as an equivalent for *115* the robe de chambre, and so it was stipulated and agreed upon that I should lay in my black silk breeches all night.

3dly. It was insisted upon, and stipulated for by the lady, that after Monsieur was got to bed, and the candle and fire extinguished, that Monsieur should not speak one single word the whole night. *120*

Granted; provided Monsieur's saying his prayers might not be deem'd an infraction of the treaty.

There was but one point forgot in this treaty, and that was the manner in which the lady and myself should be obliged to undress and get to bed—there was but one way of doing it, and that I leave *125*

---

110 lay] lie   111 inasmuch] inasmuch as   117 lay] lie   125 was but
one] was one

123–128. *There . . . complaint.*] Cf. *Letters*, No. 221, Nov. 1767, p. 403: "If [*A Sentimental Journey*] is not thought a chaste book, mercy on them that read it, for they must have warm imaginations indeed!" Cf. also Tristram's observation, in Vol. II, that the "truest respect which you can pay to the reader's understanding, is to . . . leave him something to imagine, in his turn, as well as yourself. For my own part, I am eternally paying him compliments of this kind, and do all that lies in my power to keep his imagination as busy as my own" (*TS*, 2.11.109); and his answer to the charges of indecency that were leveled against the first two volumes of his *Life and Opinions,* largely as a result of his having paid his reader so many "compliments" of this kind: "heaven is witness, how the world has revenged itself upon me for leaving so many openings to equivocal strictures,—and for depending

to the reader to devise; protesting as I do it, that if it is not the most
delicate in nature, 'tis the fault of his own imagination—against
which this is not my first complaint.

Now when we were got to bed, whether it was the novelty of the
130 situation, or what it was, I know not; but so it was, I could not shut
my eyes; I tried this side and that, and turn'd and turn'd again,
till a full hour after midnight; when Nature and patience both wearing out—O my God! said I——

—You have broke the treaty, Monsieur, said the lady, who had
135 no more slept than myself.—I begg'd a thousand pardons—but
insisted it was no more than an ejaculation—she maintain'd 'twas
an entire infraction of the treaty—I maintain'd it was provided for
in the clause of the third article.

The lady would by no means give up her point, tho' she weak-
140 ened her barrier by it; for in the warmth of the dispute, I could hear
two or three corking pins fall out of the curtain to the ground.

Upon my word and honour, Madame, said I—stretching my arm
out of bed, by way of asseveration—

—(I was going to have added, that I would not have trespass'd
145 against the remotest idea of decorum for the world)—

—But the Fille de Chambre hearing there were words between
us, and fearing that hostilities would ensue in course, had crept
silently out of her closet, and it being totally dark, had stolen so

---

126 do it, that] do, that   127 'tis] it is   134 broke] broken   136 'twas]
it was   139 her point] the point   143 way of asseveration] way asseveration
A2, way of asseveration *M2*   146 hearing . . . words] hearing words

---

so much as I have done, all along, upon the cleanliness of my reader's imaginations" (*TS*, 3.31.218; cf. also 2.2.84, 3.33.221, 3.36.226).

close to our beds, that she had got herself into the narrow passage
which separated them, and had advanc'd so far up as to be in a line *150*
betwixt her mistress and me—

So that when I stretch'd out my hand, I caught hold of the Fille
de Chambre's

END OF VOL. II.

153–154 Chambre's / END OF VOL. II.] Chambre's— / End of the 2^d Vol. [If *M2* transcribes *S2* here as accurately as *M1* transcribes *S1* at the end of Vol. I (see p. 183.
55–56*tn*, above), there Was a dash after "Chambre's—" (sic) in *S2* which Sterne deleted
in *S2* or in the proofs of *A2*, after *M2* was transcribed from *S2*. On the unauthorized
insertion of a dash after "Chambre's" in the "New Edition" of *A Sentimental Journey*
(1768) and in subsequent editions, see App. D, "New Edition," p.320.]

152–154. *So . . . II.*] Cf. the way Don Quixote, lying in darkness in his bed
at the inn, "stretch'd out his Arms to receive his fancy'd Damsel, and caught
hold of *Maritornes*," a serving-maid (*Don Quixote*, 1.3.2.100; on Sterne's
familiarity with the Motteux-Ozell trans. of *Don Quixote*, see p. 140.46–47*n*,
above).

Many editions of *A Sentimental Journey* (e.g., the "New Edition" publ.
1768; see App. D, p. 320) close the opening Sterne left to equivocal strictures
between "Chambre's" and "END" by inserting a dash after "Chambre's—"
(sic); and many compound the error by omitting "END OF VOL. II." See
Tristram's discussion (and illustration) of "that ornamental figure in oratory,
which Rhetoricians stile the *Aposeopesis*," in *TS*, 2.6.100–101. See also the
bawdy, heavy-handed sequel to this chapter in *Yorick's Sentimental Journey
Continued by Eugenius* (see p. 164.65*n*, above), ch. i, "The Case of Delicacy
Compleated."

PLATE 3.
Laurence Sterne (Carmontelle).

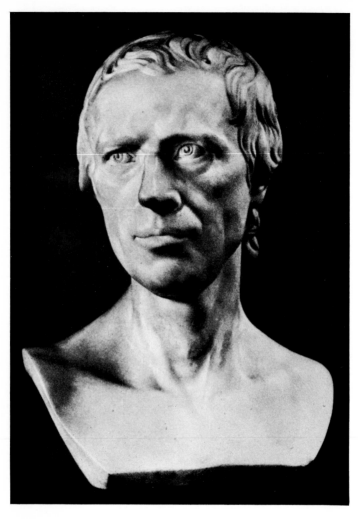

PLATE 4.
Laurence Sterne (Nollekens).

PLATE 5.
A *désobligeante*. See p. 76.

PLATE 6.
The old man lamenting the death of his ass (Stothard).
See pp. 138–141.

PLATE 7.
"A Tour to Foreign Parts" (Bunbury). See p. 79.36–42.

PLATE 8.
"The Dance at Amiens" (Rowlandson). See p. 149.

PLATE 9.
"Yorick Feeling the Grisset's Pulse" (Rowlandson).
See p. 166.

PLATE 10.
Yorick and Maria (Stothard). See pp. 270–273.

PLATE 11.
The Grace (Stothard).

PLATE 12.
"The Grace" (Newton). See pp. 283–284.

APPENDIXES

APPENDIX A

§1 *General Description*. Egerton MS. 1610 (British Museum) is a bound volume, approximately 6 x 8½ inches. It contains 218 leaves: a preliminary and a final leaf, blank except for two memoranda;[1] the 161 extant leaves of *S1*;[2] and 55 additional leaves, some of which are interleaved with *S1*, comprising the material described in §2, below. The preliminary and final leaves are unnumbered; the rest, including *S1* and the material interleaved with it, have been continuously numbered 1–216 by the British Museum.[3]

§2 *History*. Egerton 1610 was acquired by the British Museum in 1853.[4] The material bound with *S1* casts some light on the history of Egerton 1610 before 1853 and on the history of *S1* itself. Two items are of particular interest in this regard.

(a) A title page (in longhand):

The / Sentimental Journey / through France / Written by / Lawrence [sic] Sterne M.A. / [line] / This Manuscript is in the / Autograph of the Author. / William Upcott. / Islington, 1843.

(b) The following letter:

10 Upper Thames St / July 7ᵗʰ 1843. / Dear Sir, / In answer to your enquiries about the Manuscript of the Sentimental Journey, I will with pleasure send you all the information I possess on the subject. For

---

[1] See n. 3 and n. 4, below.

[2] See App. B, §3.

[3] These numbers are in pencil, and the following penciled memorandum on the recto of the final leaf, records the official museum foliation of the leaves: "216 Folios January 1929. P. E. T. E. / Examined [i.e., checked] by E. F. D." (I am indebted to the Dept. of MSS., British Museum, for information about the Museum's handling of Egerton 1610 and about the binding of the MS.)

[4] See *British Museum Additional MSS, 1848–1853* (London, 1868), p. 364. The following memorandum, on the recto of the preliminary leaf of Egerton 1610, records its acquisition by the Museum from William and Thomas Boone, booksellers: "Purchased of Messrˢ Boone; / 12 March 1853." (in the hand of Sir Frederic Madden, Keeper of MSS., 1837–1866).

nearly forty years past it has been in my Father's possession, and belonged, before that time to my grandfather, John Farnworth,[5] who I believe valued it highly. He was a man of considerable talent and a most intimate friend and companion of the well known, eccentric Parson Harvest. M.ʳ Harvest was a contemporary and brother wit of Sterne's and I think very probably (though of this I cannot speak confidently) that the manuscript came through him to my grandfather. I conclude there was some sort of connection between the author and our family, as it was not the only article belonging to my grandfather, which was prized as having once been the property of Sterne. As we never contemplated parting with it and never heard the smallest doubt expressed as to its being the original manuscript, we neglected gaining as much information on the subject as we might easily have done during the life time of the elder branches of my grandfather's family; I now regret it, as it would have enabled me to furnish you with a more circumstantial account. Believe me to be dear Sir, with sincere regard / Yours very truly / Jemima Day—[6]

The addressee of Day's letter is not indicated. However, the fact that the title page bearing Upcott's name and Day's letter are both dated 1843 suggests that Day's letter may have been written to Upcott, in response to an inquiry from him about *S1*.[7]

The other items bound with *S1* in Egerton 1610 strengthen this possibility, for they indicate that Upcott may have assembled Egerton 1610 himself. These items include a preface and (interleaved at appropriate places in *S1*) illustrations from various editions of *A Sentimental Journey*,[8] and various plates and other material.[9] All

---

⁵ Possibly "Farneworth" or "Farnesworth."

⁶ Possibly "Jeremiah Day"; cited as "Mrs. Jemima Day" in the British Museum catalogue. I have not been able to identify Day, Farnworth (?), or Harvest.

⁷ For Upcott's career as an antiquarian and collector of MSS. see *DNB*.

⁸ The preface and most of the illustrations appeared in the edition publ. by J. E. Nicholls (London, [1840?]), with engravings by Bastin and G. Nicholls from original drawings by Jacque and Fussell (*Brit. Mus. Cat.* O 12643). The illustrations on fols. 24ᵛ, 70ᵛ, and 181ᵛ (lower half), as numbered by the British Museum, appeared in the edition printed by J. Cundee and sold by T. Hurst and C. Chapple (London, 1803). The illustration on fol. 74ᵛ, of Yorick and the Monk exchanging snuffboxes, appeared (with slight variations in heading and date) in Sterne's *Works*, publ. by Strahan et al., 10 vols. (London, 1780), Vol. V, facing p. 36.

⁹ (1) fol. 1ᵛ (as numbered by the British Museum), the bust portrait of Sterne by Ravenet after Reynolds; (2) fol. 5ᵛ, frontispiece to *The Beauties of*

these items, and Day's letter, are affixed to sheets approximately the same size as the original sheets of *S1* (about 6 x 8 in.). The items I have been able to identify and date appeared elsewhere before 1843 (the date of Upcott's title page). Finally, Upcott's collections contained many grangerized volumes which he made up himself.[10] These facts indicate, I think, that Upcott may have assembled Egerton 1610, and had it bound,[11] in its present form. Upcott died in 1845; I have been unable to find a record of Egerton 1610 in the sale catalogues of his collections, but he may have disposed of the MS. before his death.

Sterne (London, 1793); (3) fol. 8, facsimile of a letter from Sterne to Garrick publ. London, 1835 (see *Letters*, No. 80, p. 146); (4) fol. 9ᵛ, print depicting the tombstone erected to Sterne by two freemasons (see *Life*, pp. 494–495; Howes, p. 46, n. 9); (5) fols. 165ᵛ, 166ᵛ, "Vue de Paris de L'Institut" and "Paris de Pont Neuf vers L'Occident," publ. in *Paris and Its Environs* (London, 1830), facing pp. 179, 167; (6) fol. 90ᵛ, bust portrait of Tobias Smollett engraved by Francis Aliamet, frontispiece to Smollett's *Complete History of England*, 3d ed., Vol. I (London, 1758), and frontispiece to his *Continuation of the Complete History of England*, "New Edition," Vol. I (London, 1761); (7) fol. 98ᵛ, bust portrait of David Hume (see p. 122.28n, above), which I have not been able to date; (8) fol. 99ᵛ, bust portrait of John Home (see p. 122.28n, above), engraved by W. Ridley, which appeared in *The European Magazine and London Review*, XLV (June 1804), facing p. 403. (I have not been able to identify the plates on fols. 11ᵛ, 95ᵛ, 164ᵛ, 181ᵛ [upper half].)

[10] See the memoirs of Upcott in the *Gentleman's Magazine*, new ser., XXIV (Nov. 1845), 540–541, and in the *Temple Bar; A London Magazine*, XLVII (May–Aug. 1876), 89–104. The sale catalogues of Upcott's collections list many grangerized volumes.

[11] The binding is blue morocco on boards. According to the Dept. of MSS., British Museum, it is generally nineteenth-century in appearance and shows no evidence of rebinding by the Museum. On the spine, in gold lettering, appears: "Sterne's Sentimental Journey Thro' France. Original Manuscript."; and, lower down, in slightly smaller letters, "Mus. Brit. Bibl. Egerton 1610."

APPENDIX B

S1—STERNE'S HOLOGRAPH MS. OF VOL. I

§1 *General Description.* S1 is a carefully revised fair copy. The text is written on one side of what were originally loose sheets,[1] and appears on the rectos of the leaves as bound in Egerton 1610. The versos are blank, except for the following, in Sterne's hand: two notes and one insertion in the text;[2] several readings which Sterne rejected as he was writing out S1;[3] a canceled folio number and an illegible canceled phrase.[4] As in the first edition, chapters begin at the top of a new folio.[5]

§2 *Printer's Copy.* (1) The beginning of each signature in A1 is usually designated in S1 by a square bracket opening to the right, and by "Vol. I" plus the appropriate signature letter and the number of the page in A1 with which the signature begins (e.g., "Vol. I. G 81"), written near the bracket (usually in the extreme left-hand margin).[6] (2) The word "metals" (p. 68.16, above) appears

---

[1] See n. 3, below. S1 is described by Cross in *Life*, pp. 471–477, 631.

[2] See textual notes to pp. 66.16–19, 117.36, 140.47–49, above; and p. 125.21–22*tn*.

[3] See textual notes to pp. 82.74–76, 88.34–36, 103.54–55, 110.10–11, 124.8–9, 131.13, 132.21, 148.47–48, 151.78, above. The position of these rejected readings (see p. 82.74–76*tn*) indicates that the leaves of S1 were originally loose sheets. The following canceled reading appears upside down at the bottom of fol. 128ᵛ of S1: "⟨philosopher who first cried *eureka*,⟩". Fol. 128 begins with "so unfolding" (p. 152.90, above) and ends with "desesperer" (p. 153.8, above). The canceled reading seems unrelated to this part of the text, and I have not been able to determine where Sterne may have originally intended it to appear. (For the folio numbers cited in referring to the text of S1, see §3.)

[4] On fols. 82ᵛ and 32ᵛ, respectively. The following, not in Sterne's hand, appear on the versos of folios: "Sentimental Journey" (fol. 27ᵛ); a printer's query [see §2, (2)].

[5] Except for the chapters commencing on pp. 76, 104, 130, 145, 153, above, which begin in S1 on the same folio on which the preceding chapter ends; these exceptions are apparently inconsistencies in the way Sterne wrote out S1. A line usually appears above and below the title of each chapter in S1.

[6] See F. A. Pottle, "Printer's Copy in the Eighteenth Century," *Papers of the*

in *S1* as "ₓmettles"; the following query, presumably by the printer, is written opposite it, on the blank verso of the preceding folio (4ᵛ): "ₓQy. shoud not this be Metals?"[7] (3) The following note appears on the first folio of *S1*, to the right of the title of the first chapter: "13 Sheets / N⁰ 2500 / 150 fine."[8] Presumably a printers memorandum, this note indicates the number of sheets required to print the 13 signatures of *A1* in 8vo and the number of sets to be printed on "ordinary" paper (2,500) and on "fine," i.e., large, "imperial" paper (150).[9]

§3 *Present State and Foliation*. In its present, incomplete state, *S1* consists of 161 folios of text written on the rectos of the leaves.[10]

Present Foliation. The folios of the text are numbered continuously [1]–55 and 70–174.[11] This series of numbers constitutes the *present*, as distinguished from the *original*, foliation of *S1* (see §4) *and is always cited in this edition in referring to the text of S1*.[12]

Bibliographical Society of America, XXVII (1933), 65–73. The designation in *S1* of sig. K (which commences at the beginning of the chapter entitled "Nampont. The Postillion", p. 142, above) lacks the square bracket. Two sigs. are not designated in *S1*: sig. B, which commences at the beginning of the first chapter (p. 65, above), and sig. L, which was apparently omitted inadvertently. (Sig. F begins on one of the folios now missing from *S1*; see §3.)

[7] The "x" next to and the line under "ₓmettles" and the query are in pencil. ("Metal" is spelled "mettle" in *Tristram Shandy*, IV, 247, 6.23.448.) "Vol. I" appears above the title of the chapter commencing on p. 128, above; it is not in Sterne's hand and may have been written by the printer.

[8] Cross gives the number "150" incorrectly as "135" in *Life*, p. 603; he gives it correctly on p. 631.

[9] See App. D, §2.

[10] Except for the hiatus described below, *S1* comprises the text of *A1* from the first through the last chapter (pp. 65–183, above). *S1* presumably had a title page (now lost) from which the title page of *M1* was transcribed (see App. C, §1).

[11] The text of fol. 52 is written on two separate leaves, the second of which is unnumbered (see App. C, §5). Thus, although there are 160 numbered folios of text, the MS. consists of 161 leaves, and, beginning with fol. 53, the number of each folio is one number lower than the actual numerical position of the leaf on which it appears (i.e., fol. 53 is on leaf 54ʳ, and so on).

[12] This series (written in ink) has been crossed out in pencil, presumably by the clerk in the British Museum who renumbered the folios of *S1* in foliating Egerton 1610 (see App. A, §1, n. 3).

S1 breaks off, at the end of fol. 55, with the words "beg of this dis-" (see p. 104.19–20, above) and recommences, at the beginning of fol. 70, with the chapter which starts on p. 113, above. An examination of *M1* (which was transcribed folio for folio from *S1*) confirms the assumption that the missing portion of *S1* comprised the text of *A1* from "-tressed lady" (p. 104.20, above) through the chapter which ends on p. 112, above, and that this portion of *S1* consisted of 14 folios numbered 56–69.

§4 *Canceled Original Foliation.* Two other series of numbers, both of which have been canceled, appear on the folios of *S1*.[13] The first series begins on fol. 17 and ends on fol. 55, the last folio before the present hiatus in *S1* (comprising fols. 56–69): this series originally ran continuously from ⟨18⟩, on fol. 17, through ⟨56⟩, on fol. 55.[14] The second series begins on fol. 70, the first folio after the present hiatus in *S1:* it runs continuously from ⟨72⟩, on fol. 70, through ⟨176⟩, on fol. 174 (the last folio of *S1*). These canceled numbers are in Sterne's hand, and he evidently used them to number the folios of *S1* as he was writing out the MS.[15] They thus constitute the *original,* as distinguished from the *present,* foliation of *S1*.

The relationship between these canceled folio numbers and the present folio numbers of *S1* may be explained as follows. Fols. [1]–16, which have no canceled numbers, are numbered only in Sterne's hand. However, fols. 17–49, 53–55,[16] and 70–174, which

[13] These numbers are written (and deleted) in ink. In addition to the numbers in these series, other canceled folio numbers appear on the following folios of *S1:* 74–77, 82^v, 89^v, 115, 133, 158–159. My efforts to determine the significance of the canceled numbers, except for those on fols. 89^v and 74–77 (see §5 and §6) have proved inconclusive.

[14] Because Sterne revised and recopied fols. 50–52 of *S1* after *M1* was transcribed from *S1* (see App. C, §5), ⟨50⟩ and ⟨51⟩ in this series are now missing.

[15] That is, he numbered each folio before writing it out. In two places where he started a folio and then turned the sheet over and began the folio again with the same version, or with a revised version, of what he had first written, the verso, on which the rejected version appears, has a folio number corresponding to the canceled number on the recto. See the textual notes to pp. 124.8–9, 148.47–48, above.

[16] Fols. 50–52 are numbered in Sterne's hand only; see App. C, §5.

do have canceled numbers in Sterne's hand, are numbered also in another hand which is, I believe, that of the *M1* copyist.[17] An explanation for this fact suggests itself if we recall, first, that fol. 17, the initial folio which is numbered in the *M1* copyist's hand, is also the initial folio bearing a canceled number in Sterne's hand (⟨18⟩); and second, that the text and the folio numbers of fols. [1]–49, 53–55, and 70–174 of *M1*, which was transcribed from *S1*, correspond exactly with fols. [1]–49, 53–55, and 70–174 of *S1*.[18]

Together, these facts suggest an explanation of the relationship between the canceled and the present folio numbers of *S1*. In writing out *S1*, Sterne numbered the first 16 folios correctly, but he misnumbered the 17th folio "18," and continued this error at least through fol. 55, the last folio preceding the present hiatus in *S1*. Before transcribing *M1* from *S1*, the *M1* copyist corrected this error by canceling Sterne's incorrect folio numbers (⟨18⟩–⟨56⟩) and renumbering these folios 17–55. However, with respect to fols. 70–174, following the present hiatus in *S1*, we encounter a difficulty: on these folios the canceled original numbers (⟨72⟩–⟨176⟩) in Sterne's hand are *two* numbers higher than the present folio numbers (70–174) in the *M1* copyist's hand. This change from one number to two in the differential between the canceled and the present folio numbers apparently occurred in the folios now missing from *S1* (56–69).

§5 The verbal parallels between a canceled reading on fol. 89ᵛ of *S1* and two passages in the final text indicate that the canceled reading and these two passages are related: see p. 110.10–11*tn*, above. Their relationship is confirmed by the analysis in §4 of the foliation of *S1*. The canceled reading on fol. 89ᵛ appears upside down at the bottom of fol. 89ᵛ and commences in the right-hand margin; and fol. 89ᵛ is numbered 69 in Sterne's hand. The two passages in the final text to which the canceled passage on fol. 89ᵛ

---

[17] The original numbers, in Sterne's hand, appear in the upper right-hand corners of the folios; the present numbers, in the *M1* copyist's hand, are usually to the left of the original numbers. The *M1* copyist modified many of the original numbers to incorporate them into the new numbering, by altering one digit, by superimposing one digit on another, or by deleting one digit and adding another.

[18] See App. C, §3, (2).

of *S1* is related appear on fols. 67 and 68 of *M1*, respectively. These folios in *M1* were presumably transcribed from the missing portion of *S1*, comprising fols. 56–69. As we have seen, the numbering of the extant folios of *S1* indicates that when Sterne first inscribed the folios now missing from *S1* (56–69) he assigned them numbers which were one or two numbers higher than the numbers the *M1* copyist assigned to these folios before transcribing them. Assuming that, when he was writing out *S1*, Sterne numbered fol. 89^v "69", we would expect the canceled passage on fol. 89^v to be related to the text of fols. 67 or 68 of *M1*, as is the case.

§6 There is bibliographical evidence that when Sterne first inscribed the last of the three chapters entitled "In the Street. Calais" (cited hereafter as ch. 18),[19] it probably appeared at an earlier point in the text. And there are grounds for believing (1) that this chapter originally followed the last of the three chapters entitled "The Remise Door. Calais" (cited hereafter as ch. 13),[20] and (2) that after he had first inscribed ch. 18, Sterne rewrote the first part and moved this chapter to its present position in the text.

The evidence that when Sterne first inscribed ch. 18 it appeared at an earlier point in the text is as follows. At present, the folios of ch. 18 are numbered 72–77. The following canceled numbers (in Sterne's hand) appear on these folios: 72 ⟨74⟩; 73 ⟨?75⟩; 74 ⟨76⟩ ⟨61⟩; ⟨7⟩7∧5∧ ⟨62⟩; 76 ⟨78⟩ ⟨63⟩; 77 ⟨?64⟩∼⟨79⟩∼.[21] The canceled numbers ⟨61⟩–⟨?64⟩ on the last four folios of ch. 18 (fols. 74–77) probably indicate that when Sterne first inscribed these folios he numbered them 61–64.[22] Assuming that Sterne inscribed these four folios and the canceled numbers ⟨61⟩–⟨?64⟩ on them in the process of writing out *S1*, these folios occupied a position somewhere in the portion of *S1* which is now missing (comprising fols. 56–69) when they were first inscribed.

---

[19] Pp. 114–120, above.

[20] Pp. 104–106, above.

[21] ⟨79⟩ is superimposed on a number which, though nearly illegible, appears to be 64. The canceled numbers ⟨61⟩–⟨?64⟩ appear in the extreme upper right-hand corners of the folios. The uncanceled numbers are in the hand of the *M1* copyist (see §4).

[22] Sterne apparently numbered each folio of *S1* before writing it out; see n. 15, above.

I have been unable to determine exactly where, in the missing portion of *S1*, the last four folios of ch. 18 may have originally appeared, but the following analysis is offered as a hypothesis.

We must first account for the fact that the first two folios of ch. 18 (72 and 73) bear only the canceled numbers ⟨74⟩ and ⟨75⟩, respectively. An examination of these folios (see facsimiles of fols. 72 and 73, following p. 320, below) indicates that (1) whereas Sterne revised fols. 74–77 of ch. 18 after he wrote them out, fols. 72 and 73 are free of alterations; (2) Sterne's handwriting on these folios is somewhat larger than it is on many of the folios of *S1*, and this difference becomes more pronounced toward the bottom of fol. 73, where the words and dashes appear to have been spaced out so as to fill the folio; (3) fol. 73 ends with a passage which is obviously a version of a canceled passage at the top of fol. 74 (see facsimile of fol. 74, following p. 320, below); and this canceled passage is separated from the rest of the text of fol. 74 by a line extending from the left-hand margin halfway across the page.

The concluding passage on fol. 73 appears to be a revised and expanded version of the canceled passage at the top of fol. 74. The relationship between these two passages[23] and the general appearance of fols. 72 and 73 suggest that the text of fols. 72 and 73 may have been revised from an earlier version of the first part of ch. 18. Let us assume, for the moment, that this hypothesis is correct and, further: (1) that this earlier version filled one folio and continued through the canceled passage which now appears at the top of fol. 74; and (2) that this folio was numbered 60. On the basis of this hypothesis, when Sterne first inscribed ch. 18 it consisted of five folios numbered 60–64.

As we have noted (§4), when Sterne first inscribed fols. 17–55 of *S1* he numbered them 18–56, and the *M1* copyist subsequently canceled these numbers and renumbered these folios 17–55. If Sterne continued the sequence of numbers running 18–56 when he inscribed the first eight of the folios which are now missing from *S1*, he would have numbered them 57–64. The texts of fol. 55 in *M1* and of fol. 55 in *S1* (the last folio before the present hiatus in

---

[23] We would normally expect the canceled passage at the top of fol. 74 to *precede* what appears to be a revised version of that passage at the bottom of fol. 73.

S1) correspond exactly. Let us suppose that the text of fols. 56–58 in *M1* also corresponds exactly with the text of fols. 56–68 in *S1*, which are now missing,[24] and that Sterne numbered the first two of these folios 57–58. When Sterne first inscribed the last four folios of what is now ch. 18, he numbered these folios 61–64; this portion of ch. 18 presumably, therefore, originally occupied a position somewhere within the first eight of the folios now missing from *S1*. If the suggestion is correct that, when ch. 18 was first inscribed, it commenced with a different version of the text which filled one folio, numbered 60,[25] this hypothetical folio would have occupied a position corresponding to fol. 59 of *M1*.

In *M1* we find that ch. 13, the last of the three chapters entitled "The Remise Door. Calais",[26] ends on fol. 58 of *M1*, and that what is now the *second* chapter entitled "In the Street. Calais" (cited hereafter as ch. 14)[27] begins on fol. 59 of *M1*. According to the hypothesis presented above with regard to the position occupied by ch. 18 when it was first inscribed, ch. 18 originally appeared between chs. 13 and 14.

In terms of the context formed by the conclusion of ch. 13 and the beginning of ch. 14, there is no reason why ch. 18 could not have originally come between them. At the conclusion of ch. 13, Yorick is about to offer to share his chaise with the lady, but he finds that while he has been weighing the propriety of doing so, she has glided off. Her manner suggests that she may be considering asking to share his chaise; and, at the end of ch. 13, not caring to interrupt her, he takes "a short turn or two before the door of the Remise" while she walks "musing on one side" (pp. 105–106,

---

[24] Fol. 55 in *M1* and in *S1* both end with the words "beg of this dis-" (see §3). Fol. 56 in *M1* begins with "-tressed lady", which indicates that the text of this folio in *M1* and of the equivalent folio in *S1*, now lost and probably numbered 56 (by the *M1* copyist), corresponded at least this far. The fact that the canceled reading on fol. 89ᵛ of *S1* (originally numbered 69 by Sterne) corresponds with parts of the text of fols. 67 and 68 of *M1* (see §5) indicates that the contents of these folios in *M1* and of fols. 67 and 68 in *S1* probably corresponded.

[25] And continued through the end of the canceled passage at the top of fol. 74, which Sterne numbered 61 when he first inscribed it.

[26] Pp. 104–106, above.

[27] Pp. 107–108, above.

above). Chapter 14 commences with Yorick's reflections on the "widowed" character and distressed circumstances he has imputed to the lady. Although his observations here are closely related to the content of ch. 13, they summarize his feelings about the lady up to this point and do not necessarily have to follow immediately after the conclusion of ch. 13.

Chapter 18 could, then, have intervened between chs. 13 and 14 without disrupting the narrative. Furthermore, except for the first paragraph, the contents of ch. 18 are not incompatible with the context formed by chs. 13 and 14. Let us suppose that ch. 18 originally lacked the present first paragraph (in which Yorick purchases a chaise and walks off toward the hotel; see p. 114.1–5, above) and commenced instead with what is now the second paragraph, in which the striking of the town clock makes him realize that he has been little more than an hour in Calais. His remarks here, on the "large volume of adventures [that] may be grasped within this little span of life by him who interests his heart in every thing" (p. 114.8–12), accurately characterize his travels thus far. And his reflections on Smelfungus and Mundungus, which conclude ch. 18 (pp. 119–120), are entirely appropriate to the situation in which he finds himself with the lady at the end of ch. 13 and the beginning of ch. 14. Unlike these splenetic travelers, he has allowed himself to be seduced out of his road by "Love" and "Pity" (p. 119.52–53) for the lady; and he is even considering sharing his chaise with her.

Ch. 18 now begins with a paragraph in which Yorick purchases a chaise and, having ordered post-horses, walks off toward the hotel (p. 114.1–5). If the hypothesis is correct that ch. 18 originally followed ch. 13, it obviously could not have begun with the present first paragraph. A possible solution to this difficulty is offered by the evidence presented above that the two folios with which ch. 18 now begins may have been substituted for a single folio containing most of an earlier version of the first part of the chapter. If we assume that this earlier version lacked the paragraph with which ch. 18 now begins, the process by which Sterne revised this chapter and shifted it to its present position may be hypothetically reconstructed as follows. (1) When Sterne first inscribed ch. 18, it consisted of five folios numbered 60–64 and lacked the present first paragraph. (2) Having decided to move ch. 18 to its present position,[28] Sterne revised the first folio of the chapter (originally numbered 60) by adding the present first paragraph and by revising and expanding the canceled passage which now appears at the top of fol. 74. He then wrote out a fair copy of the revised, expanded version of the first part of the chapter,[29] spacing out his writing so that it would exactly fill two folios, and canceled the concluding portion of the original version, which now appears at the top of fol. 74 (originally numbered 61). (3) He discarded the original first folio of the chapter (numbered 60), and replaced it with two new folios bearing the revised and expanded version of the first part of the chapter. He numbered these two folios 74 and 75, and, having canceled the numbers on the other (original) folios of the chapter (61–64), he renumbered these folios 76–79.

One problem remains to be considered. If ch. 18 did originally follow ch. 13, and if, as seems evident from the generally fair appearance of *S1*, Sterne transcribed *S1*, as a fair copy, from a draft of the text of Vol. I in which ch. 19 (the first chapter entitled "Montriul"; see pp. 121–123, above) was in its present position, ch. 19 would have followed the last of the three chapters entitled "The Remise. Calais" (now ch. 17; see p. 113, above). There would seem to be no reason why this could not have been the case. Chapter 17 ends with the lady's bidding adieu to Yorick, after Mons. Dessein has informed her of the arrival of her brother. Chapter 19 commences with a description of the inconveniences which prompt Yorick to hire La Fleur. If ch. 19 had originally followed immediately after ch. 17, the transition between these chapters would have

---

[28] He apparently moved ch. 18 while inscribing the part of *S1* which is now missing (comprising fols. 56–69), and before he inscribed ch. 17 (p. 113, above). Ch. 17 begins on fol. 70 of *S1*, the first folio after the present hiatus in *S1*. Sterne apparently numbered each folio of *S1* before writing it out (see n. 15). The folios of ch. 17 are numbered 70 and 71 in the *M1* copyist's hand, and each folio has only one canceled folio number in Sterne's hand (⟨72⟩ and ⟨73⟩, respectively), which corresponds with its present position in *S1*. Each folio of ch. 17 would have an additional canceled number in Sterne's hand if he had numbered and inscribed these folios *before* their position was changed by moving ch. 18 to its present position.

[29] For an instance in which Sterne unquestionably revised and recopied two folios in *S1*, see App. C, §5.

been somewhat abrupt, but no more so than the transitions between many of the other chapters in *A Sentimental Journey*.

If Sterne did move ch. 18 from a position between chs. 13 and 14 to its present position, he may have done so because he felt that his remarks in ch. 18, particularly on the contrast between Yorick's travels and those of Smelfungus and Mundungus, would be a more effective conclusion to his adventures in Calais than would his farewell to the lady at the end of ch. 17 (p. 113). Furthermore, in their present position, his reflections on traveling in ch. 18 provide a general commentary on the principles of traveling which are exemplified by his experiences in Calais (including his sentimental commerce with the fair lady) and which will be illustrated by the rest of his travels.

APPENDIX C

§1 *General Description.*[1] Bound in 2 vols.; the leaves measure approximately 8 x 6¼ inches. The text is written on the rectos of the leaves.[2]

M1 consists of 178 leaves: a preliminary blank leaf; title page: A / Sentimental Journey / through / France and Italy / By / Mͬ Yorick / [line] / Vol. 1.; 174 folios of text numbered continuously [1]–174;[3] an unnumbered blank leaf between fols. 88 and 89; a final blank leaf after the last folio of the text.

M2 consists of 187 leaves: a preliminary blank leaf; title page: A Sentimental Journey / Through / France & Italy / By Mͬ Yorick. / [line] / Vol. 2. / [line]; 184 folios of text numbered continuously [1]–184; an unnumbered blank leaf after the last folio of the text.

§2 *Handwriting.* The following portions of the Morgan MS., comprising most of the MS., appear to be in one hand:[4] the title

---

[1] The Morgan MS. (MA 1046–1047) is briefly described in *Life*, p. 631. A bookplate with the name of "The Hon! Martha Agnew of Lochnaw" is affixed to the inner side of the front board of *M1*, and "M. Agnew" is written above the title of the first chapter in *M1* and *M2;* on Martha Agnew's identity, see *Life*, p. 631.

[2] The versos are blank except for the note on the *Droits d'aubaine;* as in *S1*, this note is written on fol. [1]ᵛ of *M1*, opposite *"Droits d'aubaine"* (on fol. 2); see p. 66.16–19*tn*, above.

[3] The upper right-hand corners of fols. 89–92 are worn, and the numbers of these folios are partially or wholly missing.

[4] George K. Boyce considers the Morgan MS. to be largely in a hand which is not Sterne's ("Modern Literary Manuscripts in the Morgan Library," *PMLA,* LXVII [1952], 21). Cross states that the MS. is "mainly in two . . . hands, perhaps his wife's and daughter's" (*Life*, p. 631). As Cross pointed out, in advising the Morgan Library to purchase the MS. (in a letter dtd. 16 June 1926, to Belle da Costa Greene, Curator of Autograph MSS. [cited with the Library's kind permission]), Lydia had copied out parts of *Tristram Shandy* for Sterne (see *Letters*, No. 79, p. 143), and she and Mrs. Sterne were in Coxwold with him during October 1767, and nearby in York during November and December, while he was completing the *Journey*. However, none of the handwriting of the Morgan MS. seems to me to resemble Lydia's and Mrs. Sterne's hands.

page and the entire text of *M1*, and the title page and fols. [1]–85 and 87–156 of *M2*. The remaining folios of *M2* are clearly in a different hand, and, unlike the rest of the MS., they have catchwords.[5] I have not been able to identify either of these hands.[6]

§3 *Relationship between M1 and S1.* That *M1* is a fair copy of *S1* is indicated by the following evidence. (1) Aside from corrections of slips of the pen, *M1* is free of alterations, except for the occasional deletion or insertion of a word. These alterations bring *M1* into agreement with *S1* and are clearly corrections by the *M1* copyist of errors made in transcribing *M1* from *S1*.[7] (2) The text of fols. 1–49, 53–55, and 70–174 of *M1* corresponds folio for folio with fols. 1–49, 53–55, and 70–174 of *S1*,[8] and it is evident that the *M1* copyist deliberately maintained this correspondence.[9] Furthermore, the

---

[5] I.e., fol. 86, comprising the text of the chapter entitled "The Mystery. Paris" through "philosophic" (see p. 239.1–9, above; "serious" [p. 239.9, above], the first word on fol. 87, appears as catchword on fol. 86); and fols. 157–184, comprising the text of pp. 277–291, above. (Catchwords are omitted in fols. 157–184 from the folios on which chapters conclude.)

[6] Cross (*Life*, p. 631), Boyce (see n. 4, above), and T. J. Brown ("English Literary Autographs XXVII: Laurence Sterne, 1713–1768," *Book Collector*, VII [1958], 285) all state that the Morgan MS. is partly in Sterne's hand. However, if they are referring to the folios of the Morgan MS. specified in n. 5, above, the handwriting of these folios is not, in my opinion, in Sterne's holograph. Sterne's hand varies, but one detail seems to remain constant—the ampersand. There is no resemblance between Sterne's ampersands and those in the Morgan MS.

[7] These corrections were probably made by the *M1* copyist in writing out the MS. Aside from slips of the pen, the uncorrected scribal errors in *M1* involve the occasional omission of a word or phrase. These errors are the kind that would not ordinarily have been noticed by the copyist in writing out the MS., but probably would have been detected if *M1* had been collated with *S1*, which apparently was not done.

[8] Since Sterne revised and recopied fols. 50–52 of *S1* after *M1* was transcribed from it, the texts of these folios in the two MSS. do not correspond (see §5); and fols. 56–69 of *S1* are missing (see App. B, §3).

[9] For example: (*a*) On fol. 139 of *M1*, the last word appears below the end of the last line of text, and on several folios of *M1* enough space remains for two or three additional lines of text (e.g., fol. 111). These anomalies in *M1* serve to maintain the folio-for-folio correspondence between the texts of *M1* and of *S1*. (*b*) On fol. 104 of *S1*, the last word appears below the end of the last line of text, and this anomaly is followed on fol. 104 of *M1*. (*c*) On fols.

M1 copyist renumbered the folios of *S1* before transcribing *M1* from *S1*.[10] (3) There are anomalies in the text of *M1* which were evidently caused by anomalies in the text of *S1*.[11] (4) The format and the accidentals of *S1* are generally followed in *M1*.[12]

That *M1* was transcribed from *S1* before Sterne had completed the numerous revisions he made in *S1* prior to giving it to the printer is clear. In most of the instances where Sterne revised *S1*, *M1* follows the revised reading. However, *M1* occasionally follows the unrevised reading in *S1*, and in most cases this fact cannot be attributed to the copyist's having overlooked the revision in *S1*.[13] The most extensive revision Sterne made in *S1* after *M1* was transcribed from it is described in §5.

§4 *Relationship between M2 and S2 (lost)*. That *M2* has the same relationship to *S2* (now lost) that *M1* has to *S1* is indicated by the following evidence. (1) Like *M1*, *M2* is a fair copy, free of alterations except for the occasional deletion or insertion of a word, and corrections of slips of the pen. (2) As in *M1*, there are several instances in *M2* where the copyist was apparently seeking to maintain a folio-for-folio correspondence between *M2* and another text,

55 ("dis-[-tressed]"; see App. B, §3) and 163 of *S1*, the final word in the final line is hyphenated, and fols. 55 and 163 of *M1* follow *S1* in this regard.

[10] See App. B, §4.

[11] In one place where Sterne revised *S1* by superimposing one word on another, the new word ("such"—see p. 157.24*tn*, above) is very unclear; a blank is left in place of this word in *M1*, presumably because the *M1* copyist could not decipher it. In making the revision "⟨at⟩ // to" (p. 87.9*tn*, above), Sterne erased "⟨at⟩" very slightly; the *M1* copyist evidently overlooked this erasure initially, for *M1* also reads "⟨at⟩ // to".

[12] (1) As in *S1*, chapters usually begin at the head of a new folio, and a line usually appears above and below the chapter titles; exceptions in *S1* are invariably followed in *M1*. (2) The line in *S1* separating Sterne's footnote on p. 76, above, from the text (see p. 76.8*tn*, above) is transcribed in *M1*. (3) Sterne's frequent failure to capitalize the first word in a sentence (after a period and at the beginning of a paragraph), his idiosyncratic spellings (e.g., "mettles" [see App. B, §2, (2)], "Glascow", "magazeen", "summ"), and the errors in his French are usually followed in *M1*. (4) *M1* regularly substitutes "and" for "&" in *S1* (and vice versa); frequently omits commas in *S1* and occasionally inserts commas not in *S1*; omits two or three dashes in *S1* and inserts one dash not in *S1* (at the end of a paragraph).

[13] See, e.g., p. 120.61–63*tn*, above.

presumably that of *S2*.[14] (3) As noted in §3, *M1* follows the format and accidentals of *S1* faithfully in most respects, and the format and accidentals of *M2* correspond closely with those in *M1* (and in *S1*), and with those in *A2*.[15] (4) That Sterne revised *S2* after *M2* was transcribed from it is indicated both by the nature of the differences in wording between *M2* and *A2*, which was evidently printed from *S2*,[16] and by one of the differences in accidentals between *M2* and *A2*: Sterne initially wrote "Le Fleur" throughout *S1*. In most instances he revised "Le" to "La" in *S1*; where he failed to do so, this revision was invariably made in *A1*.[17] *M1* was transcribed from *S1* before he made this revision, for *M1* reads "Le" throughout. *M2* also reads "Le" throughout, and in three places *A2* reads "Le" rather than "La".[18] These facts suggest that (*a*) *M2* was transcribed from *S2* when *S2* read "Le"; (*b*) after *M2* was transcribed from *S2* Sterne revised "Le" to "La" in *S2*; (*c*) as in *S1*, he occasionally failed to make this revision in *S2*; (*d*) where *A2* reads "Le" it is following an unrevised "Le" in *S2*.

§5 *Revision of Fols. 50–52 S1*. A comparison of the texts of fols. 50–52 in *M1* and in *S1* indicates that, after *M1* was transcribed from *S1*, Sterne revised the text of fols. 50–52 of *S1*, wrote out the revised version on three new folios, and discarded the original fols. 50–51, which comprised most of the original version. Since Sterne made this revision after *M1* was transcribed from *S1*, *M1* provides

---

[14] On several folios of *M2* the last word appears below the end of the last line of text (e.g., fols. 12, 31, 43); in some of these instances the *M2* copyist may have been following an anomaly in *S2* similar to the one on fol. 104 of *S1* (see n. 9, (*b*), above). And some folios of *M2* are only partially filled (e.g., fol. 146); see n. 9, (*a*), above.

[15] One correspondence between the format of *M2* and *A2* strongly confirms the other evidence that *M2* was transcribed from *S2* and that *S2* was the printer's copy for *A2*: the lines in *A2* separating Sterne's footnotes from the text (see p. 256.21*tn*, above) also appear in *M2* (two of the lines do not run the full width of the text in *M2*, as they do in *A2*). This fact suggests that these lines in *M2* and *A2* were almost certainly copied from *S2*. (The line in *S1* separating Sterne's footnote on p. 76, above, from the text [see p. 76.8*tn*, above] is transcribed in *M1*, but omitted in *A1*.)

[16] See p. 56, above.

[17] See p. 124.7*tn*, above.

[18] See textual notes to p. 193, ll. 24, 26, 31.

a transcript of the part of the original version which was written on
the folios he discarded from *S1* (50–51).

The texts of fols. 50–52 in *M1* and in *S1* read as follows.

M1	*S1*
[Fol. 50]	[Fol. 50]
heart.	heart.[19]
The poor monk blush'd as	The poor monk blush'd as
red as scarlet: Mon Dieu!	red as scarlet: Mon dieu!
said he, pressing his hands	said he pressing his hands
together—you never used me	together,—You never used me
unkindly—I should think,	unkindly—I should think,
said the Lady, he is not	said the Lady, He is not
likely. I blush'd in my	likely. I blush'd in my
turn—but from what	turn; but from what
movements,	⟨motions⟩ movements,
I leave to the few who feel,	I leave to the few who feel,
to analyse—excuse me	to analyse.—excuse me,
dear Madam, said I, I treated	Madame, replied I—I treatd
him most unkindly, and from no	him most unkindly; & from no
provocations—'tis impossible;	provocations—'tis impossible:
said the Lady—Mon Seigʳ!	said the Lady.—My God!
cried the monk, with a warmth	cried the monk with a warmth
of asseveration which seem'd	of Asseveration which seem'd
not to belong to him,—	not to belong to him—
you used me kindly Sir:	the Fault was in me; & in the
I persisted in my point—	⟨?pros⟩ indiscretion of my Zeal—
the Lady opposed it—	the Lady opposed ⟨?him⟩~it~
the dispute grew warm—	
the monk would not have my	
box—the Lady encouraged	
him in it	
[Fol. 51]	[Fol. 51]
I insisted positively upon	and I joind with her in
his accepting it—the monk	maintaining ⟨That a heart so
peremptorily refused.	goo⟩ ∧it was impossible,∧
	That a Spirit so regulated
	as his, could give offence to
	any.
'Tis strange in the	I knew not that
eagerness of contention,	Contention could be renderd
how easily a man may suffer	so sweet & pleasurable

---

[19] See p. 99.11, above. The folios of *M1* and *S1* transcribed here are reproduced following p. 320, below.

the cause of it, to slip out
of his mind: for tho' the
monks reasons for not
taking the box were the most
flattering that could be, yet
I was actually piqued at his
perseverance and could
not help telling him, it was
unkind— / —but you have
brought it upon yourself,
said the Lady smiling, by
your treatment of him in the
hôtel— / —a la bonne heure;
cried the monk—so I beg we
may set one trespass against
the other and end the dispute
my dear Sir for ever.
   In saying this,
he rub'd his horn
   [end fol. 51]

‸a thing‸ to the nerves as I
then felt it—⟨it begot a
silence⟩ We remain'd silent,
without any Sensation of that
foolish pain wch takes place,
when in such a circle you look
for ten minutes in one
anothers faces without saying
a word.

Whilst this lasted,
the Monk, rubb'd his horn
box upon the sleeve of his
tunick; & as soon as it had
acquired a little air of
brightness by the friction—
he made a low bow, & said
twas too late to say
whether it was the weakness
or goodness our[20] tempers which
   [end fol. 51]

[Fol. 52A]
had involved us in this
contest—but be it as it
would—he beg'd We might
exchanges[21] boxes—
in saying this,
he presented his to me with
one hand, as he took mine from
me in the other; and having
kiss'd it—with a stream of
good nature in his eyes
he put it into his bosome
—and took his leave.[22]

[20] *A1* reads "goodness of our" (see p. 100.31*tn*, above).
[21] *A1* reads "exchange" (see p. 101.32*tn*, above).
[22] Fol. 52A of *S1* is only half filled; see facsimile following p. 320, below.

M1	*S1*
[Fol. 52]	[Fol. 52B]²³
upon his sleeve, and	⟨upon his sleeve, and
presented it to me with	presented it to me with
one hand, as he took mine from	one hand, as he took mine from
me in the other; and having	me in the other; and having
kiss'd it, with a stream of	kiss'd it,—with a stream of
good nature in his eyes	good nature in his eyes
he put it into his bosome	he put it into his b∧o∧some
—and took his leave.	—and took his leave.⟩
I guard . . . disappointment	I guard . . . disappointment
[end fol. 52]	[end fol. 52B]

By examining the folios in *M1* and *S1* which are transcribed above, and reproduced following p. 320, below, we can reconstruct Sterne's revision of this portion of *S1*. (1) Sterne's holograph on fols. 50–52A differs from its normal appearance in *S1*, which is typified by fol. 52B.²⁴ (2) The versions of the text given on fols. 50–52 in *M1* and on fols. 50–52A in *S1* differ extensively; and, unlike the texts of the other folios in the two MSS., the texts of these folios do not correspond folio for folio. However, the text of fol. 52 in *M1* and the text of fol. 52B in *S1*, including the canceled paragraph with which this folio commences, do correspond folio for folio and agree in wording. (3) Fols. 50–52 in *S1* have only one folio number, in Sterne's hand, whereas fols. 17–49 and 53–55 have a canceled number in Sterne's hand, with which he numbered these folios when he first inscribed them, and another number, one digit lower, with which the *M1* copyist renumbered these folios before transcribing *M1* from *S1*.²⁵ (4) Fol. 52A is only half filled, and the number of fol. 52B, in the *M1* copyist's hand (52), has been canceled and has not been replaced with another number.

---

²³ This folio is numbered "⟨52⟩ ⟨53⟩"; see facsimile following p. 320, below, and n. 24, below.

²⁴ Fol. 52A = the folio in *S1* which is now numbered 52 and is only half filled; fol. 52B = the next folio, which bears the canceled number ⟨52⟩, in the *M1* copyist's hand, and ⟨53⟩, in Sterne's hand (see the facsimiles of these folios following p. 320, below). The text of fol. 52A and the uncanceled portion of fol. 52B ("I guard . . . disappointment") together make up the "A" and "B" portions of what is now fol. 52, the text of which is written on two separate leaves.

²⁵ See App. B, §4.

The foregoing evidence indicates that the text of fols. 50 and 51 and the initial paragraph of fol. 52 of *M1* ("upon . . . leave.") were transcribed from an earlier version of this part of the text of *S1*. As in *M1*, this earlier version filled two folios in *S1*, numbered 50 and 51, and extended through the initial, canceled paragraph on fol. 52B ("⟨upon . . . leave.⟩"), which corresponds exactly with the initial paragraph on fol. 52 of *M1*. After *M1* was transcribed from *S1*, Sterne substituted the present version of the text, on fols. 50–52A of *S1*, for the earlier version. He discarded the original fols. 50 and 51, and canceled the concluding paragraph of the earlier version, at the top of the original fol. 52, which is now fol. 52B. He also canceled the *M1* copyist's number on this folio (52), so that the uncanceled portion of the text of this folio ("I guard . . . disappointment") became the concluding portion of the new fol. 52 (fol. 52B), the initial portion of which appears at the top of fol. 52A.

APPENDIX D

FIRST EDITION

§1 Publ. London, 27 Feb. 1768,[1] by Thomas Becket and Peter Abraham De Hondt; 2 vols., 8vo.

Vol. I [A]², a⁸, B–N⁸, O⁶. Pp. [i]–xx, [1]–203.
[A]1ʳ (p. [i]), half-title, verso blank: A / Sentimental Journey, / &c. &c. / Vol. I.; [A]2ʳ (p. [iii]), title, verso blank (see facsimile, p. 63, above); a1ʳ–a8ᵛ (pp. [v]–xx), subscribers; B1ʳ–O6ʳ (pp. [1]–203), text; O6ᵛ, blank.

Vol. II [A]², B–O⁸. Pp. [1]–208 (pp. 34, 35 misnumbered 33, 34).
[A]1ʳ, half-title, verso blank: A / Sentimental Journey, / &c. &c. / Vol. II.; [A]2ʳ, title, verso blank (see facsimile, p. 185, above); B1ʳ–O8ᵛ (pp. [1]–208), text.

§2 The first edition was printed in two styles: on ordinary paper (approx. 6¼ x 3¾ in.) and on large ("imperial") paper (approx. 7⅛ x 4¼ in.).[2] The two styles have the same collation (see §1). There were 281 subscribers to the first edition; they took 334 sets, 199 on ordinary paper and 135 on large paper. Those subscribing for large-paper sets have a star after their names.

§3 The following advertisement was printed as a separate sheet, to be inserted in the sets[3] for subscribers:

---

[1] See *Public Advertiser* for that date (cited in *Letters*, p. 414, n. 3). Cross states that the date of publication was 24 or 25 February and cites *Lloyd's Evening Post* for 24–26 February (*Life*, p. 603); however, the notice in that issue announced that *A Sentimental Journey* would be published "To-morrow," presumably 27 February. (The first edition was registered at Stationer's Hall on 27 February; see *Life*, p. 477*n*.)

[2] For the number of copies printed in each style, see App. B, §2, (3).

[3] In both styles; see *Life*, p. 478*n*. For the price of both styles and the premium paid by subscribers, see *Life*, pp. 477, 478*n*.

Advertisement.

The Author begs leave to acknowledge to his Subscribers, that they have a further claim upon him for Two Volumes more than these delivered to them now, and which nothing but ill health could have prevented him, from having ready along with these. The Work will be compleated and delivered to the Subscribers early the next Winter.[4]

§4 A collation of my large-paper copy of the first edition, from which the present edition is reprinted, with two other large-paper copies revealed no variant readings. A collation of my large-paper copy with four ordinary-paper copies revealed the following variants in some ordinary-paper copies:

Ref. in present text		*Large-paper*	*Ordinary-paper*
151.59	(1)	angry·	angry:[5]
153.15	(2)	vous	vaus
193.39	(3)	If	If,
194.47, 196.35, 203.33	(4)	La	Là[6]
230.9	(5)	*François*	*Francois*
230.9	(6)	*polis.*	*poli.s*
252.16–17	(7)	who have	whho ave

§5 *Emendations.* The emendations I have made in the present edition in the text of my large-paper copy of the first edition are recorded in the following textual notes: pp. 77.16; 160.33; 187, title; 187.10; 187.12; 188.28; 189.40; 189.53; 190.72; 190.74; 193.13; 193.24; 193.26; 193.31; 197.58; 197.70; 198.83; 201.8; 203.40; 204.14; 204.27; 209.5; 221.10; 223.20; 231.22; 231.28; 232.39; 234.1; 236.62; 246.4; 248.62; 253.32; 254.56; 255.81; 259.57; 268, title; 269.15; 272.15; 273.31; 277.4; 285.19; 286.34; 286.48; 290.143.

---

[4] Sterne died before he could complete the two volumes of travels through Italy he had projected; see Introduction, pp. 20–21, above.
[5] The lower dot of the colon after "angry" appears in only one of the ordinary-paper copies I examined and in none of the large-paper copies.
[6] This variant appears in Vol. II of one of my ordinary-paper copies, on pp. 17.1, 21.12, 32.11 and catchword.

§6 *Compound words hyphenated at the end of the line.*[7]

(1) *Present edition.* The following compounds which are hyphenated at the end of the line in the present edition are hyphenated within the line in the first edition.

82.73	fore- / runners	178.54	side- / box
96.10	ill- / timed	217.60	fellow- / feeling
135.10	jack- / boots	241.4	bed- / chamber
137.59	post- / house	245.27	two- / sous
151.77	self- / same	286.41	bed- / chamber
168.18	side- / ways		

(2) *First edition.* The following compounds (or possible compounds) are hyphenated at the end of the line in the first edition. Their form in the present edition is given below, followed by their form elsewhere in the first edition and/or in *S1* or in *M2*.

89.6	Hyde-park] Hyde park *S1*
89.7	sword's-man] sword's man *S1*
89.15	overreach'd] overreach'd *S1*
90.23	fore-fingers] fore-fingers *A1* [p. 164.64, above], forefingers *S1*
135.3	jack-boot] jack-boots *A1* [p. 137.56, above], jack boot *S1*
151.59	well-meaning] well- / meaning *S1*
159.8	periwig-maker's] pery-wig makerⱽ'sⱽ *S1*
160.30	nine-pence] nine-pence *S1*
175.20	apple-trees] [*S1* reads either "appletrees" or "apple trees"]
248.47	self-denials] self- / denials *S1*
255.87	broken-hearted] broken hearted *M2*
288.100	bed-chamber] bed-chamber *A2* [p. 286.31, above], Bedchamber *M2*

(3) *Present and first editions.* The following compounds (or possible compounds) are hyphenated at the end of the line both in the present edition and in the first edition.

---

[7] I am indebted here to the section on word-division in Nathaniel Hawthorne, *The Scarlet Letter*, ed. William Charvat, Fredson Bowers, et al., Hawthorne Centenary Ed., I (1962), 283–285.

83.95   laughing- / stock] laughing stock *S1*
        [i.e., "laughing-stock"]
135.1   post- / chaise] post-chaise *A1* [p. 135.2,
        above] [i.e., "post-chaise"]

§7 *Dash: Special Cases.* In the five instances where one line ends
and the next line begins with a dash in the first edition, a dash of
normal length (1 em) has been used in the present edition. (In the
instances which occur in *A1*, there is no evidence that the compositor was trying to reproduce an extra-long dash in *S1*.)

85.130 motion.—'Twas] motion.— / —'Twas *A1*
125.29 said I—*O qu'oui!*] said I— / —*O qu'oui! A1*[8]
140.37 concern—La Fleur] concern— / —La Fleur *A1*
190.71 Pierre—You] Pierre— / —You *A2*
225.12 moments!—long] moments!— / —long *A2*

SECOND EDITION

Publ. 29 March 1768[9] by Becket and De Hondt; 2 vols., 8vo (same
size as ordinary-paper copies of the first edition). The second edition has the same collation as the first, except that in both volumes
the half-title is omitted, and the title page reads: A / Sentimental
Journey / . . . Vol. I. [II.] / [line] / The Second Edition. / [dou-
ble line] / London: . . . MDCCLXVIII.

The text follows that of the first edition almost invariably page for
page, and usually line for line. None of the few, minor differences in
wording between the second edition and the first is sufficiently important to suggest that Sterne revised the first edition before his
death.[10]

---

[8] *S1* reads "said I.— ∧—O qu'oui!∧" here (the insertion is above the line).
The compositor evidently printed the redundant dash before "O qu'oui!",
which duplicates the dash following "said I.—".

[9] See *Life*, p. 604.

[10] A few of the obvious errors in the first edition were emended in the second, and new errors were introduced. Except for such changes, I have found
only two substantive variants between the first edition and the second; both
are indifferent (the reading in the first edition is given first): foot] feet (see
p. 167.30, above); finger to] finger at (see p. 179.91, above). In his edition

"NEW" EDITION

Publ. by Becket and De Hondt, after the second edition.[11] This edition has no authority, but it is of interest as the first in which a dash is inserted after "Chambre's—" (sic), at the end of the last sentence (p. 291, above). This unauthorized change, which eliminates Yorick's final equivocation, has been made in many subsequent editions.

---

of *A Sentimental Journey* (London, 1929), Sir Herbert Read records three other variants between his text, described (p. xliii) as based on the second edition, and Sterne's holograph MS. of Vol. I (*S1*): see Read's edition, p. 228, n. 25; and p. 229, n. 34, the first and third variants (*"an"*, *"up"*). Sir Herbert informed me in a letter (dtd. 4 July 1963) that he collated *S1* with the text of the Shakespeare Head Press edition of *A Sentimental Journey* (Oxford, 1927), which is described (in the prefatory note on the text) as "founded on a careful comparison of the second and other early editions." The variants recorded by Sir Herbert occur in the Shakespeare Head edition but not, so far as I have been able to determine, in the second edition.

[11] The title page is the same as that of the second edition except for the substitution of "A New Edition." for "The Second Edition." An unauthorized edition, without a printer's or a publisher's name, and two Dublin editions were also published in 1768; see *Life*, p. 604.

FACSIMILES

In the Street
Calais.

I never finish'd a twelve gui-
:nea bargain so expeditiously in my
life: my time seem'd heavy upon
the loss of the Lady, & knowing every
moment of it would be as two, till I put
myself into motion — I ordered post
horses directly, and walk'd it to —
:wards the Hotel.

Lord! said I, hearing the town
clock strike four, and recollecting

that I had been little more than a
single hour in Calais —
— What a large Volume of ad-
=ventures may be grasped with-
=in this little span of life by him
who interests his heart in every
thing, and who, having eyes to
see, what time and chance are
perpetually holding out to him
as he journieth on his way, misses
nothing he can fairly lay
his hands on —
— If this wont turn out some —
=thing — another will — no
matter — 'tis an essay upon
human Nature — I get my la=
=bour for my pains — 'tis enough

the pleasures of the experiment had kept
my senses, and the best part of my
blood awake, & lay'd the gross to sleep.
I pity the man who can travel from
Dan to Beersheba, and cry, 'tis all
barren — and so it is; & so is all the
world to him who will not cultivate
the fruits it offers —
in it to call forth my affections — if I
could not do better, I would fasten them upon
some sweet myrtle, or seek some melan-
=choly cypress to connect myself to — I
would court their shade, and greet
them kindly for their protection — I
would cut my name upon them;

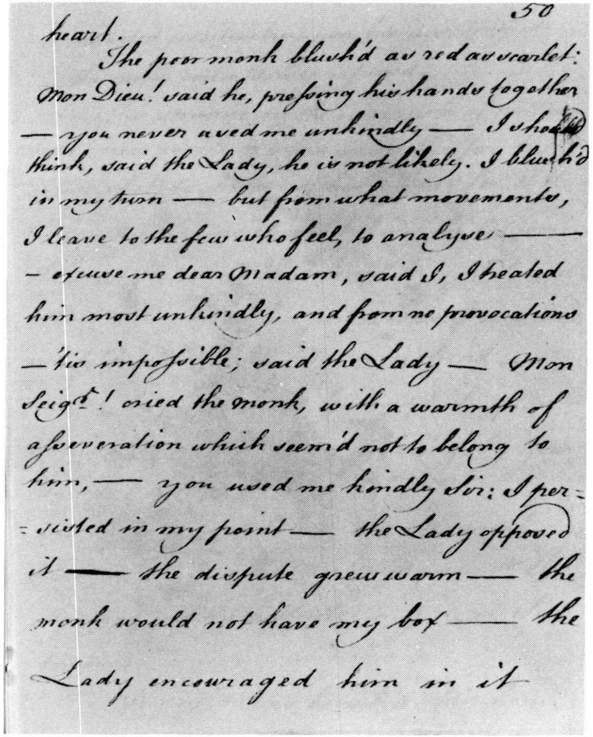

50

heart.
The poor monk blush'd as red as scarlet:
Mon Dieu! said he, pressing his hands together
— you never used me unkindly — I should
think, said the Lady, he is not likely. I blush'd
in my turn — but from what movements,
I leave to the few who feel, to analyse —
— excuse me dear Madam, said I, I treated
him most unkindly, and from no provocations
— 'tis impossible; said the Lady — Mon
Seig.r! cried the monk, with a warmth of
asseveration which seem'd not to belong to
him, — you used me kindly Sir: I per-
= sisted in my point — the Lady opposed
it — the dispute grew warm — the
monk would not have my box — the
Lady encouraged him in it

M1
Fol. 50

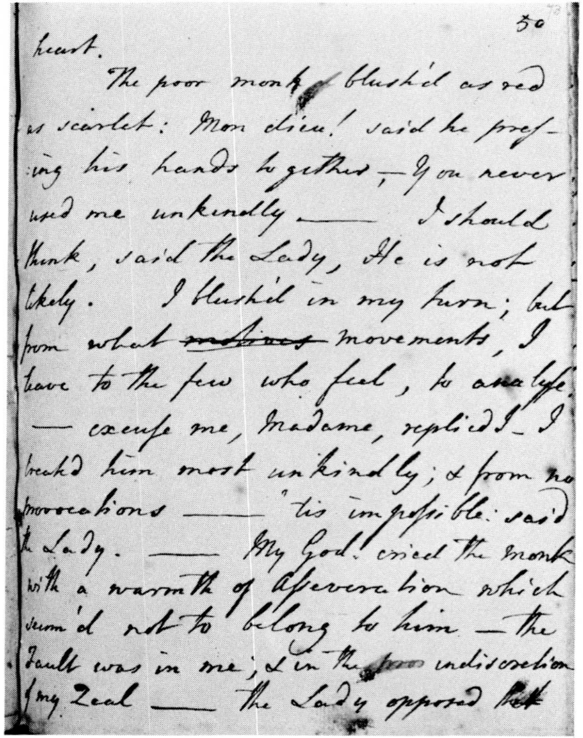

50

heart.
The poor monk ~~s~~ blush'd as red
as scarlet: Mon dieu! said he pres-
-sing his hands together, — You never
used me unkindly — I should
think, said the Lady, He is not
likely. I blush'd in my turn; but
from what ~~motives~~ movements, I
leave to the few who feel, to analyse,
— excuse me, Madame, replied I — I
treated him most unkindly; & from no
provocations — 'tis impossible: said
the Lady. — My God! cried the monk
with a warmth of Asseveration which
seem'd not to belong to him — the
fault was in me; & in the ~~pro~~ indiscretion
of my Zeal — the Lady opposed ~~her~~

S1
Fol. 50

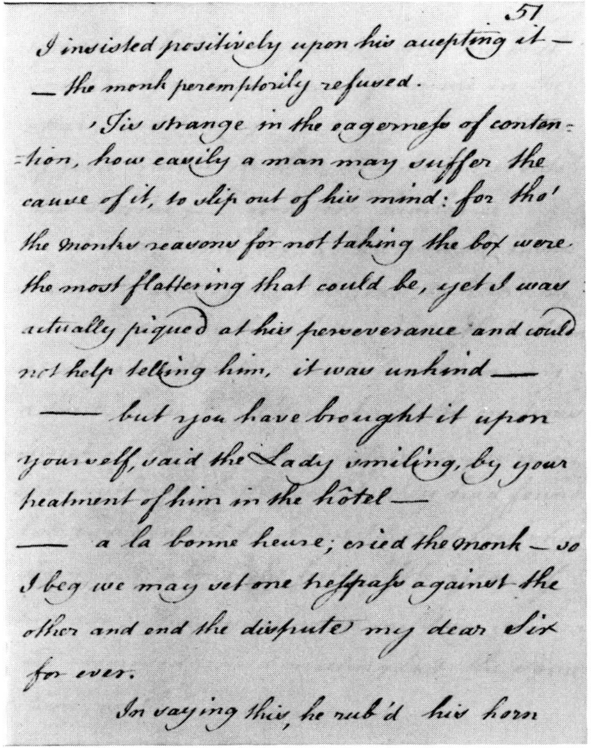

S1
Fol. 51

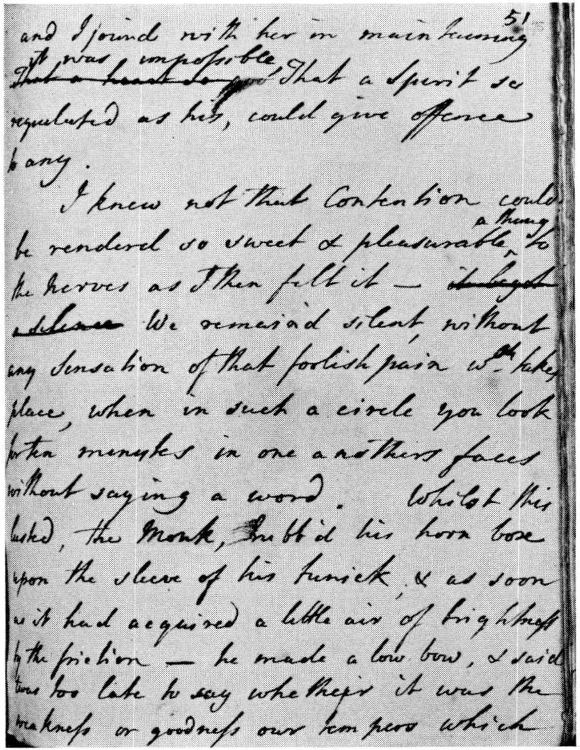

M1
Fol. 51

S_1
Fol. 52A

52

upon his sleeve, and presented it to me with one hand, as he took mine from one in the other; and having kiss'd it, with a steam afford nature in those eyes he put it onto his breame — and took his leave.

I guard this box, as I would the instru= mental parts of my religion, to help my mind on to something better: in truth Seldom go abroad without it; and oft and many a time, have I call'd up by it the countenance Spirit of its owner to regulate my own, in the jostlings of the world; they had found full employment for it, and learnt from his story, till about the forty fifth year of his age, when upon some military services ill acquired, and meeting at the same time with a disappointment

M1
Fol. 52

upon his sleeve, and presented it to me with one hand, as he took mine from me in the other's; having kiss'd it they with a ... good nature in his eyes he put it into his [frame] and took his leave.

I guard this box, as I would the instrumental parts of my religion, to help my mind on to something better: in truth Seldom go abroad without it; and oft and many a time, have I call'd up by it, the courteous Spirit of its owner to regulate my own, in the jostlings of the world; they had found them full employment for it, as Seemt from his story, till about the forty fifth year of this age, when upon some military services ill requited, & meeting at the same time with a disappointment

S1
Fol. 52B

Then follow the Travellers of Neceffity.

The delinquent & felonious Traveller,

The unfortunate & innocent Traveller

The fimple Traveller -

and laft of all (if you pleafe) The Sentimental Traveller (mean-ing thereby myfelf, who have travell'd, of which I am now fitting down to give an account — as much out of Neceffity, and the befon ote Voyager, as any one in the clafs.

I am well aware, at the fame time, that both my travels & obfer-vations will be altogether of a different caft from any of my fore-runners, that I might have infifted upon a while

S1

Fol. 24

Then follow the Travellers of Neceffity.

The delinquent and felonious Traveller,

The unfortunate and innocent Traveller,

The fimple Traveller,   And

[28]

And laft of all (if you pleafe) The Sentimental Traveller (meaning thereby myfelf) who have travell'd, and of which I am now fitting down to give an account—as much out of *Neceffity,* and the *befon de* Voyager, as any one in the clafs.

I am well aware, at the fame time, as both my travels and obfervations will be altogether of a different caft from any of my fore-runners; that I might have infifted upon a whole

A1

Portions of pp. 27, 28

APPENDIX E

ADDITIONAL NOTES TO *A Sentimental Journey*

Page 65.8–9. *"the coat I have on, said I, looking at the sleeve, will* *Note to p. 65.8–9* *do"*] Yorick may simply be referring to the condition of his "dusty black coat."[1] However, Sterne tends to use quotation marks for special emphasis, and Yorick may also be referring to its color. Is he, perhaps, implying that his black coat and, by extension, his character as heteroclite parson will be suitable to his role as the Sentimental Traveller?

In answer to a correspondent who had read the MS. of the first two volumes of *Tristram Shandy* and had criticized their humor as imprudent for a divine and "too free & gay for the solemn colour of [his] coat,"[2] Sterne replied:

I will use all reasonable caution—Only with this caution along with it, not to spoil My Book;—that is the air and originality of it, which must resemble the Author . . . A Very Able Critick & One of My Colour too—who has Read Over Tristram—Made Answer Upon My saying I Would consider the colour of My Coat, as I corrected it—That that very Idea in My head would render My Book not worth a groat—still I promise to be Cautious—but I deny I have gone as farr as Swift—He keeps a due distance from Rabelais—& I keep a due distance from him—Swift has said a hundred things I durst Not Say—Unless I was Dean of St. Patricks———[3]

Curtis points out that, in citing the advice of a "Very Able Critick," Sterne is apparently referring to the counsel of a friend who described his conversation with Sterne in a letter dated 15 April 1760.[4] According to the letter, in June 1759 he discussed with Sterne the MS. of Vols. I and II of *Tristram Shandy:*

---

[1] See p. 156.13, above.

[2] Cf. Owen Ruffhead's charge, quoted p. 6, above, that Tristram's jerkin cuts "an antic figure" upon Sterne's "prunella gown and cassock."

[3] *Letters*, No. 38A, Summer 1759, p. 76. (Cf. No. 38B, pp. 78–79.)

[4] *European Magazine*, XXI (March 1792), 169. Curtis (*Letters*, p. 77, n. 1) quotes this letter and notes that Sterne's letter (quoted above) was first published in the *Gentleman's Magazine*, XLIX (July 1779), 345, and was reprinted in several periodicals the following month.

Note to p. 65.8–9 I thought I discovered a vein of humour which must take with readers of taste, but I took the liberty to point out some gross allusions, which I apprehended would be matter of just offence, especially when coming from a clergyman, as they would betray a forgetfulness of his character. —He observed, that an attention to his character would damp his fire, and check the flow of his humour; and that if he went on and hoped to be read, he must not look at his band or cassock. I told him, that an over-attention to his character might perhaps have that effect; but that there was no occasion for him to think all the time he was writing his book, that he was writing sermons; that it was no difficult matter to avoid the dirtiness of Swift on the one hand, and the looseness of Rabelais on the other; and that if he steered in the middle course, he might not only make a very entertaining, but a very instructive and useful book!

Note to p. 67.21 Page 67.21. *Eliza*] Mrs. Elizabeth Sclater Draper, whom Sterne had met in January 1767, while he was in London soliciting subscriptions for *A Sentimental Journey*.[1] Born in 1744 in India, she had been orphaned at the age of four and later sent to school in England. In 1757 she returned to India and the following year married Daniel Draper, an official of the East India Company. She and her husband visited England in about 1765; when Sterne met her, Draper had gone back to India, leaving her to settle their children in school and to recover her health. At the beginning of April 1767 she sailed for Bombay to rejoin her husband, at his command.[2]

Sterne's sentimental effusions over Eliza are recorded in his letters to her and in the *Journal to Eliza*, which he commenced soon after her departure for India and continued (intermittently) through the summer and fall of 1767 while he was writing *A Sentimental Journey*. His letters to her and the *Journal* are a baffling combination of affection and compassion, affectation and calculation; and the sincerity of his feelings for her has often been questioned in the same terms in which Thackeray challenged all Sterne's writings: "How much was deliberate calculation and imposture . . . and how much true feeling . . . ?"[3] To pose the problem in these terms, however, is to ask for impossible distinctions. As Yorick's *Sentimental Journey* so brilliantly demonstrates,

---

[1] See p. 17, above.
[2] See *Letters*, p. 298, n. 1; *Life*, pp. 428 ff. In 1773 she eloped from her husband, whom she had come to detest.
[3] See p. 26, above.

all human relationships are a subtle compound of calculation and *Note to*
p. 67.21
"true feeling," particularly for a man like Sterne, whose extraordinary self-consciousness is embodied in Tristram and Yorick, and
can be gauged by his love for Uncle Toby, that amiable paradigm
of perfectly unself-conscious innocence and goodness.

That the lachrymose sentimentality of the *Journal* is, to some
degree, a sincere expression of Sterne's feelings for Eliza and of his
need for this kind of relationship with women, seems undeniable.
The influence of his emotional involvement with Eliza on some
aspects of *A Sentimental Journey* is attested by the verbal parallels
between the book and Sterne's letters and *Journal* to her, and
by the striking similarities between Sterne's image of and feelings
for Eliza, and Yorick's description of some of the women he meets
in his travels.[4]

Cross, however, surely exaggerates in claiming that the *Journal*

completely reveals the pathological state of the emotions . . . whence
sprang the *Sentimental Journey*, during the composition of which Sterne
was fast dying of consumption . . . Each work is the counterpart of
the other. In the journal, we have the crude expression of the maudlin
sentiment which often accompanies a wasting disease; in the *Sentimental
Journey*, we have sentiment refined to an art so exquisite as to place the
author among the first masters of English prose.[5]

Except for his letters to Eliza, Sterne's correspondence suggests
that he was in what was for him comparatively good health, and in
good spirits, while composing *A Sentimental Journey*, and there is
no convincing evidence that his chronic consumption was un-
usually severe during this period. Furthermore, the plan and
method of *A Sentimental Journey* evolved over a period of time,
partly in response to influences antecedent to and less sentimental
than the trauma of love and mortal illness.[6]

The *Journal* itself is suspect as a spontaneous overflow of
Sterne's pitiful (let alone pathological) emotions. Its pathos is art-
fully contrived and sustained, and as Professor McKillop has remarked, it "manipulates facts and feelings in such a way that it

---

[4] See esp. p. 93.30–34n, above.
[5] *Life*, p. 460.
[6] See pp. 1–17, above; and Putney, pp. 350–352.

Note to
p. 67.21

may be considered another exercise in Yorickan fiction; [Sterne] evidently played with the idea of making literary capital of his amour as he was making literary capital of his travels."[7] Sterne publicized his affair with Eliza in a manner which suggests that he may have wanted to arouse the interest of the fashionable world in the way he might treat his latest "literary amour or flirtation"[8] in his new travel work.[9] The *Journal* is written partly under the

[7] McKillop, p. 215. See also Putney (pp. 352–353) who comments that the *Journal* "does not merit the confidence it has been accorded . . . the entire relationship between Sterne and Mrs. Draper needs to be reëxamined with the knowledge that it is the business of the absent lover, especially of a merely sentimental mistress, to invent woes he has never felt."

[8] McKillop, p. 215. Richard Griffith, to whom Sterne "communicated" part of *A Sentimental Journey* while he was writing the book (see p. 18, above), observed: "he was making every one a Confidant in that Platonic [affair], I suppose, as he did me, on the Second Day of our Acquaintance. But, in Truth, there was nothing in the Affair worth making a Secret of—The World, that knew of their Correspondence, knew the worst of it, which was merely a simple Folly. Any other Idea of the Matter would be more than the most abandoned Vice could render probable. To intrigue with a Vampire! To sink into the Arms of *Death alive!*" (*A Series of Genuine Letters, between Henry and Frances* [London, 1786], V, 199–200; quoted from *Letters*, p. 306, n. 2).

[9] Sterne circulated the story of his affair and displayed his picture of Eliza (see p. 67.20–21n, above) among his acquaintances: see esp. *Letters*, No. 189, London, March 1767, p. 312; *Journal*, pp. 339, 346, 365, 379 ("Your picture has gone round the Table after supper"—at Crazy Castle, frequented by the Demoniacs [see p. 164.65n, above]; it would be interesting to know what was said on that occasion). Sterne's ref. to "my journal to Mrs. [Draper]" in a letter to the Earl of Shelburne (*Letters*, No. 196, London, 21 May 1767, p· 344) indicates that Shelburne, at least, knew of the *Journal*'s existence; and certain aspects of the *Journal* itself suggest that Sterne may have anticipated the possibility of its eventual publication: (1) The prefatory note to the *Journal* (*Letters*, p. 322), in which Sterne states that it is "wrote under the fictitious Names of Yorick & Draper [!]" and describes the circumstances of its composition, is written on a separate sheet and has the air of having been composed with this possibility in mind. (2) In the entry for 17 June (p. 358), in which he tells Eliza that he has brought her name and picture into *A Sentimental Journey* (see p. 67.20–21n, above), he recounts their relationship and imagines their marriage after Draper's death; and in the entry for 18 June he tells her, "This last Sheet [the entry for 17 June] has put it out of my power, ever to send you this Journal to India . . ." (p. 359). He could have removed this sheet from the *Journal*, and his disclaimer sounds suspiciously like an excuse for keeping it, perhaps for his own purposes.

pseudonym of Yorick and carries sentimental pathos to such lengths as to invite comparison with Yorick's quixotically sentimental commerce with the women he encounters in *A Sentimental Journey*, particularly with the fair lady in Calais.[10] As Sterne remarked to a friend, "I . . . must ever have some dulcinea in my head";[11] and, as Don Quixote observes, *Note to p. 67.21*

a Knight-Errant cannot be without a Mistress; 'tis not more essential for the Skies to have Stars; than 'tis to us to be in Love. Insomuch, that I dare affirm, that no History ever made mention of any Knight-Errant that was not a Lover . . . as to the Use which I make of the Lady *Dulcinea*, she is equal to the greatest Princesses in the World . . . to cut off all Objections at once, I imagine that All I say of her is really so, without the least Addition or Diminution . . .[12]

Soon after he met Eliza, Sterne assured her: "Not Swift so loved his Stella, Scarron his Maintenon, or Waller his Sacharissa, as I will love, and sing thee, my wife elect! All those names, eminent as they were, shall give place to thine, Eliza."[13] In *A Sentimental Jour-*

Although nothing can be proved, it is interesting to speculate whether the comic romance Sterne was writing at the time of his death (see *Letters*, No. 234, quoted p. 20, above) had any connection with the *Journal*. In the entry for 24 April (pp. 329–330), he tells Eliza "as whimsical a Story . . . and as comically disastrous as ever befell one of our ⟨Shan⟩ family—Shandy's Nose, . . . his Sash-Window are fools to it"—about the sufferings he is experiencing from what the doctors have diagnosed as an attack of venereal disease, though "I have had no commerce whatever with the Sex . . . these 15 Years—" In the letter to the Earl of Shelburne cited above, in which he refers to the *Journal*, he transposes this story almost verbatim from the *Journal*, observes that it "would make no bad anecdote in Tristram Shandy's Life," and tells Shelburne that he has mentioned it in the *Journal* (*Letters*, pp. 343–344)• The story would have made no bad anecdote in a comic romance either; in any case, after he has recounted it to Eliza, his references to what he is suffering for her sake become somewhat equivocal.

[10] See p. 93.30–34*n*, above.
[11] *Letters*, No. 148, quoted p. 128.17–25*n*, above.
[12] *Don Quixote*, 1.2.5.77, 1.3.11.194–195.
[13] *Letters*, No. 192, p. 319. In view of Sterne's determination to make Eliza more famous than Swift's Stella, was his decision to write the *Journal to Eliza* influenced, perhaps, by John Hawkesworth's publication the year before of parts of Swift's journal to Stella, in *Letters, Written by the late Jonathan Swift, D.D. . . . and Several of his Friends* (London, 1766)?

ney, Sterne kept his promise to celebrate Eliza's name, but he did so
in his own way and with his unfailing sense of humor.[14]

Note to pp. 78–85

Pages 78–85. *Preface*] Yorick's observations, in the Preface to his
Journey, on travel and on the difficulties of gaining "useful knowl-
edge and real improvements" abroad, are partially anticipated in
Yorick's sermon on the Prodigal Son.[1]

After elaborating on the "interesting and pathetic" aspects of
the story, which the Biblical account "left to be supplied by the
heart,"[2] and reflecting on its moral significance, Parson Yorick
remarks: "The intention of this parable is so clear from the occasion of it"[3] and its "uses have been so ably set forth, in so many
good sermons . . . that I shall turn aside from them at present,
and content myself with some reflections upon that fatal passion
which led him,——and so many thousands after the example, *to
gather all he had together, and take his journey into a far country.*"
The sermon concludes with the following passage,[4] which sum-

---

[14] See Putney's excellent analysis of "the ambiguous role" Eliza plays in *A
Sentimental Journey* "as the mistress to whom Yorick could scarcely be true"
("Laurence Sterne, Apostle of Laughter," *The Age of Johnson: Essays Pre-
sented to Chauncey Brewster Tinker* [New Haven, 1949], pp. 169–170).

[1] First published in Vol. III of *The Sermons of Mr. Yorick.* Sterne delivered
Vols. III and IV of the *Sermons* to Becket in October 1765, just before leaving
England on his second trip abroad, and they were published on 22 January
1766, while he was in Italy (*Letters,* No. 152, p. 261; *Life,* p. 603). ("The
Prodigal Son" commences with the remarks on the efficacy of stories and
"fables" as a means of moral instruction quoted in the Introduction, p. 43,
n. 50, above.) Sterne's "Satyr against Traveling (as puppies travel)" (*Letters,*
No. 134, Nov. 1764, p. 231), in Vol. VII of *Tristram Shandy,* was published in
January 1765.

[2] *Sermons,* I, 227 (III.v). For a parallel between Yorick's description of the
return of the Prodigal and *A Sentimental Journey,* see p. 283.15–27*n,* above.

[3] He gives a brief interpretation of it as a rebuke to the scribes and pharisees.
See Luke 15:1–2, 11–32.

[4] *Sermons,* I, 233–237 (III.v); quoted by Vrooman, pp. 103–105. It is impossible to determine when this passage was written. However, as Vrooman
points out (pp. 106–107), there is some evidence suggesting that Sterne may
have added it to "The Prodigal Son" in preparing Vols. III and IV of the
Sermons for the press, during the summer and early fall of 1765 (see *Letters,*
Nos. 146, 148, 149, pp. 254–257). Sterne had a large number of sermons to

marizes many of the objections made by Englishmen to the Grand *Note to*
Tour as a means of education: *pp. 78–85*

The love of variety, or curiosity of seeing new things, which is the
same, or at least a sister passion to it,——seems wove into the frame of
every son and daughter of Adam; we usually speak of it as one of nature's levities, tho' planted within us for the solid purposes of carrying
forwards the mind to fresh enquiry and knowledge: strip us of it, the
mind (I fear) would doze for ever over the present page; and we should
all of us rest at ease with such objects as presented themselves in the
parish or province where we first drew our breath.

It is to this spur which is ever in our sides, that we owe the impatience
of this desire for travelling: the passion is no way bad,——but as others
are,——in it's mismanagement or excess;——order it rightly the advantages are worth the pursuit; the chief of which are——to learn the languages, the laws and customs, and understand the government and
interest of other nations,——to acquire an urbanity and confidence of
behaviour, and fit the mind more easily for conversation and discourse;
——to take us out of the company of our aunts and grandmothers, and
from the track of nursery mistakes; and by shewing us new objects, or old
ones in new lights, to reform our judgments——by tasting perpetually
the varieties of nature, to know what *is good*——by observing the address
and arts of men, to conceive what *is sincere,*——and by seeing the dif-

---

choose from, most of which were probably composed during his early career
in the church (those he rejected were published, posthumously, in 1769, in
Vols. V–VII of the *Sermons*); and he probably did not compose the entire
"Prodigal Son" sermon for inclusion in Vol. III. It seems more likely that he
simply added his reflections on foreign travel to this sermon in preparing it
for the press; this possibility is strengthened by the abrupt and rather tenuous
transition between his recounting of the Biblical parable and his remarks on
travel, and, perhaps, by the authoritative tone of his comments (cf. esp. his
description of a traveling tutor "such as my eyes have seen!"). (Cross suggests
initially that this sermon "may have been prepared solely for the press" and
later states that it was "revised and redecorated"; see *Life,* pp. 372, 380.)

It is worth noting that Richard Hurd's *Dialogues on the Uses of Foreign
Travel; Considered as a Part of An English Gentleman's Education: Between
Lord Shaftesbury and Mr. Locke* was published in January 1764 (see *Gentleman's Magazine,* XXXIV [Jan. 1764], 47), shortly before Sterne began ready-
ing Vols. III and IV of the *Sermons* for publication. I have found no evidence
that Sterne borrowed directly from Hurd's *Dialogues* in "The Prodigal Son";
however, their objections to the Grand Tour as a means of education, though
commonplace, correspond rather closely, and both are cast in a dialogue (a
form which, admittedly, Sterne uses frequently in the *Sermons.*)

pp. 78–85 ference of so many various humours and manners,——to look into ourselves and form our own.[5]

This is some part of the cargo we might return with; but the impulse
of seeing new sights, augmented with that of getting clear from all lessons both of wisdom and reproof at home——carries our youth too early
out, to turn this venture to much account; on the contrary, if the scene
painted of the prodigal in his travels, looks more like a copy than an
original,—will it not be well if such an adventurer, with so unpromising
a setting out,—without *carte*,—without compass,——be not cast away
for ever,—and may he not be said to escape well[6]——if he returns to his
country, only as naked, as he first left it?[7]

---

[5] Cf. "by shewing . . . our own" (above) with "through . . . by" (p.
217.63–65, above). Vrooman suggests that Sterne's reflections in "The
Prodigal Son" on travel as a means of education may have been influenced by
Locke's remarks on this subject in *Some Thoughts Concerning Education*. Cf.,
e.g., the first two paragraphs quoted above from the sermon with Locke's
view that the really valuable aspects of travel "may be reduced to these two;
first, Language, secondly, an Improvement in Wisdom and Prudence, by seeing Men, and conversing with People of Tempers, Customs and Ways of Living, different from one another, and especially from those of his Parish and
Neighbourhood" (*Education*, ed. R. H. Quick [Cambridge, 1913], §212, p.
184; quoted by Vrooman, p. 105, n. 1; see also n. 9, below). Cf. also *Spectator*
No. 364 (III, 368): "Certainly the true End of visiting forreign Parts, is to
look into their Customs and Policies, and observe in what Particulars they
excell or come short of our own; to unlearn some odd Peculiarities in our
Manners, and wear off such awkard Stiffnesses and Affectations in our Behaviour, as may possibly have been contracted from constantly associating
with one Nation of Men, by a more free, general, and mixed Conversation."

[6] After describing the temptations of the "house of feasting" in a sermon,
Yorick remarks that "no doubt, numbers of all ages escape unhurt, and get
off this dangerous sea without shipwreck. Yet, are they not to be reckoned
amongst the more fortunate adventurers? . . . we may be allowed to describe this fair and flattering coast—we may point out the unsuspected dangers of it, and warn the unwary passenger, where they lay. We may shew him
what hazards his youth and inexperience will run, how little he can gain by
the venture, and how much wiser and better it would be [as is implied in the
text] [Ecclesiastes 7:2–3; bracketed phrase is Sterne's] to seek occasions rather
to improve his little stock of virtue than incautiously expose it to so unequal
a chance, where the best he can hope is to return safe with what treasure he
carried out—but where probably, he may be so unfortunate as to lose it all—
be lost himself, and undone for ever" (*Sermons*, I, 20 [I.ii]). This passage
should be compared with the passages from *Quo Vadis?* quoted in n. 7, below.

[7] In writing his critique of foreign travel in "The Prodigal Son," Sterne may

But you will send an able pilot with your son——a scholar.—— *Note to pp. 78–85* If wisdom can speak in no other language but Greek or Latin,——you do well——or if mathematicks will make a man a gentleman,——or natural philosophy but teach him to make a bow,——he may be of some service in introducing your son into good societies, and supporting him in them when he has done——but the upshot will be generally this, that in the most pressing occasions of address,——if he is a mere man of reading, the unhappy youth will have the tutor to carry,——and not the tutor to carry him.

But you will avoid this extreme; he shall be escorted by one who knows the world, not merely from books—but from his own experience:——a man who has been employed on such services, and thrice made the *tour of Europe, with success.*

——That is, without breaking his own, or his pupil's neck;——for if he is such as my eyes have seen! some broken *Swiss valet de chambre,*— some general undertaker, who will perform the journey in so many months "IF GOD PERMIT,"—much knowledge will not accrue;——some profit at least,—he will learn the amount to a halfpenny, of every stage from Calais to Rome;——he will be carried to the best inns,——instructed where there is the best wine, and sup a livre cheaper, than if the youth had been left to make the tour and the bargain himself.——Look

---

have also had in mind Bishop Joseph Hall's *Quo Vadis?*, from which he borrowed extensively in the Preface to *A Sentimental Journey* (as well as in *Tristram Shandy*); see App. E, pp. 332–336, note to pp. 83.100–85.126, below. Although the parallels are not sufficiently close to establish direct borrowing, cf. "the impulse of seeing new sights . . . left it?" (above) with the following passages in *Quo Vadis?* (ed. cit., p. 334, n. 4, below): "It is the affectation of too early ripeness that makes [parents] prodigal of their children's safety and hopes. . . . How can these novices, that are turned loose into the main ere they know either coast or compass, avoid these rocks and shelves, upon which both their estates and souls are miserably wrecked?" (iii.530, iv.532); "let our merchants take heed, lest they go so far . . . that while they buy all other things good-cheap, they make not an ill match for their souls; lest they end their prosperous adventures in the shipwreck of a good conscience" (i.529–530); "he hath escaped well that returns but what he carried; but he is worthy of memory that returns either more good or less evil" (xx.557); if Englishmen arm themselves against the blandishments of the papists by adding to "the sound knowledge of the principles of religion . . . those lessons which they are taught by the state . . . there may be hope they shall bring back the same souls they carried" (xxiii.561). Hall alludes to the Prodigal Son: "It was the younger son in the gospel who . . . turns unthrift, because he got his portion too soon into his hands, and wandered into a far country. The eye of the parent and the ferule of the master is all too little to bring our sons to good" (v.534).

Note to
pp. 78–85 at our governor! I beseech you:——see, he is an inch taller as he relates
the advantages.——

——And here endeth his pride—his knowledge and his use.

But when your son gets abroad, he will be taken out of his hand, by
his society with men of rank and letters, with whom he will pass the
greatest part of his time.

Let me observe in the first place,—that company which is really good,
is very rare——and very shy: but you have surmounted this difficulty;
and procured him the best letters of recommendation to the most
eminent and respectable in every capital,——

And I answer, that he will obtain all by them, which courtesy strictly
stands obliged to pay on such occasions,—but no more.

There is nothing in which we are so much deceived, as in the advantages proposed from our connections and discourse with the literati,
&c. in foreign parts; especially if the experiment is made before we are
matured by years or study.

Conversation is a traffic; and if you enter into it, without some stock
of knowledge, to ballance the account perpetually betwixt you,——the
trade drops at once: and this is the reason,——however it may be
boasted to the contrary, why travellers have so little (especially good)
conversation with natives,——owing to their suspicion,—or perhaps
conviction, that there is nothing to be extracted from the conversation
of young itinerants, worth the trouble of their bad language,—or the
interruption of their visits.

The pain on these occasions is usually reciprocal; the consequence of
which is, that the disappointed youth seeks an easier society;[8] and as bad
company is always ready,—and ever lying in wait,—the career is soon
finished; and the poor prodigal returns the same object of pity, with the
prodigal in the gospel.[9]

---

[8] Cf. "Conversation is a traffic . . . society" (above), with "conversation
. . . party," pp. 78.19–79.23, above.

[9] Cf. "But when . . . gospel" (above) with the following comments by
Locke in *Some Thoughts Concerning Education*: noting that if young men are
sent abroad with a tutor at too late an age they are often unwilling to submit to
his authority, Locke maintains that a young gentleman should "be *sent
abroad* . . . either when he is younger, under a Tutor, whom he might be
the better for; or when he is some Years older, without a Governor; when he is
of Age to govern himself, and make Observations of what he finds in other
Countries worthy his Notice, and that might be of Use to him after his Return; and when too, being throughly acquainted with the Laws and Fashions,
the natural and moral Advantages and Defects of his own Country, he has
something to exchange with those abroad, from whose Conversation he hoped
to reap any Knowledge. . . . He that is sent out to *travel* at the Age, and
with the Thoughts of a Man designing to improve himself, may get into the

Page 83.84–96. *The man . . . people.*] Although the vineyards *Note to p. 83.84–96* and wines of the Dutch colony at the Cape of Good Hope are mentioned in several seventeenth- and eighteenth-century accounts of the colony with which Sterne and his readers might have been familiar,[1] I have found no specific reference in these accounts to the Dutchman "who first transplanted the grape of Burgundy" to the Cape.

Sterne may not have a particular person in mind here, and his allusion to Burgundy grapes is appropriate to a journey through France. However, I have found one reference he and his readers might have known to the planting of the first grapevines and the making of the first wine by the Dutch at the Cape, during the governorship of Jan van Riebeeck,[2] who established the colony in

Conversation and Acquaintance of Persons of Condition where he comes; which, tho' a Thing of most Advantage to a Gentleman that travels, yet I ask, amongst our young Men that go abroad under Tutors, what one is there of an hundred, that ever visits any Person of Quality? Much less makes an Acquaintance with such, from whose Conversation he may learn what is good Breeding in that Country, and what is worth Observation in it; tho' from such Persons it is, one may learn more in one Day, than in a Year's Rambling from one Inn to another. Nor indeed, is it to be wondered; for Men of Worth and Parts will not easily admit the Familiarity of Boys who yet need the Care of a Tutor; tho' a young Gentleman and Stranger, appearing like a Man, and shewing a Desire to inform himself in the Customs, Manners, Laws, and Government of the Country he is in, will find welcome Assistance and Entertainment amongst the best and most knowing Persons every where, who will be ready to receive, encourage and countenance an ingenuous and inquisitive Foreigner" (*Education,* ed. Quick, §§212, 214, 215, pp. 185–186, quoted in part by Vrooman, pp. 105–106, n. 1).

[1] In addition to Kolben's account (below), see e.g.: William Dampier, *A New Voyage Round the World* (London: James Knapton, 1703), I, 532 ff. (apparently the 5th ed. of this popular work; see Edward G. Cox, *A Reference Guide to the Literature of Travel* [Univ. of Washington Publications in Language and Literature, IX, Seattle, 1935], I, 43); John Harris, *Navigantium atque Itinerantium Bibliotheca; Or, A Complete Collection of Voyages and Travels,* I (London, 1744), sec. xv, "The Voyage of William Funnell round the World, as Mate to Captain William Dampier," p. 146; John Ovington, *A Voyage to Suratt in the Year 1689,* ed. H. G. Rawlinson (London, 1929), pp. 283–293; François Leguat, *A New Voyage to the East-Indies* (London, 1708), I, 33; II, 277.

[2] See Van Riebeeck's *Journal,* ed. H. B. Thom (Capetown and Amsterdam, 1952–1958), III, 10; the entry for 2 Feb. 1659 records the first wine-making

1652 (for the Dutch East India Company) and governed it from
1652 to 1662. The reference is in *The Present State of the Cape of
Good-Hope . . . By Peter Kolben,* 2 vols. (trans. from the orig. German by Guido Medley).[3] Kolben, who spent 1704–1713 at the Cape,
states:

His Excellency [Van Riebeeck] . . . having provided himself in *Europe*
with such Plants and Seeds as he judg'd would be proper at the *Cape* &
he could conveniently carry with him, set and sow'd the same in a Piece
of Ground he chose at the Distance of two Leagues up in the Country,
partly a Hill and partly a Vale, dividing the Ground into a Vineyard, a
Fruit- a Flower- and a Kitchen-Garden. Every Thing prosper'd . . .
well, and he reap'd in due Season the Fruits of his Labours . . .[4]

During the eighteenth century, Kolben's book was one of the
most popular accounts of the Cape colony.[5] A reader familiar with
Kolben's reference to Van Riebeeck's vineyard (or with other references to it) might well have assumed that the Dutchman to whom
Yorick alludes in *A Sentimental Journey* is Van Riebeeck.

Pages 83.100–85.126. *Knowledge . . . going*—] Yorick's observations on traveling in this paragraph are largely adapted from
Bishop Joseph Hall's *Quo Vadis? A Just Censure of Travel, As It is*

---

at the Cape, from grapes planted two years before (there is no mention of
Burgundy grapes).

[3] London: W. Innys, 1731. The first German edition was publ. Nürnberg,
1719. "Kolben" is Medley's englishing of German "Kolb."

[4] I, 20–21. In describing the vineyards and wines of the Cape Colony,
Kolben remarks that the Dutch had great difficulty in establishing their vine-
yards with stock imported from Europe (he mentions the Rhine, but not
Burgundy) and from Persia. He observes that the "*Cape*-Wines . . . lose,
by Standing about Two Years, the *Capian* Taste, and assume That of the
Wines of the *Canaries*" (II, 80; see pp. 75–81).

[5] A second edition of Vol. I of Medley's translation was published by
W. Innys and R. Manby (London, 1738). Parts of Vol. I, including an
abridged version of the description of Van Riebeeck's garden and vineyard,
were printed in *The World Displayed,* Vol. X (London: J. Newberry, 1760;
2d ed., 1768), see esp. pp. 50–51. Another index of the currency of Kolben's
book is Smollett's recommendation of "the ingenious Peter Kolben's *Natural
History of the Cape of Good Hope*" in *Peregrine Pickle* (1751), ch. xvii (Smollett
is referring to "The Natural History of the Cape" in Vol. II). (On Smollett's
use of Kolben's descriptions of the Hottentots, see Kahrl, *Tobias Smollett,*
p. 151.)

Commonly Undertaken by the Gentlemen of our Nation.[1] For easy reference, the paragraph is given here, and the phrases Sterne appropriated from *Quo Vadis?* with little or no change are italicized:

Knowledge and improvements are to be got by sailing and posting for
that purpose; but whether useful knowledge and real improvements, is
all a lottery—and even where the adventurer is successful, the acquired
stock must be used with caution and sobriety to turn to any profit—but
as the chances run prodigiously the other way both as to the acquisition
and application, I am of opinion, That a man would act as wisely, if he
could prevail upon himself, to live contented without foreign knowledge
or foreign improvements, especially if he lives in a country that has no
absolute want of either—and indeed, much grief of heart has it oft and
many a time cost me, when I have observed how *many a foul step* the inquisitive Traveller *has measured* to see sights and look into discoveries,
all which, as Sancho Pança said to Don Quixote, *they might have seen dry-
shod* at home. *It is an age so full of light, that there is scarce a country* or
corner of Europe *whose beams are not crossed and interchanged with others
—Knowledge* in most of its branches, and *in most affairs, is like music in*
an Italian *street, whereof those may partake, who pay nothing*—But there
is *no nation under heaven*—and *God is my record,*[2] (*before whose tribunal
I must one day come and give an account of this* work)—that I do not
speak it vauntingly—But there is *no nation under heaven abounding
with more variety of learning—where the sciences may be more fitly woo'd,
or more surely won* than here—*where art is encouraged, and will so soon
rise high*—where Nature (take her all together) has so little to answer
for—and, to close all, where there is more wit and variety of character
to feed the mind with—*Where then, my dear countrymen, are you going—*

In the following excerpts from *Quo Vadis?* I have quoted enough
of Hall's text to show how Sterne adapted to his own purposes one
aspect of the learned bishop's strictures on traveling abroad in
pursuit of "Knowledge and improvements."[3] The portions of *Quo*

---

[1] Publ. London, 1617; Hall (1574–1656) traveled on the Continent in 1605
and 1616. Vrooman points out (pp. 49–50), that Sterne paraphrases *Quo
Vadis?* in *Tristram Shandy,* 7.13.492–493 (see my article, "Sterne's Borrowings from Bishop Joseph Hall's *Quo Vadis?*" *English Language Notes,* II
[1965], 197, n. 4). For Sterne's indebtedness to Hall in his *Sermons,* see
Hammond, esp. pp. 37, n. 1; pp. 125–132.

[2] "*God . . . record*": this phrase appears in Philippians 1:8 and is also
used by Hall; see the excerpts from *Quo Vadis?* below.

[3] Hall censures foreign travel by the English chiefly because it exposes them
to the dangers of Catholicism.

Vadis? Sterne appropriated in the foregoing paragraph are italicized and are arranged in the order in which he incorporated them into Yorick's remarks:

. . . perhaps it is . . . the learning of . . . the state, wherein our traveller hopes for perfection. The site and form of cities, the fashion of government, the manners of people . . . is that wherein his own eye shall be his best intelligencer; the knowledge whereof shall well requite his labour, whether for discourse or for use.

What if I say that, save the soothing up of our fancy in all this, these lessons may be as well taken out at home? I have known some that have travelled no farther than their own closet, which could both teach and correct the greatest traveller, after all his tedious and costly pererrations.

What do we but lose the benefit of so many journals, maps, historical descriptions, relations, if we cannot with these helps travel by our own fireside?

He that travels into foreign countries talks perhaps with a peasant, or a pilgrim, or a citizen, or a courtier, and must needs take such information as partial rumour or weak conjecture can give him; but he that travels into learned and credible authors talks with them who have spent themselves in bolting out the truth of all passages . . .

The ordinary traveller propounds some prime cities to himself, and thither he walks right forward: if he meet with aught that is memorable in the way he takes it up; but how many thousand matters of note fall beside him on either hand, of the knowledge whereof he is not guilty! whereas some grave and painful author hath collected into one view whatsoever his country affords worthy of mark; *having measured many a foul step for that which we may see dryshod,* and worn out many years in the search of that which one hour shall make no less ours than it was his own. . . . *this age is so full of light, that there is no one country* of the habitable world *whose beams are not crossed and interchanged with other. Knowledge of all affairs is like music in the streets, whereof those may partake which pay nothing.* [x.539–540][4]

. . . travel professeth to advance . . . the supreme power of our understanding; which if from hence [England] it may be manifestly improved, he should not be worthy to tread upon the earth that would not emulate Drake and Candish [Cavendish] in compassing it.

But . . . *no nation under heaven* [viii.536–537] . . . *God is my record* [iv.533][5] . . . *before whose tribunal I shall once come to give an account of this* "Censure" [xix.554] . . . Blessed be God, who hath made

---

[4] *Quo Vadis?,* sect. x, pp. 539–540, in Hall's *Works,* ed. Philip Wynter (Oxford, 1863), Vol. IX; all quotations are from this edition.

[5] See n. 2, above.

this word as true as it is great, *no nation under heaven so aboundeth with*
all variety of learning as this island! . . . set aside the study of civil
law, which indeed finds better helps abroad, *all sciences* (the word may
seem proud, but it is true)[6] *may be both more fitly wooed and more surely
won* within our four seas: for what learning is that which the seas, or
Alps, or Pyrennees have engrossed from us? what profession, either
liberal or manuary, wherein the greatest masters have not been at least
equalled by our homebred islanders? [viii.537, 536] . . . *Where art is
encouraged, it will soon rise high* and go far [xii.543] . . . Here grows
that wealth which ye go but to spend abroad. Here is that sweet peace
which the rest of the world admires and envies. Here is that gracious
and well tempered government which *no nation under heaven* may dare
once offer to parallel. Here all liberal arts reign and triumph . . .
Whither go ye then, worthy countrymen,[7] or what seek ye? [xxi.558]

Yorick's final question—"Where then, my dear countrymen, are
you going"—is surely intended to recall the title (if not the corresponding phrases) of *Quo Vadis?* to readers acquainted with
Hall's treatise.[8] The humor of Yorick's remarks depends partly on
his allusion to and borrowings from Hall's *Just Censure of Travel,
As It is Commonly Undertaken by the Gentlemen of our Nation.* Like
Hall, Sterne believed that most of the "Knowledge and improvements" the ordinary traveler gains from journeying in foreign
nations can be obtained more effectively by reading about them
"dry-shod at home." As a comic proof of his point, he incorporated
this aspect of Hall's censure of travel into *A Sentimental Journey,*
without traveling any farther than his own closet.[9]

By doing so, he humorously illustrated the differences between
the *"inquisitive traveller"* (p. 85, above) and Yorick, the Senti-

---

6 "(the . . . true)": cf. "that . . . vauntingly" in the paragraph quoted
from *A Sentimental Journey,* above.

7 Hall uses the phrase "dear countrymen" in *Quo Vadis?,* xx.557.

8 "Quo vadis?" is the Vulgate rendering of John 13:36, 16:5: "Whither
goest thou?"

9 Yorick's use of Hall in *A Sentimental Journey* is analogous to the way
Tristram puts "this and that together" from Piganiol de la Force, *Nouveau
voyage de France,* 2 vols. (Paris, 1755), a standard guidebook, to prove that
without knowing anything at firsthand about Calais, he can write so detailed
a description of it that the reader will take him for "the town clerk of *Calais*
itself" (*TS,* 7.4–5.482–486). The borrowings from Piganiol (II, 226–232) in
this portion of *Tristram Shandy* are analyzed by Vrooman, pp. 54–60 (see also
Life, p. 355; *Letters,* p. 232, n. 4).

Note to pp. 83.100– 85.126 mental Traveller, who must go "abroad" in order to carry on "sentimental commerce" with his fellowmen. And he also thereby emphasized the *"Novelty of [his] Vehicle"* (p. 82, above)—that is, the novelty of *A Sentimental Journey* as a travel book in which, rather than attempting "to swell the catalogues we have of pictures, statues, and churches," Yorick recounts "a quiet journey of the heart in pursuit of NATURE, and those affections which rise out of her, which make us love each other—and the world, better than we do" (p. 219, above).

Note to p. 87.2–3 Page 87.2–3. *Mons. Dessein, the master of the hôtel*] Dessein was well known to English travelers. Sometime during the Seven Years War (1756–1763) he leased the Lyon d'Argent in Calais from Louis-Guillaume Grandsire, who had managed it during the 1740's and 1750's.[1] Dessein prospered so well that in 1764 Grandsire, angered by Dessin's success and his own inability to drive out his tenant, set up the sign of the Lion immediately opposite his own premises at Calais and endeavoured to pilfer his rival's trade. Dessin was candid enough to publish this treachery in the *London Chronicle* (3–5 July 1764, 13) and to invite the nobility and gentry still to partake of his provisions and wines. But trouble was brewing. On 25 Sept. 1764 a serious fire broke out at the Lyon d'Argent . . . and on 26 Oct. 1764 another fire destroyed the inn. Both fires appear to have been set by Dessin, who forthwith solicited subscriptions from the English, exaggerating the extent of his loss and privately intending to use the money, not for the rebuilding of Grandsire's house, but for the purchase of a handsome hotel in the rue Royale, which he named the Hôtel d'Angleterre. Furious at such deception, the ruined Grandsire attacked his late tenant in the *Public Advertiser* (Monday, 24 Dec. 1764 [p. 3]). But his advantage was offset by Dessin's appearance in the following March at Tom Davies's bookshop in London, where, under the patronage of Lord Shelburne,[2]

---

[1] See *Letters,* p. 175, n. 6. Dessein, "it is said, had been a favorite waiter at the Silver Lion with the English passing through Calais, and had assumed his peculiar name from a compliment of one of them, who remarked: '*Il a du dessein, ce gaillard là*' " (*Life,* p. 382; Cross does not specify his source). Curtis notes that Dessein's actual name was Pierre Quillacq and gives his dates as 1726–1793 (*Letters,* p. 177, n. 4).

[2] "A witness of the fire, [Shelburne] had penned a supplicatory note for Dessin which was published in the *Public Advertiser* (9 March 1765 [p. 4]), subscribed twenty louis towards the purchase of the Hôtel d'Angleterre, besides inducing others, among them Lord Spencer, to do likewise" (*Letters,* p. 344, n. 1). Sterne knew both Shelburne and Spencer; see *Letters,* No. 196, pp. 342–344; p. 259, n. 1.

he solicited further subscriptions (id., Saturday, 9 March 1765 [p. 4]). *Note to p. 87.2–3* Established by such means in his new and elegant hostelry, he waited for Sterne to invest him with glory.[3]

The Hôtel d'Angleterre was considered one of the finest in Europe. William Cole stopped there in Nov. 1765, soon after it opened, and described it as "a fine large Quadrangle, with most sumptuous Apartments & elegantly furnished . . . the Master of it a very civil & obliging Man."[4] In 1767 Philip Thicknesse declared that "no hotel in France is equal to [it] . . . *Monsieur Dessein* knows the *goùt* of both nations, and blends them with propriety; and he has the advantage of a palace as it were, to do it in."[5]

A shrewd businessman as well as an obliging host, Dessein augmented the income from his hotel by renting chaises to English travelers and by converting their English currency into French at a highly profitable rate. Thicknesse observed in 1776 that he had "become one of the richest men in *Calais*" by "studying the *Gout* of the English nation, and changing their gold into French currency."[6]

Dessein benefited greatly from the publication of *A Sentimental Journey*, which made him famous throughout Europe. He designated one of the rooms in the Hôtel d'Angleterre "STERNE'S CHAMBER," and there "numberless Englishmen down to Thackeray slept, in the fancy that they were lying in the very place where Sterne once stretched his lean shanks."[7] According to Frederic Reynolds, who stayed at the hotel in 1782, Dessein told him: "Your countryman, Monsieur Sterne, von great, von vary great

---

[3] *Letters,* pp. 177–178, n. 4. Dessein purchased the hotel in December 1764 and opened it in March 1765 (*Letters,* p. 261, n. 1). According to Philip Thicknesse, "The Hotel d'Angleterre . . . is a very elegant hotel, and you will find here, good provisions, good wine, a decent landlord, and a reasonable bill. It is called the Hotel d'Angleterre, because it was opened, in some measure, by the liberality of some Englishmen of rank and fashion, in consequence of the very grievous hardships imposed upon Mons. Dessin, by the proprietor of the Silver Lion, Mons. Grandsire" (*Observations,* pp. 2–3).

[4] *Journey to Paris,* p. 358 (quoted in *Letters,* p. 261, n. 1). Cf. Sterne's opinion of Dessein, quoted p. 89.11*n,* above.

[5] *Useful Hints,* pp. 279–280 (quoted in *Life,* p. 383).

[6] *A Year's Journey into France, and Part of Spain* (London, 1777), I, 10 (cited in *Life,* p. 383).

[7] *Life,* p. 383.

man, and he carry me vid him to posterity. He gain moche money by his Journey of Sentiment—mais moi—I—make more through de means of dat, than he, by all his ouvrages reunies—Ha, ha!"[8]

Page 120.54–64. *Peace . . . eternity.*] Yorick's prophecy that Smelfungus and Mundungus would be unhappy even in heaven is partially adapted from one of Sterne's sermons, "Our Conversation in Heaven,"[1] in which he offers the following reflections on St. Paul's warnings in Philippians 3:17–20 against the danger of forfeiting eternal beatitude for the pleasures of the flesh:

. . . many walk . . . who mind earthly things, . . . relish them, making them the only object of their wishes,—taking aim at nothing better, and nothing higher.—But *our* conversation, says [St. Paul] . . . is in heaven.[2]—We christians . . . have greater and nobler views;—here we consider ourselves only as pilgrims and strangers.—Our home is in another country, where we are continually tending; there our hearts and affections are placed; and when the few days of our pilgrimage shall be over, there shall we return, where a quiet habitation and a perpetual rest is designed and prepared for us for ever. . . . It is observable, that St. Peter represents the state of christians under the same image, of strangers on earth, whose city and proper home, is heaven:—he makes use of that relation of citizens of heaven, as a strong argument for a pure and holy life,—beseeching them *as* pilgrims and strangers *here*, as men whose interests and connections are of so short a date, and so trifling a nature,—to abstain from fleshly lusts, which war against the soul,[3] that is, unfit it for its heavenly country, and give it a disrelish to the enjoyment of that pure and spiritualized happiness, of which that region must consist . . . The apostle tells us, that without holiness no man shall see God;[4]—by which no doubt he means, that a virtuous life is the only medium of happiness and terms of salvation,—which can only give us admission into heaven.—*But some of our divines carry the assertion further, that without holiness,—without some previous*

---

[8] *Life and Times of Frederic Reynolds, Written by Himself* (London, 1826), I, 180 (quoted in *Life,* p. 384).

[1] Preached at York in 1750 (*Life,* p. 620; *Letters,* No. 10, p. 26, p. 29, n. 8); publ. in 1769 as Sermon No. 2 in Vol. V of *Sermons by The late Rev. Mr. Sterne.*

[2] Philippians 3:20.

[3] Cf. I Peter 2:11: "Dearly beloved, I beseech you as strangers and pilgrims, abstain from fleshly lusts, which war against the soul."

[4] Hebrews 12:14: "Follow peace with all men, and holiness, without which no man shall see the Lord."

similitude wrought in the faculties of the mind, corresponding with the
nature of the purest of beings, who is to be the object of our fruition here-
after;—that it is not morally only, but physically impossible for it to be
happy,—and that an impure and polluted soul, is not only unworthy of so
pure a presence as the spirit of God, but even incapable of enjoying it, could
it be admitted [italics added].[5]

And here, not to feign a long hypothesis, as some have done, of a sinner's being admitted into heaven, with a particular description of his condition and behaviour there,—we need only consider, that *the supreme good, like any other good, is of a relative nature, and consequently the enjoyment of it must require some qualification in the faculty, as well as the enjoyment of any other good does;—there must be something antecedent in the disposition and temper, which will render that good a good to that individual,—otherwise though (it is true) it may be possessed,—yet it never can be enjoyed* [italics added].[6] . . .

---

[5] For similar passages in the sermons of John Tillotson, see Hammond, p. 159.

[6] "And here . . . *enjoyed*": quoted almost verbatim from John Norris, *Practical Discourses Upon the Beatitudes*, "Discourse the Sixth" (see Hammond, p. 142). Cf. *Sermons*, II, 24–25 (IV.viii): "Let us . . . consider the traces which even the most insensible man may have proof of, from what he may perceive springing up within him from some casual act of generosity; and tho' this is a pleasure which properly belongs to the good, yet let him try the experiment;——let him comfort the captive, or cover the naked with a garment, and he will feel what is meant by that moral delight arising in the mind from the conscience of a humane action.

"But to know it right, we must call upon the compassionate . . . for this, like all other pleasures, is of a relative nature, and consequently the enjoyment of it, requires some qualification in the faculty, as much as the enjoyment of any other good does:—there must be something antecedent in the disposition and temper which will render that good,——a good to that individual; otherwise, tho' 'tis true it may be possessed,——yet it never can be enjoyed"; and *Sermons*, II, 219–220 (VII.xiv), "Follow Peace" (Hebrews 12:14): religion teaches us "to subdue all those unfriendly dispositions in our nature, which unfit us for happiness, and the social enjoyment of the many blessings which God has enabled us to partake of in this world, miserable as it is, in many respects.—Could christianity persuade the professors of it into this temper, and engage us, as its doctrine requires, to go on and exalt our natures, and, after the subduction of the most unfriendly of our passions, to plant, in the room of them, all those (more natural to the soil) humane and benevolent inclinations, which, in imitation of the perfections of God, should dispose us to extend our love and goodness to our fellow creatures, according to the extent of our abilities; . . . could this be accomplished,—the world . . . might be considered by us as a foretaste of what we should enter upon hereafter. . . . Follow peace . . . because, adds the Apostle, without this

340   *Appendix E*

Note to p.   We see, even in the common intercourses of society,—how tedious it
120.54–64 is to be in the company of a person whose humour is disagreeable to our
own, though perhaps in all other respects of the greatest worth and excellency.[7]—How then can we imagine that an ill-disposed soul, whose
conversation never reached to heaven, but whose appetites and desires,
to the last hour, have grovel'd upon this unclean spot of earth;—how
can we imagine it should hereafter take pleasure in God, or be able to
taste joy or satisfaction from his presence, who is so infinitely pure, that
he even putteth no trust in his saints . . . *The consideration of this has
led some writers so far, as to say, with some degree of irreverence in the expression,—that it was not in the power of God to make a wicked man happy,
if the soul was separated from the body, with all its vicious habits and inclinations unreformed;*[8]—*which thought, a very able divine in our church has
pursued so far, as to declare his belief,—that could the happiest mansion in
heaven be supposed to be alotted to a gross and polluted spirit, it would be so
far from being happy in it, that it would do penance there to all eternity:—
by which he meant, it would carry such appetites along with it, for which
there could be found no suitable objects* [italics added].—A sufficient cause
for constant torment;—for those that it found there, would be so dis-
proportioned, that they would rather vex and upbraid it, than satisfy its
wants.[9]—This, it is true, is mere speculation,—and what concerns us not

---

frame of mind, no man shall see the Lord. For heaven is the region, as well as
the recompense, of peace and benevolence; and such as do not desire and pro-
mote it here, are not qualified to enjoy it hereafter." Cf. also Tillotson: "To
see God is to be happy; but, unless we be like him, we cannot see him. The
sight and presence of God himself would be no happiness to that man who is
not like to God in the temper and disposition of his mind" (quoted from
Hammond, p. 159).

[7] Cf. the passage quoted from John Norris n. 9, below.

[8] Cf. Samuel Clarke: "I will not presume to affirm, (though some have done
it, not without appearance of reason,) that if God should transplant such
[wicked] persons into Heaven, he *could* not make them happy there" (quoted
from Hammond, p. 116).

[9] The "able divine" Sterne cites is John Norris. Cf. the following passage
in Norris's *Practical Discourses Upon the Beatitudes*, "Discourse the Sixth"
(quoted from Hammond, p. 142): "We see that even in this Life, 'tis very
tedious to be in the Company of a Person whose Humour is disagreeable to
ours, tho perhaps in other respects of sufficient Worth and Excellency. And
how then can we imagine that an ill-disposed Soul should take any Pleasure
in God, who is to her infinitely more unlike, and therefore disagreeable, than
one Man can be supposed to be to another? For my part, I rather think that
should an impure Soul be afforded a Mansion in Heaven, she would be so far
from being happy in it, that she would do *Penance* there to all Eternity. For

to know;—it being enough for our purpose, that such an experiment is *Note to p.*
120.54-64
never likely to be tried,—that we stand upon different terms with God,—
that a virtuous life is the foundation of all our happiness,—that as God
has no pleasure in wickedness, neither shall any evil dwell with him;—
and that, if we expect our happiness to be in heaven,—we must have our
conversation in heaven, whilst upon earth,—make it the frequent subject
of our thoughts and meditations,—let every step we take tend that way,
—every action of our lives be conducted by that great mark of the prize
of our high-calling, forgetting those things which are behind;—forgetting this world,—disengaging our thoughts and affections from it,
and thereby transforming them to the likeness of what we hope to be
hereafter.—How can we expect the inheritance of the saints of light,
upon other terms than what they themselves obtained it?—

Can that body expect to rise and shine in glory, that is a slave to lust,
or dies in the fiery pursuit of an impure desire? Can that heart ever
become the lightsome seat of peace and joy, that burns hot as an oven
with anger, rage, envy, lust, and strife? full of wicked imaginations, set
only to devise and entertain evil?[10]

The principle expressed in the foregoing pasage—that man
knows and enjoys God, the Supreme Good, primarily by virtue
of a faculty which participates in and is essentially of the same
nature as its divine object—is characteristically Latitudinarian.
Equally Latitudinarian is the tendency here, as elsewhere in
Sterne's sermons, to deëmphasize grace, which is seen by the
Latitudinarians primarily as coöperating with the man who has
already chosen the good.[11] As Sterne remarks in another sermon,
"it is evident" from many passages in Scripture

that the assistances of grace were not intended to destroy, but to co-
operate with the endeavours of man,—and are derived from God in
the same manner as all natural powers.—Indeed, without this interpretation, how could the Almighty address himself to man as a rational
being?—how could his actions be his own?—how could he be considered as a blameable or rewardable creature?[12]

---

besides that a sensualized Soul would carry such Appetites with her thither
for which she could find no suitable Object, which would be a constant Torment; those that she *does* find there would be so disproportionate, that they
would rather vex and upbraid, then satisfie her Indigence."

[10] *Sermons*, II, 94–98 (V.ii).

[11] I am indebted here to Rader, "Idea and Structure in Fielding's Novels,"
pp. 22–29.

[12] *Sermons*, II, 195 (VI.xi).

Yorick's ironic benediction upon Smelfungus and Mundungus (p. 120.54–64, above) is (characteristically) both comic and serious. He implies that, if they were admitted to heaven, God probably *would* not redeem them from their splenetic vices, since they had rejected the virtuous and redeeming joys and pleasures of their pilgrimage on earth. But, as in the passages quoted above from Sterne's sermon, he stops well short of saying that God *could* not redeem them.

Note to p. 123.34 Page 123.34. *La Fleur*] An account of La Fleur's life and of his experiences as Sterne's valet, purportedly given to the writer by Sterne himself, appeared (in 1790) in three articles entitled "Sterne's La Fleur."[1] Cross states that the account "has behind it a real La Fleur and vague traditions,"[2] but it seems to be entirely fictitious.

Curtis suggests that Sterne may have taken La Fleur's name from a "quixotic character . . . in *Le Glorieux* (1732), the comedy by Philippe Néricault-Destouches. In this play La Fleur is a lackey, who is rendered miserable because his master is too proud to speak with him."[3] According to William Jackson,[4] Sterne took La Fleur's name and "a little trait of his character" from Bayle's *Dictionary* (from which he had often borrowed in *Tristram Shandy*). In the article on "James Sadeur" in the *Dictionary*, there is a brief anecdote about a footman called "Le Fleur."[5] However, I can see no

---

[1] *European Magazine*, XVIII (July–Dec. 1790), 173–174, 268, 346–347.

[2] *Life*, p. 408n.

[3] *Letters*, p. 268, n. 2. Cross (*Life*, p. 407) states that Sterne took La Fleur's name "from current French comedy."

[4] *The Four Ages* (London, 1798), pp. 245–246; cited by Ferriar, II, 48n.

[5] *A General Dictionary, Historical and Critical; in which a new . . . Translation of that of . . . Mr. Bayle . . . is included*, 10 vols. (London, 1734–1741), IX, 11, n. [C]. The fact that Sterne also used the misspelling "Le Fleur" when he first wrote out *S1* (see p. 124.7*tn*, above) may indicate that he did take the name from this translation of Bayle's *Dictionnaire*. The English translation publ. London, 1734–1738, entitled *The Dictionary Historical and Critical of Mr. Peter Bayle*, 2d ed., reads "La Fleur"; the translation publ. London, 1710, entitled *An Historical and Critical Dictionary, by Monsieur Bayle*, does not have the passage referring to La Fleur. (For the English translations of Bayle's *Dictionnaire*, see L. P. Courtines, *Bayle's Relations with England and the English* [New York, 1938], p. 234.)

basis for Jackson's claim that Sterne derived a trait of La Fleur's character from Bayle.[6]

Page 172.38. *the Marquesina di F****] identified by Cross[1] and others as the beautiful Marchesa Fagnani, née Costanza Brusati in Milan,[2] who became mistress to George Selwyn and to the fourth Duke of Queensbury, and whose daughter Maria ("Mie-Mie") Fagnani married the notorious third Marquis of Hertford (the original of Lord Steyne in *Vanity Fair*). The identification appears to have derived mainly from a remark by Arthur Young, who passed the Marchesa's house near Milan in 1789 and reflected that she "has been much in England, and celebrated here for being the lady with whom our inimitable Sterne had the rencontre at Milan, which he has described so agreeably."[3]

Note to p. 172.38

Emilio Legnani has argued that "the Marquesina di F***" is the Marchesa Fagnani, but that the encounter with her described in *A Sentimental Journey* could not have actually happened to Sterne in Milan, because Costanza Brusati did not marry the Marchese Fagnani (of Milan) until January 1767, *after* Sterne's trip to Italy in 1765–66.[4] However, Sterne wrote *A Sentimental Journey* after Costanza Brusati had become the Marchesa Fagnani. If she is "the Marquesina di F***" he could have referred to her in the book by her married rather than by her maiden name.

Legnani argues that Sterne fabricated Yorick's encounter with

[6] Jackson states in a confusing note (*The Four Ages*, p. 246) that the reference to La Fleur "is to be found in the New Voyage into Terra Australis, by James Sadeur (a feigned name)." "James [Jacques] Sadeur" is a pseudonym for Gabriel Foigny (or "de Foigny"), and Jackson is presumably referring to the English translation of Foigny's *La Terre australe connue* (1676) entitled *A new discovery of Terra incognita Australis by Mr. Sadeur* (see Geoffroy Atkinson, *The Extraordinary Voyage in French Literature Before 1700* [New York, 1920], pp. 36, 178). However, it is clear that the anecdote about La Fleur was told to Bayle by "a gentleman" who recounted it to him apropos of a passage in Foigny's book.

[1] *Life*, p. 400.

[2] In 1747; she died in 1804.

[3] *Travels During the Years 1787, 1788 and 1789* (Dublin, 1793), I, 424, entry for 7 Oct. 1789.

[4] "L'Avventura Milanese di Sterne con la 'Marquesina di F***' fu 'fabbricata di pianta,' " *English Miscellany*, VI (1955), 247–257.

Note to   the Marchesa at the suggestion of Alessandro Verri, whom he had
p. 172.38   met in Milan.[5] Sterne saw Verri again in London, sometime between
7 Jan. and 11 Feb. 1767, before he went down to Coxwold to write
A Sentimental Journey. According to Verri, Sterne was working on
("facendo") the *"Viaggio Sentimentale d'Italia"* and told him he
intended, as Verri puts it, to fabricate out of whole cloth ("fabbri-
care di pianta") several adventures in Milan.[6] Legnani notes that
during the period when he saw Sterne in London, Verri learned
that Costanza Brusati had become the Marchesa Fagnani. According to Legnani, Verri disliked the Marchesa. On the assumption
that Yorick's encounter with "the Marquesina di F***" casts a
disreputable light on her character, Legnani concludes that Verri
suggested this incident to Sterne in order to impugn the Marchesa's reputation. Although Legnani has shown that Verri could
have told Sterne about the Marchesa's marriage, his conclusion
that he did so and that he also suggested this incident to Sterne is
speculation.

Note to   Page 173.58 *chichesbeo*] properly *cicisbeo* (called a *cavaliere servente*
p. 173.58   in Venice): the recognized admirer or gallant of a married woman
in Italy, who attended her in public (*OED*); a husband was often
the *cicisbeo* of another man's wife.

    Sharp's indignant attacks on this custom as depraved and im-
moral[1] were answered by Joseph Baretti, who maintained that such
relationships were generally expressions of an honorable, virtuous,
and platonic esteem, and that Sharp's attacks were ignorant
slander.[2]

    Like Sharp, Smollett considered the custom immoral and con-
demned it with typically British righteousness. He observed that,
outside one of the gates of Florence,

---

    [5] See *Life*, p. 399.

    [6] Legnani, p. 252. Sterne told Lydia he would not "begin" *A Sentimental Journey* until he reached Coxwold (see *Letters*, No. 183, quoted p. 18, above); he was probably referring to the actual writing of the book.

    [1] *Letters from Italy;* see esp. Nos. 5, 18, 43, 48.

    [2] *An Account of the Manners and Customs of Italy; with Observations on the Mistakes of Some Travellers, with Regard to that Country* (London, 1768); see esp. Vol. I, chs. 6–8, pp. 76–116.

in the summer evenings, the quality resort to take the air in their *Note to p. 173.58* coaches. Every carriage stops, and forms a little separate conversazione. The ladies sit within, and the cicisbei stand on the foot-boards, on each side of the coach, entertaining them with their discourse. It would be no unpleasant inquiry to trace this sort of gallantry to its original, and investigate all its progress. The Italians, having been accused of jealousy, were resolved to wipe off the reproach, and, seeking to avoid it for the future, have run into the other extreme. . . . every married lady in this country has her cicisbeo, or serviente, who attends her every where, and on all occasions; and upon whose privileges the husband dares not encroach, without incurring the censure and ridicule of the whole community. For my part, I would rather be condemned for life to the gallies, than exercise the office of a cicisbeo, exposed to the intolerable caprices and dangerous resentment of an Italian virago.[3]

He commented that, in the summer evenings at Nice,

part of the noblesse may be seen assembled in a place called the Parc . . . stretched in pairs upon logs of wood, like so many seals upon the rocks by moon-light, each dame with her *cicisbeo:* for, you must understand, this Italian fashion prevails at Nice among all ranks of people; and there is not such a passion as jealousy known. The husband and the *cicisbeo* live together as sworn brothers; and the wife and the mistress embrace each other with marks of the warmest affection. I do not choose to enter into particulars. I cannot open the scandalous chronicle of Nice, without hazard of contamination. With respect to delicacy and decorum, you may peruse dean Swift's description of the Yahoos, and then you will have some idea of the *sporcherie*, that distinguishes the gallantry of Nice.[4]

Page 176.27–37. *Mr. Shandy the elder, who accounted for nothing* *Note to p. 176.27–37* *like any body else . . . leg.*] As Tristram observes, his father was "a philosopher in grain" who had "a thousand little sceptical notions of the comick kind to defend": "There was that infinitude of oddities in him, and of chances along with it, by which handle he would take a thing,—it baffled, Sir, all calculations.——The truth was, his road lay so very far on one side, from that wherein most men travelled,—that every object before him presented a face and section of itself to his eye, altogether different from the plan and elevation of it seen by the rest of mankind."[1] Walter's odd

---

[3] *Travels*, Letter No. 27, pp. 230–231.
[4] *Travels*, Letter No. 17, pp. 153–154.
[1] *TS*, 1.21.68, 1.19.53, 5.24.382.

Note to p. opinions on rearing children, codified in the TRISTRA-*pœdia* (which
176.27–37 he discusses with Yorick), are confounded by the comic cross-
accidents which befall Tristram.[2]

Walter's explanation for the large numbers of dwarfs in Paris
stems, presumably, from his experiences on Tristram's "*grand tour
through Europe*," on which, Tristram says, "my father (not caring
to trust me with any one) attended me himself, with my uncle
Toby and *Trim*, and *Obadiah*." Tristram alludes to this "*grand
tour*" in the course of his subsequent journey through France (in
Vol. VII); observing that his father's "researches" were "ever of
such a nature, that they would have found fruit even in a desert,"
he remarks:

> wherever my father went——but 'twas more remarkably so, in this
> journey through *France* and *Italy*, than in any other stages of his life——
> his road seemed to lie so much on one side of that, wherein all other
> travellers had gone before him——he saw kings and courts and silks of
> all colours, in such strange lights——and his remarks and reasonings
> upon the characters, the manners and customs of the countries we
> pass'd over, were so opposite to those of all other mortal men, par-
> ticularly those of my uncle *Toby* and *Trim*—(to say nothing of myself)—
> and to crown all—the occurrences and scrapes which we were per-
> petually meeting and getting into, in consequence of his systems and
> opiniatry—they were of so odd, so mixed and tragicomical a contexture
> —That the whole put together, it appears of so different a shade and tint
> from any tour of *Europe*, which was ever executed—That I will venture
> to pronounce—the fault must be mine and mine only—if it be not read
> by all travellers and travel-readers, till travelling is no more,—or which
> comes to the same point——till the world, finally, takes it into its head
> to stand still.——
> ——But this rich bale is not to be open'd now; except a small thread
> or two of it, merely to unravel the mystery of my father's stay at AUX-
> ERRE.[3]

To illustrate the odd, tragicomical nature of Walter's experiences
and opinions on this tour, Tristram recounts the Shandy family's
visit to the abbey of St. Germain at Auxerre. Yorick's reference in
A Sentimental Journey to Walter's remarks on the dwarfs in Paris[4] is

---

[2] See *TS*, 5.16.372, 5.30–31.389–392.

[3] *TS*, 7.27.512–513.

[4] P. 176.27–37, above.

the only other "thread" Sterne ever unraveled from the "rich bale" of the Shandy family's grand tour. Tristram's unfulfilled promise to recount their tour "hereafter"[5] may be considered part of Sterne's effort to recapture the public's interest, an effort which eventually led to *A Sentimental Journey.*

Pages 178.57–73. *A poor defenceless being . . . posture.*] As Ferriar first pointed out (I, 66–69), Sterne adapted this incident from a similar episode in Scarron's *Roman comique* (1651). William A. Eddy has shown[1] that Sterne adapted his version of the episode from the translation of *Le Roman comique* by Tom Brown et al.[2] Ragotin, Scarron's dwarfish hero, having arrived late at a crowded theater,

Note to p. 178.57–73

therefore must crowd in where he could get a Seat. His ill Fortune had placed him just behind a Country Gentleman of the largest size, who had a great loose Coat on, which not a little encreas'd his bulk. Besides his spreading Haunches, Chine and Shoulders, he was of a Stature so much taller than other Men, that altho he sat down, *Ragotin* who was but one row off him, thought he stood a tip-toe, and therefore cry'd out incessantly to him *to sit down like the rest*, not believing that one who sat on the same Bench could be so much taller than any of his Companions. The Gentleman whose name was *la Baguenodiere*, knew not for some time that *Ragotin* had spoke to him, till at length being stil'd by the title of the Gentleman with the Green Feather, whereof indeed he had a very flaunting one in his Hat, . . . he turned his Head about and saw the little *Impertinent*, who thereupon bid him somewhat roughly *to sit down.* This, nevertheless *la Baguenodiere* was so little moved at, that he turned his Face again very gravely towards the Stage, as if nothing had been said to him; hereat *Ragotin* began to call to him again *to sit down*, but which he took as little notice of as before, only turning about and looking upon him, and then returning to his former posture. This at last so vex'd *Ragotin*, that he bawled out to him again a third time, which notwithstanding *la Baguenodiere* regarded as little as formerly. During all

---

[5] *TS*, 7.28.515.

[1] "Tom Brown and *Tristram Shandy*," *Modern Language Notes*, XLIV (1929), 380.

[2] *The Whole Comical Works of Monsr Scarron*, trans. by "Mr. *Tho. Brown*, Mr. *Savage*, and Others," 2d ed., rev. and corr. (London, 1703), Scarron's *Comical Romance*, Pt. II, ch. xvii, pp. 213–214. (This version agrees with the 1st ed., publ. 1700, except for minor differences in accidentals.)

Note to p. the time the Play lasted *Ragotin* still treated him after the like manner in
178.57–73 great Fury, and *la Baguenodiere* as often look'd upon him with the same
unconcern, without speaking a Word to him; which was sufficient to
have enflam'd the most Phlegmatick Soul in the World. One might
have compar'd *la Baguenodiere* in this Adventure to a large Mastiff, and
Ragotin to a little Cur that runs barking at him by his side, which pro-
vokes the great Dog so little, that in contempt of him he only steps aside,
and lifting up his Leg, pisses against the Wall. . . . *Ragotin* began to
swear and rave thro Impatience, while *la Baguenodiere* returned him
only a cold and indifferent Glance.[3]

Note to p. Page 199.87–89. *Disguise . . . account.*] Ignatius Sancho, a culti-
199.87–89 vated Negro who had been a slave in the West Indies, wrote Sterne
in 1766 that his description of slavery as a bitter draught which
millions had been made to drink[1] was "truely affecting," and en-
treated him to write further on

slavery (as it is at this day undergone in the West Indies; that subject
handled in your own manner, would ease the Yoke of many . . . But
should only *one* be the better for it—⟨good⟩ gracious God! what a feast!
very sure I am, that Yorick is an Epicurean in Charity—universally
read & universally admired—you could not fail. dear Sir think in me,
you behold the uplifted hands of Millions of my moorish brethren . . .
hear their supplicatory address—humanity must comply.[2]

In replying to this letter, Sterne told Sancho:

There is a strange coincidence, Sancho, in the little events, as well as
the great ones of this world; for I had been writing a tender tale of the
sorrows of a ⟨distressd⟩ friendless poor negro girl, and my eyes had
scarse done smarting, When your Letter of recommendation in behalf of
so many of her brethren and Sisters came to me—but why, *her brethren?*
—or yours? Sancho,—any more than mine: it is by the finest tints and
most insensible gradations that nature descends from the fairest face
about St James's, to the sootyest complexion in Africa: at which tint of
these, is it, Sancho, that the ties of blood & nature cease? . . .
If I can weave the Tale I have wrote, into what I am about, tis at the
service of the ⟨unfortunate⟩ afflicted; and a much greater matter: for in

---

[3] The episode results in a fight between la Baguenodière and two other men
which causes a general disturbance in the theater.

[1] In *Sermons,* I, 122, quoted p. 199.87–89*n*, above.

[2] *Letters,* No. 168, London, 21 July 1766, pp. 282–283; this version of the
letter appears in Sterne's *Letter Book,* and, as Curtis points out, "Comparison
with Lydia's text will show Sterne's effective alterations."

honest truth, it casts, a great Shade upon the world, that so great a   *Note to p.* part of it, are, and have been so long bound down in chains of darkness   *199.87–89* [II Peter 2:4] & in chains of misery; . . . and so, good hearted Sancho, adieu! & be assured I will not forget y^r Letter.[3]

At this time Sterne was working on Vol. IX of *Tristram Shandy* (publ. Jan. 1767) and had evidently decided to write *A Sentimental Journey* as soon as it was completed.[4] In Vol. IX, Trim promises to tell Uncle Toby the story of "a poor negro girl" who "had suffered persecution," and he and Toby reflect on the need for universal benevolence illustrated by the oppression of her race.[5] Like several other stories promised in *Tristram Shandy,* the tale of the Negro girl is never told.[6] However, the fact that Yorick condemns slavery in the words of the passage in the *Sermons* which Sancho had praised, and describes a captive representing "the millions of my fellow creatures born to no inheritance but slavery,"[7] suggests that, in writing these portions of *A Sentimental Journey,* Sterne may have recalled his assurance to Sancho that he would not forget his letter.[8]

Page 228.11–22. *I remember the grave and learned Bevoriskius, in his*   *Note to p.* *commentary upon the generations from Adam . . . creatures!*] Ed-   *228.11–22* ward W. West has identified "Bevoriskius" as Johan van Beverwyck (or Beverwicjk), 1594–1647, a Dutch author of various learned works, including several on medicine, whose latinized name was "Beverovicius."[1] According to West:

The "Commentary on the Generations of Adam" begins at fol. 1 of a quarto book, published at Amsterdam in 1652, entitled *Joh. Van Bever-*

---

[3] *Letters,* No. 170B, Coxwold, 27 July 1766, pp. 286–287.

[4] See *Letters,* No. 169, Coxwold, 23 July 1766, quoted p. 12, above.

[5] *TS,* 9.6.606–607.

[6] See p. 255.100*n*, above. In July 1766, while he was writing Vol. IX, Sterne intended to continue *Tristram Shandy;* see *Letters,* No. 169, quoted p. 12, above.

[7] "The Captive. Paris," p. 201, above.

[8] Milic (p. xxxii) also suggests this possibility.

[1] *Notes & Queries,* 6th ser., XII (1885), 425–426. For Beverwyck's Latin works published under the name "Beverovicius," see Evert Dirk Baumann, *Johan van Beverwijck in Leven en Werken Geschetst* (Dordrecht, 1910), pp. 299–306, and the *British Museum Catalogue.*

wiick's Schat Der Gesontheydt Met Veersen verçiert door de Heer Jacob Cats,
Ridder. It has a portrait of Beverwyck on the title-page, with numerous
copper-plates in the text. The commentary has a queer little plate of
Death enclosing Adam and Eve in his net while Eve offers the apple to
her spouse.

I have not been able to identify definitely the edition of Beverwyck's *Schat der Gesontheyt* (Treasury of Health) described by
West. However, he may be referring to the edition published in
Amsterdam in 1652, in the following volume of Beverwyck's works
on medicine: *Alle de Wercken, soo in de Medicyne als Chirurgye van*
de Heer Dr. Johan van Beverwijck (J. J. Schipper). I have not seen
this edition of this volume, but the 1656 edition has a portrait of
Beverwyck on the title page and numerous copper-plates in the
text.[2] The *Schat der Gesontheydt*[3] commences on "Fol. 1" (i.e., p. 1)
of this volume. At the head of p. 1 appears the following title: "Of
the Degeneration of Man, and why he has become subject to sickness and to death itself." Below this title there is a plate depicting
Adam and Eve in Eden, holding hands and framed by a cloud,
with the word "Jehovah" (in Hebrew) above their heads. Below the
plate there commences a commentary, in prose interspersed with
verse, on Man's physical degeneration and subjection to tormenting
diseases as a result of his sinful disobedience to God.

Book III of this edition of the *Schat der Gesontheyt* discusses the
effects of various kinds of food and drink on health. Book III, ch.
xiv, entitled "Of Birds," contains the following remarks on the
physical effects of eating sparrows:

Arabic physicians forbid [sparrow] as a food, because of [the sparrow's]
short life and lecherousness. Many believe that it therefore stimulates
[*te paert helpen*] a phlegmatic man.[4]

In an edition of the *Schat der Gesontheyt* published in 1672,[5] these

---

[2] For these and other editions of this volume, see Baumann, p. 305, item
21a.

[3] The full title reads: *Ioh. van Beverwycks Schat der Gesontheydt. Met veersen*
verçiert door de Heer Iacob Cats, Ridder, &c. (Amsterdam: Ian Iacobsz Schipper,
1656).

[4] *Schat der Gesontheydt*, in *Alle de Wercken* (Amsterdam, 1656), p. 119.

[5] In the following volume: *Joh. van Beverwycks Wercken der Genees-Konste,*
Bestaende in den Schat der Gesontheyt, Schat der Ongesontheyt, Heel-Konste . . .

remarks on sparrows are considerably expanded and read in part as follows: *Note to p. 228.11–22*

Arabic physicians forbid [sparrow] as a food, because of [the sparrow's] short life and lecherousness. For example, *Orus in Hieroglyph* writes that [sparrows] copulate [*af-steken*] seven times in one hour. *J. C. Scaliger* has seen a sparrow do it ten times in one day, and *Aldrouandus* twenty times during a brief part of a day. A rich merchant from Dordrecht who keeps a flock of innumerable birds of all sorts, has told me, that he saw on various trips (and this has also been confirmed by other persons) a sparrow do it seventeen times in succession in only one-quarter of an hour, but that its wings and tail drooped markedly and it was very wet with sweat. Sparrows are then, not only thus lecherous, but also make those who eat them, that way [i.e., lecherous], according to the testimony of *Terpsicles*, of *Athen.*, in the 9th book.[6]

Considering the detailed description in this passage of the ability of sparrows to copulate frequently in a short period (as evidence of the traditional view that sparrows are naturally lecherous) and the fact that Beverwyck's latinized name was "Beverovicius," it seems likely that Yorick's recollection of the account given by "the grave and learned Bevoriskius," in "his commentary upon the generations from Adam," of the sparrows copulating on his window sill, is a reference to this passage in Beverwyck's *Schat der Gesontheyt* and to his commentary on the "Degeneration of Man" since Adam's fall. If so, one question remains: How did Sterne know Beverwyck's *Schat der Gesontheyt* and its remarks on sparrows? So far as I know, Sterne could not read Dutch, and I have been unable to find any translation of the *Schat der Gesontheyt* into Latin, French, or English. Perhaps he found a reference to the remarks on sparrows in Beverwyck's treatise, in a work such as Ephraim Chambers' *Cyclopaedia* or Bayle's *Dictionary.*[7]

---

t'Amsterdam, By de Weduwe van J. J. Schipper, Amsterdam, 1672 (see Baumann, p. 305, item 21c). Like the 1656 edition of the *Schat der Gesontheyt,* the 1672 edition commences (on p. 1) with a commentary in prose and verse on the physical "Degeneration of Man" and has the same plate of Adam and Eve below the title. (The text of the commentary differs considerably in the two editions.)

[6] *Schat der Gesontheyt,* Book III, ch. xiv, in *Wercken der Genees-Konste* (Amsterdam, 1672), pp. 155–156. I am indebted to Mr. Bond Johnson for translating Beverwyck's Dutch for me.

[7] I have found no ref. to Beverwyck in either of these works. Burton's *Anatomy of Melancholy* is quoted on p. 20 of the 1656 edition of the *Schat der*

Note to p. Page 261.4–7. *Mons. Le Compte de B**** . . . and so on.*] In
261.4–7 January 1762, after a fortnight in Paris, Sterne wrote Garrick:

> . . . my head is turned round with . . . the unexpected honours I
> have met with here. Tristram was almost as much known here as in
> London, at least among your men of condition and learning, and has got
> me introduced into so many circles ('tis comme a Londres.) I have just
> now a fortnight's dinners and suppers upon my hands . . . I hope in
> a fortnight to break through, or rather from the delights of this place,
> which in the *scavoir vivre,* exceed all the places, I believe, in this section
> of the globe— . . . I could write six volumes of what has passed comic-
> ally in this great scene, . . . but more of this hereafter—[1]

Tristram Shandy was probably not as well known in Paris as
Sterne liked to suppose. Richard Phelps, who had traveled with
him from London to Paris, remarked in February 1762:

> Tristram . . . meets with great Civilities from the people to whom he
> has been recommended, and luckily for him (I mean as an Author) he
> ascribes it entirely to the life and Opinions of Mr Shandy—but alass!
> there are not five people in Paris possess'd of a Tristram Shandy, nor
> one of those who are, who pretends to understand it. They know how-
> ever that Tristram is a great Genius in his own Country, and he would
> very probably be so in this, if he would but learn to speak [French] be-
> fore he attempts talking.[2]

Vols. I and II of *Tristram Shandy* were not translated until 1776,
and the book was known in Paris mainly by reputation and
through the reviews in the French journals.[3]

On 8 March 1762 Sterne wrote a friend:

> The french Love such a nonsensical fellow as I am, & I have found little
> difficulties in getting into some of the best Circles; & am moving on
> with ten times the rapidity I ever moved before; for Lo! I am going this
> night to the Prince of Contis—There is nothing in this place wch has
> given me more pleasure than the Connections I have made wth Y^e
> Crebillions, D'Allemberg, Bufon, Diderot & the rest of a large Circle of
> men of wit & learning whom I meet twice a week at Baron de Holbach's,

---

Gesontheyt. According to Baumann (p. 303, item 18a), five editions of the *Schat
der Gesontheyt* had appeared by 1642. Burton could, therefore, have known
Beverwyck's treatise on health, but I have found no ref. to it in the 6th ed. of
the *Anatomy of Melancholy*, publ. 1651.

[1] *Letters,* No. 83, pp. 151–152.
[2] Cash, "Sterne Letters."
[3] See *Life,* p. 296; *Letters,* p. 152, n. 3.

& Pelletiers Tables—what makes these men truly entertaining & desirable, is, that they have the art, notwithstanding their Wits, of living together without biting or scratching—an infinitude of gaity & civility reigns among them—& w^t is no small art, Every man leaves the Room wth a better Opinion of his own Talents than when he enterd.[4]

Page 278.15–16. *thee, great—great* SENSORIUM *of the world!*] Ephraim Chambers' *Cyclopaedia*, from which Walter Shandy's speculations on the sensorium are partly drawn,[1] defines the sensorium as "the seat of the common sense; or that part or place where the sensible soul is supposed more immediately to reside. . . . The *sensory* is supposed to be that part of the brain wherein the nerves from all the organs of sense, terminate."[2] *Note to p. 278.15–16*

Chambers notes that Newton "considers the universe, as the *sensory* of the godhead." In Query 28 of the *Opticks* Newton writes:

. . . does it not appear from Phænomena that there is a Being incorporeal, living, intelligent, omnipresent, who in infinite Space, as it were in his Sensory, sees the things themselves intimately, and throughly perceives them, and comprehends them wholly by their immediate presence to himself: Of which things the Images only carried through the Organs of Sense into our little Sensoriums, are there seen and beheld by that which in us perceives and thinks.[3]

This passage was a chief point of controversy in the famous correspondence between Leibniz and Samuel Clarke debating various aspects of Newton's thought,[4] and it was given wide currency by

[4] Cash, "Sterne Letters."

[1] *TS*, 2.19.147–149. Sterne's borrowings here from Chambers' articles on "sensory" and "soul" are noted by Bernard L. Greenberg, "Laurence Sterne and Chambers' *Cyclopaedia*," *Modern Language Notes*, LXIX (1954), 561–562. "Sensorium" is used also in *TS*, 2.10.108, 3.38.231, 9.26.638.

[2] *Cyclopaedia: Or, An Universal Dictionary of Arts and Sciences*, 5th ed. (London, 1741–1743), article on "Sensory, Sensorium *commune*." "Sensorium" is defined in the *OED* as "the seat of sensation . . . the percipient centre to which sense-impressions are transmitted by the nerves."

[3] *Opticks*, 4th ed. (London, 1730), p. 345; see also Query 31, p. 379, ref. to God's "boundless uniform Sensorium."

[4] The correspondence, edited by Clarke, was first published in 1717, and was reprinted in Clarke's *Works* in 1738; it was one of the works on moral philosophy and metaphysics "recommended or in use" at Cambridge at least as late as 1730, three years before Sterne entered the university (see Christopher Wordsworth, *Scholae Academicae* [Cambridge, 1877], p. 129).

Leibniz interpreted the passage quoted above from the *Opticks* literally, to

Note to p. 278.15–16 Addison's admiring reference to it in *Spectator* No. 565 (IV, 531–532). Addison remarks that we can

utterly extinguish . . . [the] melancholy Thought, of our being over-looked by our Maker in the Multiplicity of his Works, and the Infinity of those Objects among which he seems to be incessantly employed, if we consider, in the first place, that he is Omnipresent; and, in the second, that he is Omniscient.

If we consider him in his Omnipresence: His Being passes through, actuates and supports the whole Frame of Nature. His Creation, and every Part of it, is full of him. There is nothing he has made, that is either so distant, so little, or so inconsiderable, which he does not essentially inhabit. His Substance is within the Substance of every Being, whether material or immaterial, and as intimately present to it, as that Being is to it self. . . .

In the second Place, he is Omniscient as well as Omnipresent. His Omniscience indeed necessarily and naturally flows from his Omnipresence; he cannot but be conscious of every Motion that arises in the whole material World, which he thus essentially pervades, and of every Thought that is stirring in the intellectual World, to every part of which he is thus intimately united. Several Moralists have considered the Creation as the Temple of God, which he has built with his own Hands, and which is filled with his Presence. Others have considered infinite Space as the Receptacle, or rather the Habitation of the Almighty: But the noblest and most exalted way of considering this infinite Space is that of Sir *Isaac Newton,* who calls it the *Sensorium* of the Godhead. Brutes and Men have their *Sensoriola,* or little *Sensoriums,* by which they apprehend the Presence, and perceive the Actions of a few Objects that lie contiguous to them. Their Knowledge and Observation turns within a very narrow Circle. But as God Almighty cannot but perceive and know every thing in which he resides, Infinite Space gives Room to Infinite Knowledge, and is, as it were, an Organ to Omniscience.[5]

---

mean that God needed space as an organ by which to perceive things. Clarke replied that, on the contrary, Newton meant that God, "being omnipresent, perceives all things by his immediate presence to them, in all space wherever they are, without the intervention or assistance of any organ or medium whatsoever," and said that in supposing "infinite space to be (as it were) the *sensorium* of the Omnipresent Being," Newton was using a "similitude" comparing God's perception of things to man's (quoted from *The Leibniz-Clarke Correspondence,* ed. H. G. Alexander [Manchester, 1956], p. 13). (For Sterne's borrowings from Clarke in his *Sermons,* see Hammond, pp. 112–122.)

[5] This passage and the dispute between Leibniz and Clarke over the passage quoted above from the *Opticks* are cited by Arthur Cash in connection with

Page 286.28–34. *I . . . an English gentleman*] Yorick's encounter with the lady in "The Case of Delicacy" is apparently based on a similar experience of John Craufurd of Errol (Scotland), one of the gayest of the young wits in London and Paris, whom Sterne first met in Paris, in 1765.[1] The anecdote is recounted in the memoirs of John Macdonald, Craufurd's footman. According to Macdonald, he and Craufurd stopped at an inn between Verviers and Aix-la-Chapelle for the night:

Note to p. 286.28–34

There was a great deal of company in the house, but the best room was not engaged. My master was let in there, he being an English gentleman, and supper was ordered. Half an hour after this, a Flemish lady and her maid arrived in a chaise. She begged to lodge there all night. She was told the rooms were all full. She said she would make any shift, if there was an empty bed. The landlady said they were all taken up where such a lady as she could sleep, but one, which was very good, in the closet of the English gentleman's room. "Then give Madame Blond's compliments to the English gentleman, and that I desire the favour he will let me sit in the room with him till bed-time." . . . She said she should be glad to sit in his room, as all the apartments were engaged. He said she was extremely welcome . . . After supper her maid and the housemaid made the bed in the closet ready. My master politely said to her: "Madame Blond, if you like, you may have this bed, as it will hold yourself and maid, and I will sleep in the closet." She said: "By no means; I am extremely obliged to you for the privilege of the little bed." "Come, Madam, we will play at cards for the large bed." They did so, and she lost. When the maid came to put her to bed, she gave her maid strict charge to bolt the closet-door. Madam Blond spoke to my master in French the whole evening. She bade him good night, and desired the maid again to be sure to bolt the door; for the bolt was in my master's room. Next day Madam Blond went to Spa, and Mr Craufurd to Aix-la-Chapelle . . .[2]

Yorick's apostrophe to the "great SENSORIUM of the world" (*Sterne's Comedy of Moral Sentiments,* p. 94, n. 4). Cash suggests that the spirit of Yorick's apostrophe is closer to Leibniz's interpretation of Newton than to Clarke's and Addison's.

[1] See *Life,* pp. 392–393; *Letters,* p. 263, n. 7.

[2] *Memoirs of an Eighteenth Century Footman, John Macdonald, Travels,* (*1745–1779*), ed. John Beresford (London, 1927), pp. 86–87. Macdonald's memoirs were originally published (as *Travels, in Various Parts of Europe, Asia, and Africa*) in 1790, and his version of Craufurd's experience may have been influenced by *A Sentimental Journey.* (The chronology of Macdonald's memoirs is vague, but this incident apparently took place in 1766 or 1767.) For Macdonald's eye-witness account of Sterne's death, see *Memoirs,* ed. Beresford, pp. 91–92 (quoted in *Letters,* pp. 419–420, n. 3).

INDEX

INDEX

In addition to those listed on pp. xv–xvii, the following abbreviations are used in the index: S = Sterne; *ASJ* = *A Sentimental Journey*. References to the nine volumes of the first edition of *Tristram Shandy* (*TS*) and to the seven volumes of the first edition of Sterne's *Sermons* are given in roman numerals. Critical and scholarly studies published in the twentieth century are selectively indexed, usually by author only. References followed by *n* are to the explanatory notes below the text and in Appendix E.

I

GENERAL INDEX

Addison, Joseph
Cato: paraphrased in *ASJ*, 277.12–14*n;* Dr. Johnson on, 278.14*n*
Remarks on Several Parts of Italy: ridiculed in *TS* VII as pedantry that could have been written "dry shod," 84.112–113*n*, 278.14*n;* mentioned, 15 n. 48
See also *Spectator*
Agnew, Martha, and Morgan MS., 308 n. 1
Alembert, Jean le Rond d': and *L'Encyclopédie*, 265.69*n;* S meets at baron d'Holbach's, 352
Atkinson, Geoffroy, 343 n. 6

Baretti, Joseph, defense of Italian cicisbei against Sharp, 344
Barrow, Isaac, on cheerfulness and religion, 38 n. 39
Bartholomew, St., Smollett compared with, in *ASJ*, 118.43–44*n*
Bayle, Pierre, *Dictionary:* and La Fleur, 342; mentioned, 351
Becket, Thomas, publisher (with P. A. De Hondt) of: *ASJ*, 49, 316, 319–320; *Sermons* III–IV, 52 n. 11; *TS* V–VI, 8; *TS* V–IX, 52 n. 11, 53 n. 13
Beverwyck, Johan van, *Schat der Gesontheyt*, poss. ref. to, in *ASJ*, 349–351 (228.11–12*n*)

Bevoriskius. *See* Beverwyck, Johan van
Bible, the
Acts 2:1–11, 257.11–12*n*
I Corinthians: 3:16 and 6:19, 218.69–70*n;* 13:12, 44 n. 53, 47
II Corinthians: 6:16, 218.69–70*n;* 11:23–27, 126.13–15*n*
Daniel 2:1–11, 245.33–37*n*
Deuteronomy 5:6 and 6:12, 247.46*n*
Ecclesiastes 9:11, 114.10*n*
II Esdras 10:31, 94.39–41*n*
Exodus: 13:3, 13:14, and 20:2, 247.46*n;* 20:26, 83.92–96*n*
Ezekiel: 17:1–10, 261.2–3*n;* 16:36–37, 22:10, and 23:18, 83.92–96*n*
Genesis: 2:18, 167.31*n* and 237.8–11*n;* 9:20–22, 83.92–96*n;* 9:23, 217.61–62*n;* 16:12, 89.17–18*n;* 42:9, 216.24–25*n*
Hebrews 12:14, 338 n. 4 and 339 n. 6
Isaiah: 25:8, 146.22*n;* 42:1, 248.51*n*
Jeremiah: 6:16, 101.38–39*n;* 17:9, 42 n. 49
Job 29:13, 68.18–23*n*
John: 2:21, 218.69–70*n;* 13:36 and 16:5, 335 n. 8; 20:19, 120.54*n*
I John 5:3, 29 n. 17
Judges 20:1, 115.17*n*
I Kings 1:52, 278.16–17*n*

359

Sterne (*Continued*)

117.*33n*; S describes "temple" erected by Pity in her bosom, 218.69–70*n;* in a "sungilt cottage," 273.21–23*n;* and Morgan MS., 308 n. 4

Sterne, Laurence

as clergyman: authorship of *TS* and pseudonym in *Sermons of Mr. Yorick* criticized, 5–11, 16 n. 51, 321–322 (65.8–9*n*); archbishop of York asked to censure, 16 n. 51; frustrated hopes for preferment (and mitre), 105.31–32*n*, 200.99–100*n*

coat-of-arms, and Yorick's in *ASJ*, 205.37–40*n*

death, and desire to die jesting, 20, 201.10–17*n*

finances and literary fortunes: *TS*, 5 and n. 16, 7, 8 and n. 30, 10; *Sermons*, 5 n. 19; *ASJ*, 10, 17–18, 222.16–19*n*, 227.39–40*n;* wrote "not to be *fed* but to be *famous*," 8

health: on European travels, 2 and nn. 6, and 8, 12 and n. 40, 79.30*n*, 82.67–71*n*, 215.12*n*, 226.33–35*n*, 287.70*n;* during composition of *ASJ*, 18–21, 323; "miscarried of" *TS* X by fever, 12 n. 42; sexual impotence, 243.57*n;* venereal disease, 243.57*n*, 277.8–9*n* ("chastisement"), 324 n. 9 (on 325)

portraits of, xi (frontispiece, Plates 3, 4)

travels in Europe:

first trip: 1–3; death reported in London papers, 2 and n. 6, 192.7–8*n;* reception in Paris, 2, 155.5–9*n*, 261–266*nn*, 352–353 (261.4–7*n*); and "hints and projects" for writing, 2–3; inspires *TS* VII, 8; S at Dessein's Lyon d'Argent in Calais, 87.2–3*n;* and date of Yorick's journey, 192.7–8*n;* S's application for passports,

Sterne (*Continued*)

192.11*n*, 226.33–35*n;* S in danger of arrest as spy, 216.24–25*n;* his comparison of French and old coins reported in papers, 232.34–42*n*

second trip: 11–12; anecdote about S's shirts, 13 n. 45; reported in papers, 17; S at Dessein's Hôtel d'Angleterre, 87.2–3*n;* S's return to England via Calais, 102.46–47*n;* S's meeting with Smollett, 117.33*n;* S in Italy, 11–12, 117.33*n*, 172.37–40*n*, 267.93*n;* S orders periwig, 158*n;* S anticipates French vintage, 268.1–10*n;* delay in Savoy mountains, 286.24*n*

third trip (projected), 79.37–41*n*, 261.4–7*n*

travels (projected) as tutor or governor, 79.37–41*n*

and Tristram Shandy: "Chevalier Shandy," 2, 226.33–35*n;* shandying in London after publ. of *TS* I and II, 5; S identified by himself and others with Tristram, 5–6, 17; "*Reverend Tristram . . . Harlequin-Shandy*," 16 n. 51; "the modern Democritus, Tristram Shandy," 18; shandying in Paris and converting Parisians to shandeism, 265.66–71*n;* Tristram embodies S's self-consciousness, 323

and Yorick: S criticized for use, in *Sermons of Mr. Yorick*, of pseudonym as heteroclite parson in *TS* I, 5 and n. 20; S criticed as "arch *Prebend Mr. Yorick*, alias *Tristram Shandy*," 6; character as heteroclite Parson Yorick in *TS* suitable to role in *ASJ*, 321–322; Yorick embodies S's self-consciousness, 323; Yorick as S's pseudonym in *Journal*, 325

views on: travel, 3 ("as puppies travel"), 268.1–10*n;* taste for

II

INDEX TO STERNE'S WRITINGS

Sentimental Journey, A (Continued)
82.77*n*, 336 (83.100–85.126*n*); cosmopolitan tolerance, civilized behavior, and benevolence, 33–34, 39, 75.1–11*n*, 199.87–89*n*; communication, 34–35; sentimental commerce, 35, 40, 78.17–18*n*; mortality and death, 36, 47 (final VEXATION), 192.7–8*n*, 221.11–12*n*; microcosm and macrocosm, 36–37; *"pélerinage de l'âme"* and cosmopolitan sociality, 39; benevolent, comic sense of life as "gift of God," and self-knowledge, 41–47; as "parable" or "fable," 43; benevolent idealism and shandean world, 44; man as glory, jest, riddle, 44–45; style, 46; comedy and charity, 47; life and writing as journey, 46 n. 64; page rescued from "violation," 170.2–9*n*; starling and S's name, 197.65–66*n*; problem of identity, 221.1–16*n*
See also Sterne, Laurence: and Yorick

Sermons of Mr. Yorick
Vol. I: title page, xi (Plate 1), 4
Vols. I and II: publication and reception, 5–6, 222.16–19*n*; S "on the verge of laughter" in, 222.16–19*n*
Vols. III and IV: publication and reception, 11–12; S's "ecclesiastick" children who do "penance" for *TS* and "balance" his "shandaic character," 11
and *ASJ*, 28–31, 35–47
general (including paraphrases, echoes, parallels in *ASJ*, selectively indexed): "Professing themselves to be wise, they became fools," frontispiece, 46; "a man's mind must be like your proposition," 25 n. 2; and anti-Puritan, anti-Stoic, anti-Hobbesian Latitudinarians, 28; God "infinitely kind," 28 and n. 14,

Sermons of Mr. Yorick (Continued)
44 and n. 53; man's natural benevolence and "benevolent affections," 29 and n. 14, 44 and n. 53; "innocent pleasures" on "weary pilgrimage," 29 and n. 15; "peaceable commerce" and "social intercourse" promoted by "natural bond of brotherhood," 29 and n. 15, 190.89–93*n*; "moral delight" in covering nakedness, 29 and n. 16, 339 n. 6; life not a "disastrous pilgrimage" for "saint-errants," 29 n. 17; redemptive joys of this world akin to perfect joy of next, 30–31; pleasures become licentious and excessive, 30 n. 18; "Our Conversation in Heaven," and Smelfungus and Mundungus, 31, 338–342 (120.54–64*n*); "*Sierra Morena*," 35 and n. 33; "splenetick" men (incl. puritans, stoics, Papists) who flee joy and suppose that God likes "splenetic and mortifying" actions, 38 and n. 38; God a "fountain of joy," 39 n. 41, 148.49–52*n*, 277.10–11*n*; joyful religion, 39 and n. 41, 283.15–27*n*; "cold Stoick," 237.7*n*, 283.15–27*n*; "think worthily oɩ our nature," 41–42; self-knowledge, and self-love, 42–43 and n. 48; Nathan and David, 43 n. 50; parables and moral instruction, 43 n. 50; we discern things "darkly and confusedly . . . as in a glass," 44 n. 53; man as glory, jest, riddle, 44–45 and nn. 53, 54; life and writing as a journey, 47 n. 64; benevolence and health, 68.18–23*n*; ebbs and flows, 70.6*n*; anti-Catholicism, 74.27–29*n*; "religious grudge," 75.1–11*n*; "benevolent," "peaceable commerce" and social intercourse," 78.17–18*n*; "*novelty of his* Vehicle," 82.77*n*; "some-